Middle School 3-2

기말고사 완벽대비

적중100

영어 기출 문제집

중3

지학 | 민찬규

Best Collection

구성과 특징

교과서의 주요 학습 내용을 중심으로 학습 영역별 특성에 맞춰 단계별로 다양한 학습 기회를 제공하여
단원별 학습능력 평가는 물론 중간 및 기말고사 시험 등에 완벽하게 대비할 수 있도록 내용을 구성

Words & Expressions

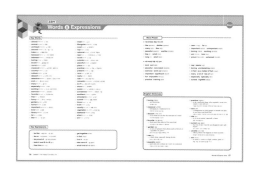

Step1   Key Words 단원별 핵심 단어 설명 및 풀이
         Key Expression 단원별 핵심 숙어 및 관용어 설명
         Word Power 반대 또는 비슷한 뜻 단어 배우기
         English Dictionary 영어로 배우는 영어 단어

Step2   실력평가 단원별 수시평가 대비 주관식, 객관식 문제풀이

Step3   서술형 대비 학업성취도 및 수행능력평가 대비 서술형 문제풀이

Conversation

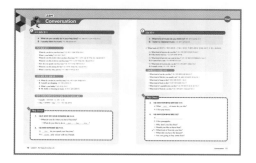

Step1   핵심 의사소통 소통에 필요한 주요 표현 방법 요약
         핵심 Check 기본적인 표현 방법 및 활용능력 확인

Step2   대화문 익히기 교과서 대화문 심층 분석 및 확인

Step3   교과서 확인학습 빈칸 채우기를 통한 문장 완성 능력 확인

Step4   기본평가 시험대비 기초 학습 능력 평가

Step5   실력평가 단원별 수시평가 대비 주관식, 객관식 문제풀이

Step6   서술형 대비 학업성취도 및 수행능력평가 대비 서술형 문제풀이

Grammar

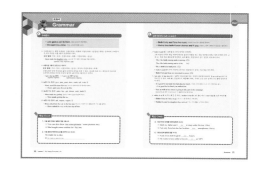

Step1   주요 문법 단원별 주요 문법 사항과 예문을 알기 쉽게 설명
         핵심 Check 기본 문법사항에 대한 이해 여부 확인

Step2   기본평가 시험대비 기초 학습 능력 평가

Step3   실력평가 단원별 수시평가 대비 주관식, 객관식 문제풀이

Step4   서술형 대비 학업성취도 및 수행능력평가 대비 서술형 문제풀이

Reading

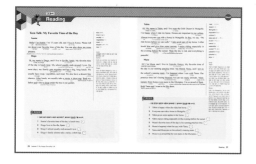

Step1   구문 분석 단원별로 제시된 문장에 대한 구문별 분석과 내용 설명
         확인문제 문장에 대한 기본적인 이해와 인지능력 확인

Step2   확인학습A 빈칸 채우기를 통한 문장 완성 능력 확인

Step3   확인학습B 제시된 우리말을 영어로 완성하여 작문 능력 키우기

Step4   실력평가 단원별 수시평가 대비 주관식, 객관식 문제풀이

Step5   서술형 대비 학업성취도 및 수행능력평가 대비 서술형 문제풀이
         교과서 구석구석 교과서에 나오는 기타 문장까지 완벽 학습

Composition

|영역별 핵심문제|

단어 및 어휘, 대화문, 문법, 독해 등 각 영역별 기출문제의 출제 유형을 분석하여 실전에 대비하고 연습할 수 있도록 문제를 배열

|단원별 예상문제|

기출문제를 분석한 후 새로운 시험 출제 경향을 더하여 새롭게 출제될 수 있는 문제를 포함하여 시험에 완벽하게 대비할 수 있도록 준비

|서술형 실전 및 창의사고력 문제|

학교 시험에서 점차 늘어나는 서술형 시험에 집중 대비하고 고득점을 취득하는데 만전을 기하기 위한 학습 코너

|단원별 모의고사|

영역별, 단계별 학습을 모두 마친 후 실전 연습을 위한 모의고사

INSIGHT on the textbook

교과서 파헤치기

- **단어Test1~3** 영어 단어 우리말 쓰기, 우리말을 영어 단어로 쓰기, 영영풀이에 해당하는 단어와 우리말 쓰기
- **대화문Test1~2** 대화문 빈칸 완성 및 전체 대화문 쓰기
- **본문Test1~5** 빈칸 완성, 우리말 쓰기, 문장 배열연습, 영어 작문하기 복습 등 단계별 반복 학습을 통해 교과서 지문에 대한 완벽한 습득
- **구석구석지문Test1~2** 지문 빈칸 완성 및 전문 영어로 쓰기

Contents

Lesson 7

Homes Everywhere

 의사소통 기능

- 바람·소원 표현하기
  I wish I could live on the water.
- 상상하여 말하기
  What would you do if you lived in Alaska?

 언어 형식

- 가정법 과거
  If I **lived** in a pueblo, **I would climb** up a ladder to enter my house.

- 5형식 동사 keep / make
  They would **keep me cool** in summer and **warm** in winter.

Words & Expressions

Key Words

- **appear**[əpíər] 동 보이다, 나타나다
- **cave**[keiv] 명 동굴
- **colorful**[kʌ́lərfəl] 형 형형색색의
- **earth**[ə:rθ] 명 흙
- **enter**[éntər] 동 ~에 들어가다
- **everywhere**[évriwer] 부 모든 곳에, 어디나
- **family name** 성(姓)
- **flat**[flæt] 형 평평한
- **floating**[flóutiŋ] 형 떠다니는
- **hidden**[hídn] 형 숨겨진
- **house**[hauz] 동 수용하다
- **however**[hauévər] 부 그러나, 하지만
- **huge**[hju:dʒ] 형 거대한, 굉장히 큰
- **imagine**[imǽdʒin] 동 상상하다
- **install**[instɔ́:l] 동 설치하다
- **invader**[invéidər] 명 침략자
- **invisible**[invízəbl] 형 눈에 보이지 않는, 투명한
- **island**[áilənd] 명 섬
- **jungle**[dʒʌ́ŋgl] 명 밀림, 정글
- **ladder**[lǽdər] 명 사다리
- **like**[laik] 전 ~와 같은
- **millionaire**[mìljənɛ́ər] 명 백만장자
- **mostly**[móustli] 부 주로, 일반적으로

- **opening**[óupəniŋ] 명 구멍
- **pole**[poul] 명 기둥, 막대기
- **raised**[reizd] 형 높이 올린
- **rise**[reiz] 동 오르다, 올라가다
- **roof**[ru:f] 명 지붕
- **share**[ʃɛər] 동 공유하다
- **sometimes**[sʌ́mtàimz] 부 때때로, 가끔
- **store**[stɔ:r] 동 저장하다, 보관하다
- **straw**[strɔ:] 명 짚, 지푸라기
- **surface**[sə́:rfis] 명 표면, 지면, 수면
- **support**[səpɔ́:rt] 동 지탱하다, 떠받치다
- **swampy**[swámpi] 형 습지의
- **take**[teik] 동 ~을 타다
- **thick**[θik] 형 두꺼운, 살찐
- **tide**[taid] 명 조수, 흐름
- **travel**[trǽvəl] 동 여행하다, 이동하다
- **unwelcome**[ənwélkəm] 형 반갑지 않은
- **usually**[jú:ʒuəli] 부 보통, 대개
- **Venetian**[vəní:ʃən] 명 베니스 사람
- **village**[vílidʒ] 명 마을, 촌락
- **walkway**[wɔ́:kwei] 명 통로
- **wheel**[hwi:l] 명 바퀴
- **wooden**[wúdn] 형 나무로 된

Key Expressions

- **all day** 하루 종일
- **all over the world** 세계 곳곳에
- **at high tide** 만조에
- **be known as** ~로 알려지다
- **be made up of** ~로 구성되다, ~로 만들어지다
- **be used for** ~로 사용되다
- **climb up** ~에 올라가다
- **come over** 들르다
- **for a while** 당분간, 잠시 동안
- **full of** ~로 가득 찬
- **go sledding** 썰매 타러 가다
- **hand down** ~을 물려주다
- **live in** ~에 살다, ~에 거주하다

- **make sense** 이치에 맞다
- **more than** ~ 이상의
- **one of** ~ 중 하나
- **on top of** ~ 위에
- **on weekends** 주말마다
- **pull A up** A를 당겨 올리다
- **stop A from ~ing** A가 ~하지 못하게 막다
- **take a look** 보다
- **upside down** 거꾸로 된, 뒤집힌
- **up to** ~까지
- **walk around** 돌아다니다
- **What is it ~ like?** ~은 어때?

Word Power

※ 서로 비슷한 뜻을 가진 어휘

- □ **appear** 나타나다 – **show up** 나타나다
- □ **hidden** 숨겨진 – **concealed** 숨겨진, 가려진
- □ **store** 저장하다, 보관하다 – **save** 모으다, 저축하다
- □ **travel** 여행하다, 이동하다 – **wander** 유랑하다, 방랑하다

- □ **earth** 흙 – **soil** 토양, 흙
- □ **huge** 거대한, 굉장히 큰 – **enormous** 거대한, 막대한
- □ **support** 지탱하다, 떠받치다 – **sustain** 지탱하다, 떠받치다

※ 서로 반대의 뜻을 가진 어휘

- □ **appear** 보이다, 나타나다 ↔ **disappear** 사라지다
- □ **enter** ~에 들어가다 ↔ **exit** 나가다, 퇴거하다
- □ **huge** 거대한, 굉장히 큰 ↔ **tiny** 매우 작은
- □ **invisible** 눈에 보이지 않는, 투명한 ↔ **visible** 눈에 보이는
- □ **thick** 두꺼운 ↔ **thin** 얇은

- □ **colorful** 형형색색의 ↔ **colorless** 색이 없는
- □ **flat** 평평한 ↔ **uneven** 울퉁불퉁한, 평탄하지 않은
- □ **install** 설치하다 ↔ **remove** 제거하다
- □ **rise** 오르다, 올라가다 ↔ **descend** 내려가다, 내려오다
- □ **unwelcome** 반갑지 않은 ↔ **welcome** 환영하는, 반가운

※ 형용사(adjective) vs 부사(adverb)

- □ **early** 이른 – **early** 이르게
- □ **far** 먼 – **far** 멀리
- □ **good** 좋은, 착한 – **well** 좋게, 제대로
- □ **high** 높은 – **high** 높이
- □ **long** 긴 – **long** 길게

- □ **enough** 충분한 – **enough** 충분히
- □ **fast** 빠른 – **fast** 빠르게
- □ **hard** 단단한, 어려운 – **hard** 열심히, 강력하게
- □ **late** 늦은 – **late** 늦게
- □ **well** 건강한, 적절한 – **well** 제대로, 완전히, 잘

English Dictionary

- □ **cave** 동굴
  - → a large hole in the side of a hill or under the ground
    언덕의 한 측면이나 땅의 아래에 있는 큰 구멍
- □ **flat** 평평한
  - → level, with no high hills or other raised parts
    언덕이나 다른 높이 올라 있는 곳이 없는, 평평한
- □ **house** 수용하다
  - → to provide a place for somebody to live
    어떤 사람에게 살 곳을 제공하다
- □ **millionaire** 백만장자
  - → a person who has a million pounds, dollars, etc.; a very rich person
    백만 달러나 백만 파운드를 갖고 있는 사람; 매우 부자인 사람
- □ **install** 설치하다
  - → to fix equipment or furniture into position so that it can be used
    장비나 가구를 사용할 수 있도록 제자리에 고정시키다
- □ **invisible** 눈에 보이지 않는, 투명한
  - → impossible to see 볼 수 없는
- □ **opening** 구멍
  - → a space or hole that somebody or something can pass through
    어떤 사람이나 사물이 지나갈 수 있는 공간이나 구멍
- □ **store** 저장하다, 보관하다
  - → to put something that is not being used in a place where it can be kept safely
    사용하지 않고 있는 어떤 사물을 안전하게 있을 수 있는 곳에 넣다
- □ **support** 지탱하다, 떠받치다
  - → to hold somebody or something in position; to prevent somebody or something from falling
    어떤 사람이나 사물을 제자리에 대다; 어떤 사람이나 사물이 떨어지는 것을 막다
- □ **swampy** 습지의
  - → very wet or covered with water land in which plants, trees, etc. are growing
    식물이나 나무 등이 자라는 매우 습하고 물로 덮인 땅
- □ **tide** 조수
  - → the regular upward and downward movement of the level of the ocean that is caused by the pull of the sun and the moon on Earth
    지구 위에 있는 태양과 달의 인력에 의해 발생하는 바다 수면 높이의 정기적인 상하 움직임
- □ **walkway** 통로
  - → a passage or path for walking along, often outside and raised above the ground
    종종 밖이나 지면에서 올라와 있는 통행을 위한 길

서답형
01 다음 짝지어진 단어의 관계가 같도록 빈칸에 알맞은 말을 쓰시오.

hidden – concealed = store : _____

02 다음 영영풀이가 가리키는 것을 고르시오.

level, with no high hills or other raised parts

① flat   ② uneven
③ visible   ④ high
⑤ ground

중요
03 다음 중 밑줄 친 부분의 뜻풀이가 바르지 <u>않은</u> 것은?
① My name will <u>appear</u> at the front of the book. (나타나다, 보이다)
② Some plastic bags were <u>floating</u> in the beach. (떠다니는)
③ The <u>surface</u> of the moon is pitted with craters. (표면)
④ Would you <u>take</u> this to the post office for me? (~을 타다)
⑤ They crush the strawberry with a heavy <u>wooden</u> press. (나무로 된)

서답형
04 다음 우리말을 주어진 어휘를 이용하여 영작하시오.
(1) 그 정부는 달갑지 않은 교육 정책을 고집하고 있다. (unwelcome, persist in)
➡ _____
_____

(2) 아기를 안고 있을 때 머리를 떠받치는 것은 중요하다. (support, hold)
➡ _____

(3) 그녀는 연세가 거의 100세이시고 주로 방에만 계신다. (nearly, mostly, keep)
➡ _____
_____

서답형
05 다음 문장의 빈칸에 들어갈 말을 〈보기〉에서 골라 쓰시오.

┤ 보기 ├
come over / all day / climb up /
known as / on weekends

(1) The construction workers sawed and hammered _____.
(2) Rain, snow and hail are collectively _____ precipitation.
(3) Why don't you _____ to Korea this summer?

06 다음 문장의 빈칸 (A)와 (B)에 각각 공통으로 들어갈 말로 바르게 짝지어진 것은?

• They could hand __(A)__ those privileges to their children.
• The box I ordered was left upside __(A)__ in the hallway.
• He tried to stop himself __(B)__ crying out in front of people.
• There is nothing to prevent us __(B)__ going there.

① over – from   ② over – to
③ down – out   ④ down – to
⑤ down – from

01 다음 주어진 영영풀이에 맞는 단어를 쓰시오.

> to fix equipment or furniture into position so that it can be used

➡ _____

02 다음 짝지어진 단어의 관계가 같도록 빈칸에 알맞은 말을 쓰시오.

> enter : exit = appear : _____

03 다음 문장의 빈칸에 들어갈 말을 〈보기〉에서 골라 쓰시오.

> ┌─ 보기 ─┐
> make sense / on top of / more than /
> pull up / walk around

(1) Jane used to like to _____ in bare feet.

(2) Can you open the doors while I _____ the shades?

(3) This sentence doesn't _____ at all .

04 다음 우리말에 맞게 빈칸에 알맞은 말을 쓰시오.

> 우리 할머니는 돌아가시기 전에 그녀의 보석들을 물려주셨다.

➡ My grandmother had _____ her jewels before she passed away.

05 다음 우리말과 일치하도록 주어진 어구를 모두 배열하여 영작하시오.

(1) 나는 왜 그들이 떠나고 싶어 하는지 짐작이 안 된다.

(why / I / leave / imagine / they / want to / cannot)

➡ _____

(2) 신도시들이 서울의 과잉 인구를 수용하기 위해 만들어졌다.

(house / to / were / Seoul's / designed / over-population / new towns)

➡ _____
_____

(3) 정원에서 놀고 있는 아이들은 오늘 행복해 보인다.

(in the garden / the children / appear / today / playing / happy)

➡ _____
_____

06 다음 우리말에 맞게 주어진 단어를 사용하여 영작하시오.

(1) 베를린에서는 많은 사람들이 보통 자전거를 타고 출근한다. (usually)

➡ _____

(2) 난 종종 혼자 있는 것을 좋아한다. (often, on my own)

➡ _____

(3) 내가 주말에 주로 하는 것은 독서이다. (mostly, during)

➡ _____

Conversation

① 바람·소원 표현하기

> A: Can you have dinner with me today?
> B: I wish I could, but I have to go home early today.

- 'I wish I could~.'는 '내가 ~하면 좋겠다.'라는 뜻으로, 바람이나 소원을 나타내는 표현이다. I wish 뒤에는 사실과 반대되거나 가능성이 거의 없는 일이 온다. 만약 가능성이 있거나 결과를 아직 모르는 것을 희망할 때는 I hope를 쓴다.

- I wish 뒤에는 could를 이용해 현재 사실과 반대되는 내용, 혹은 가능성이 없는 일을 가정한다.
  - I wish I could live on the water.
    = I want to live on the water, but I can't.
  - I wish I could travel for the rest of my life.
    = I want to travel for the rest of my life, but I can't.

- 더 알아볼 표현 I hope ~
'I hope ~'는 'I wish I could ~'와 달리 실현 가능성이 있거나 가능성이 높은 상황에서 사용한다.
  - I hope I don't have to work late tomorrow. 나는 내일 늦게까지 일하지 않았으면 좋겠다.
  - I hope you can finish your homework in time. 네가 네 숙제를 제시간에 끝낼 수 있기를 바라.

핵심 Check

1. 다음 대화의 빈칸에 알맞은 것은?

> A: What's the matter?
> B: My computer is so slow. _____ a new computer.

① I hope I could have   ② I want I can have

③ I wish I have   ④ I wish I can have

⑤ I wish I could have

② 상상하여 말하기

A: What would you do if you became the president of your country? 네가 너희 나라
의 대통령이 된다면 어떻게 하겠니?

B: I would make a law to protect the environment. 나는 환경을 보호하는 법을 만들 거야.

■ 'What would you do if ~?'는 '만약 ~라면 너는 어떻게 하겠니?'라는 뜻으로 상상하여 말하는 표현이다.

■ 비슷한 표현으로 'Suppose ~', 'What if ~?' 등을 쓸 수 있다.
  • What would you do if you lived in Alaska?
  • Suppose you lived in Alaska.
  • What if you live in Alaska?

■ 가정법 과거
  가정법 과거는 현재 사실에 반대되는 상황을 가정할 때 쓰인다.
  What would you do if you won a million dollars? 백만 달러를 얻게 된다면 뭘 할 거니?
  → If I won a million dollars, I would buy a house and a car. 내가 백만 달러를 얻게 된다면, 나는 집과 자동
    차를 살 거야.
  → 현재에는 백만 달러가 없지만 생기는 상황을 가정하는 내용이다.

핵심 Check

2. 다음 대화의 괄호 (A)와 (B)에서 알맞은 것을 고르시오.

> A: What would you do if you (A)[have / could have] a magical
>   power?
> B: I (B)[turn / would turn] back time, then I would be able to time-
>   travel.

 Listen and Speak 2 B

G: Dohun, we need to start our project on our dream country ❶to visit.

B: That's right. Which country do you want to visit, Emma?

G: ❷In my case, I want to visit Spain.

B: ❸What would you do if you visited Spain?

G: ❹I'm interested in buildings. So I would go see La Sagrada Familia.

B: Isn't ❺that the church Antoni Gaudí designed?

G: Yes, it is. ❻It would be interesting to see ❼how his design was inspired by nature.

B: Hmm... ❽How about *Gaudí and Spain* as the title for our project?

G: I love it!

G: 도훈아, 우리가 방문하고 싶은 꿈꾸는 나라에 대한 프로젝트를 시작해야 돼.

B: 맞아. Emma, 너는 어느 나라를 방문하고 싶니?

G: 내 경우에는 스페인에 가 보고 싶어.

B: 스페인에 가게 되면 뭘 할 건데?

G: 나는 건물들에 관심이 있어. 그래서 나는 La Sagrada Familia에 가 볼 거야.

B: 그 성당은 Antoni Gaudí가 디자인한 교회 아니니?

G: 응, 맞아. 그의 디자인이 어떻게 자연에서 영감을 얻었는지 보면 흥미로울 거야.

B: 흠… '가우디와 스페인'을 우리 프로젝트 제목으로 하는 건 어떠니?

G: 아주 좋아!

---

❶ to부정사의 형용사적 용법으로 our dream country를 꾸며 준다. ❷ In my case 내 경우에는 ❸ '만약 ~라면 너는 어떻게 하겠니?'라는 뜻으로 상상하여 말하는 표현이다. ❹ be interested in ~에 관심이 있다 ❺ 이때 대명사 that은 앞서 언급한 La Sagrada Familia를 가리킨다. ❻ 가주어 it ~ to 구문이 사용되었으며, 뒤에 나오는 to부정사 구문이 진주어이다. ❼ 의문사 how를 사용한 간접의문문이다. ❽ 상대방에게 무언가를 제안할 때 쓸 수 있는 표현으로, 'Why don't we ~?'로 대체할 수 있다.

Check(√) True or False

(1) Emma's dream country to visit is Spain.　　　　　　　　　T ☐ F ☐

(2) Dohun is not interested in visiting Spain.　　　　　　　　T ☐ F ☐

Real Life Communication A

Jinho: I think ❶living in a jungle would be really exciting. Don't you think so?

Claire: But there are some dangerous animals in the jungle, Jinho.

Jinho: I know. But the jungle ❷is full of adventure. ❸I wish I could live there.

Claire: ❹What would you do if you lived in the jungle?

Jinho: I would explore ❺it. Maybe I could make some animal friends.

Claire: Then where would you sleep? In a cave?

Jinho: No, I would stay in a tree house. Then I would be safe from dangerous animals.

Claire: ❻That makes sense.

Jinho: 내 생각엔 정글에서 사는 건 정말 신날 거야. 그렇게 생각하지 않니?

Claire: 근데 진호야, 정글에는 몇몇 위험한 동물들이 있어.

Jinho: 나도 알아. 하지만 정글은 모험으로 가득하잖아. 내가 거기서 살 수 있다면 좋을 텐데.

Claire: 정글에서 산다면 뭘 할 건데?

Jinho: 난 정글을 탐험할 거야. 아마도 동물 친구들도 좀 만들 수 있겠지.

Claire: 그러면 어디서 잠을 잘 건데? 동굴에서?

Jinho: 아니, 나무로 만든 집에서 지낼 거야. 그러면 위험한 동물들한테서 안전해지겠지.

Claire: 그건 말이 되네.

---

❶ 동명사 구문으로 주어로 사용되었다. ❷ be full of ~로 가득 차 있다 ❸ 'I wish I could ~.'는 '내가 ~하면 좋겠다.'라는 뜻으로, 바람이나 소원을 나타내는 표현이다. ❹ 비슷한 표현으로 'Suppose ~', 'What if ~?' 등을 쓸 수 있다. ❺ 대명사 it은 the jungle을 가리킨다. ❻ 대명사 That은 Jinho가 말한 앞 문장 전체를 가리킨다.

Check(√) True or False

(3) Jinho thinks it would be great to live in a jungle.　　　　　　　　　T ☐ F ☐

(4) Claire believes that it would be dangerous in the jungle due to some animals.　　T ☐ F ☐

Listen and Speak 1 A

G: ❶Have you heard from Julia? She's traveling in Turkey, right?

B: Yes, she sent me some pictures. Do you want to see ❷them?

G: Yes, please.

B: Okay, ❸take a look.

G: Oh, look at those cave houses! ❹They look so unique, don't they? ❺I wish I could try living there.

B: I like those balloons. ❻They look so beautiful!

G: I think Turkey is a wonderful place ❼to visit. ❽I hope to visit there some day.

B: Me too!

❶ 상대방에게 무엇을 해본 적이 있냐고 물을 때 현재완료 용법을 사용할 수 있다. ❷ 대명사 them은 앞서 언급된 some pictures를 가리킨다. ❸ take a look 보다 ❹ 대명사 They는 앞서 언급한 those cave houses를 가리킨다. ❺ '내가 ~하면 좋겠다'라는 뜻으로, 바람이나 소원을 나타내는 표현이다. I wish 뒤에는 사실과 반대되거나 가능성이 거의 없는 일이 온다. ❻ 대명사 They는 those balloons를 가리킨다. ❼ to부정사의 형용사적 용법으로 사용되었다. ❽ 가능성이 있거나 결과를 아직 모르는 것을 희망할 때는 I hope를 쓴다.

Listen and Speak 1 B

B: Will ❶it snow today?

G: I have no idea. Why are you waiting for snow, Taeho?

B: I got a new sled for my birthday. ❷I can't wait to ❸test it out.

G: ❹Let me check the weather. Umm, there will be no snow ❺for a while.

B: ❻I wish I could live in Alaska. Then I could go sledding all day!

G: ❼No kidding! Alaska is a very cold place.

B: I think ❽it would be fun. I want to build a snow house and stay there on vacation.

G: Living in a snow house sounds fun!

❶ 날씨를 이야기할 때는 대명사 it이 사용된다. ❷ I can't wait to ~. 빨리 ~하고 싶다. ❸ test out 시험해 보다 ❹ 동사 let은 목적보어로 동사원형을 취한다. ❺ for a while 잠시 동안, 한동안 ❻ '내가 ~하면 좋겠다'라는 뜻으로, 바람이나 소원을 나타내는 표현이다. ❼ 무엇이 사실임을 강조하거나 남이 방금 한 말에 동의를 표할 때, 혹은 상대방이 한 말이 사실인지를 물을 때 쓴다. ❽ 대명사 it은 B가 앞서 말했던 알래스카에 가서 사는 것(to live in Alaska)을 가리킨다.

Listen and Speak 1 C

A: Look at these houses. ❶They look very natural.

B: Wow, ❷I wish I could ❸try living here!

A: Which house would you most like to live in?

B: I wish I could live in the stone house. ❹It looks very strong.

❶ 대명사 They는 앞 문장의 these houses를 가리킨다. ❷ I wish 뒤에는 사실과 반대되거나 가능성이 거의 없는 일이 온다. ❸ try ~ing 시험삼아 ~해 보다 ❹ 대명사 It은 앞 문장의 the stone house를 가리킨다.

Listen and Speak 2 A - 1

B: This is my ❶dream house, Alice. What do you think?

G: Oh, the house has wheels! Is ❷it a kind of car?

B: Yes, ❸it can move like a car.

G: So ❹what would you do if you lived in that house?

B: ❺I would travel to many places with my family.

G: That sounds cool.

❶ dream 꿈에서나 가능할 듯한 완벽한 것 ❷ 대명사 it은 the house with wheels를 가리킨다. ❸ 앞서 가리킨 집을 의미한다. ❹ '만약 ~라면 너는 어떻게 하겠니?'라는 뜻으로 상상하여 말하는 표현이다. ❺ 'What would you do if ~?'라는 질문에 대답할 때에는 'I would ~'라고 말한다.

Listen and Speak 2 A - 2

G: What would you do ❶if you became a millionaire, Juwon?

B: I would build my own house.

G: ❷What kind of house would you build?

B: I would build a house ❸that is completely covered with mirrors.

G: Why?

B: The mirrors would make the house almost ❹invisible. Wouldn't that be cool?

G: ❺That would be cool!

❶ 현재 사실과 반대되는 내용을 가정하고 있으므로 가정법 과거 문장을 쓴다. ❷ What kind of ~ 어떤 종류의 ~ ❸ 접속사 that으로 사용되었다. ❹ invisible 보이지 않는 ❺ 대명사 That은 앞서 언급된 문장, '집을 거울로 꾸며 눈에 거의 보이지 않는 것'을 의미한다.

Listen and Speak 2 A - 3

G: Look. The house in this picture is ❶upside down.

B: That's ❷interesting. Does anybody live there?

G: No, it would not be easy to live ❸there because the inside is also upside down.

B: Really? But I want to ❹try living there.

G: What would you do if you lived in that house?

B: I would walk upside down ❺like Spider-Man. I could also see things differently.

❶ upside down 거꾸로 된 ❷ interesting 흥미롭게 하는 ❸ there는 the house in the picture를 가리킨다. ❹ try ~ing 시험삼아 ~해 보다 ❺ like ~처럼

Listen and Speak 2 C

A: ❶What would you do if you could have a magical power?

B: I would ❷turn into a bird. Then I would ❸ be able to fly freely in the sky.

A: That's cool.

❶ 비슷한 표현으로 'Suppose ~', 'What if ~?' 등을 쓸 수 있다. ❷ turn into ~ ~로 변하다 ❸ be able to ~할 수 있다

Real Life Communication B

A: ❶I wish I could stay in a house on the water during my vacation.

B: What would you do if you were ❷there?

A: I would ❸go swimming every day. I would also ❹go fishing.

B: That sounds fun.

❶ I wish 뒤에는 could를 이용해 현재 사실과 반대되는 내용, 혹은 가능성이 없는 일을 가정한다. ❷ there는 앞선 문장에서 언급된 'a house on the water'를 가리킨다. ❸ go swimming 수영하러 가다 ❹ go fishing 낚시하러 가다

Let's Check 1

B: This is my dream house. What do you think, Alice?

G: Oh, it's in the deep sea. ❶It looks so unique. So, ❷what would you do if you lived in that house?

B: ❸I have an interest in deep sea animals. So I would ❹explore the deep sea and find some unique sea animals.

G: That sounds cool!

❶ 대명사 It은 B's dream house in the deep sea를 가리킨다. ❷ 'What would you do if ~?'는 '만약 ~라면 너는 어떻게 하겠니?'라는 뜻으로 상상하여 말하는 표현이다. ❸ have an interest in ~에 관심이 있다 ❹ explore 탐험하다

Let's Check 2

A: ❶What's the matter?

B: My computer is so slow. ❷I wish I could have a new computer.

❶ '무슨 일이니?'라는 의미로 What's wrong?으로 대체할 수 있다. ❷ I wish 뒤에는 could를 이용해 현재 사실과 반대되는 내용, 혹은 가능성이 없는 일을 가정한다.

● 다음 우리말과 일치하도록 빈칸에 알맞은 말을 쓰시오.

Listen and Speak 1 A

G: _____ you heard from Julia? She's _____ in Turkey, right?

B: Yes, she sent me some pictures. Do you _____ to _____ them?

G: Yes, please.

B: Okay, _____ a look.

G: Oh, look at those cave houses! They look so _____, don't they? I wish I could try _____ there.

B: I like _____ balloons. They look so beautiful!

G: I think Turkey is a wonderful place _____ visit. I _____ to visit there _____ _____ .

B: Me _____!

Listen and Speak 1 B

B: Will _____ snow today?

G: I have no idea. _____ are you _____ _____ snow, Taeho?

B: I got a new sled for my birthday. I can't _____ to test it _____ .

G: Let me _____ the weather. Umm, there will be no snow for a while.

B: I wish I could live in Alaska. Then I _____ go sledding all day!

G: No _____! Alaska is a very cold _____ .

B: I think it would be fun. I want to _____ a snow house and _____ there on _____ .

G: _____ in a snow house _____ fun!

Listen and Speak 1 C

A: Look at _____ houses. They look very _____ .

B: Wow, I wish I could _____ living here.

A: _____ house would you _____ like to _____ _____ ?

B: I wish I could live in the stone house. It looks very _____ .

Listen and Speak 2 A-1

B: This is my dream house, Alice. _____ do you think?

G: Oh, the house has wheels! Is it a _____ of car?

B: Yes, it can move _____ a car.

G: So _____ would you do if you _____ in that house?

B: I would _____ to many places with my family.

G: That sounds _____ .

 해석

G Julia한테서 소식 들었니? 그 애는 터키에서 여행 중이잖아, 맞지?

B 응, Julia가 나한테 사진 몇 장을 보내왔어. 사진 보고 싶니?

G 응, 보고 싶어.

B 알겠어, 봐.

G 오, 저 동굴 집 좀 봐! 정말 특이하다, 그렇지 않니? 난 그곳에서 살아 봤으면 좋겠어.

B 난 저 열기구가 마음에 들어. 매우 아름다워 보여!

G 내 생각엔 터키가 방문하기에 정말 멋진 곳 같아. 언제 한 번 방문해 보고 싶다.

B 나도 그래!

B: 오늘 눈이 오는 거니?

G: 나도 모르겠어. 태호야, 왜 눈을 기다리는 거니?

B: 내 생일 선물로 새 썰매를 받았거든. 그거 빨리 시험해 보고 싶어.

G: 날씨 좀 확인해 볼게. 음, 당분간은 눈 소식이 없을 거야.

B: 알래스카에 살면 좋을 텐데! 그럼 온종일 썰매를 타러 갈 수 있을 텐데!

G: 말도 안 돼! 알래스카는 정말 추운 곳이야.

B: 내 생각엔 정말 즐거울 것 같아. 눈으로 집을 짓고 방학 때 그곳에서 지내고 싶어.

G: 눈으로 만든 집에 사는 건 재미있을 것 같아!

A: 이 집들 좀 봐. 매우 자연 그대로인 것 같아.

B: 우와, 이곳에 살아 봤으면 좋겠어.

A: 어느 집에서 가장 살아보고 싶니?

B: 돌로 만든 집에서 살아 보면 좋을 텐데. 매우 튼튼해 보여.

B: 이게 내 꿈의 집이야, Alice. 어떻게 생각하니?

G: 와, 바퀴가 달린 집이라니! 자동차의 일종이니?

B: 응, 자동차처럼 움직일 수 있어.

G: 그래서 그 집에서 살게 되면 뭘 할 거니?

B: 나는 가족들이랑 많은 곳을 여행할 거야.

G: 정말 신나게 들린다.

Listen and Speak 2 A-2

G: What would you do if you _____ a millionaire, Juwon?

B: I would _____ my own house.

G: What _____ of house would you _____?

B: I would build a house that is completely _____ with mirrors.

G: Why?

B: The _____ would make the house almost _____. Wouldn't that be cool?

G: That _____ be cool!

Listen and Speak 2 A-3

G: Look. The house in this picture is _____ down.

B: That's _____. Does anybody live there?

G: No, it would not be _____ to live there because the inside is also _____ _____.

B: Really? But I want to try living there.

G: _____ would you do if you lived in that house?

B: I would walk upside down _____ Spider-Man. I could also see things _____.

Listen and Speak 2 B

G: Dohun, we _____ to start our project on our dream country to _____.

B: That's right. _____ country do you want to visit, Emma?

G: In my _____, I want to visit Spain.

B: What _____ you do if you _____ Spain?

G: I'm _____ in buildings. So I would go see La Sagrada Familia.

B: Isn't _____ the church Antoni Gaudi _____?

G: Yes, it is. It would be interesting to see _____ his design was _____ by nature.

B: Hmm... . _____ about *Gaudí and Spain* as the title for our project?

G: I love it!

Listen and Speak 2 C

A: _____ would you do if you could have a magical power?

B: I would _____ _____ a bird. Then I would be _____ _____ _____ freely in the sky.

A: That's cool.

해석

G: 주원아, 백만장자가 되면 뭘 할 거니?

B: 나는 나만의 집을 지을 거야.

G: 어떤 집을 짓고 싶은데?

B: 나는 거울로 완전히 덮인 집을 지을 거야.

G: 왜?

B: 그 거울들이 집을 거의 안 보이게 만들어줄 거야. 멋지지 않니?

G: 그건 멋질 거야!

G: 봐, 이 사진에 있는 집은 거꾸로 되어 있어.

B: 흥미로운데. 그 집에 누가 사는 건가?

G: 아니, 내부도 거꾸로 되어 있으니까 그곳에서 살기는 쉽지 않을 거야.

B: 정말? 하지만 나는 그곳에서 살아 보고 싶어.

G: 저 집에 살게 된다면 너는 뭘 할 거니?

B: 나는 스파이더맨처럼 거꾸로 걸어다닐 거야. 난 또한 사물을 다르게 볼 수 있을 거야.

G: 도훈아, 우리가 방문하고 싶은 꿈꾸는 나라에 대한 프로젝트를 시작해야 돼.

B: 맞아. Emma, 너는 어느 나라를 방문하고 싶니?

G: 내 경우에는 스페인에 가 보고 싶어.

B: 스페인에 가게 되면 뭘 할 건데?

G: 나는 건물들에 관심이 있어. 그래서 나는 La Sagrada Familia에 가 볼 거야.

B: 그 성당은 Antoni Gaudi가 디자인한 교회 아니니?

G: 응, 맞아. 그의 디자인이 어떻게 자연에서 영감을 얻었는지 보면 흥미로울 거야.

B: 흠… '가우디와 스페인'을 우리 프로젝트 제목으로 하는 건 어떠니?

G: 아주 좋아!

A: 마법의 힘을 갖게 된다면 너는 무엇을 할 거니?

B: 난 새로 변할 거야. 그러면 하늘을 자유롭게 날 수 있겠지.

A: 그거 멋있다.

Real Life Communication A

Jinho: I think _____ in a jungle would be really _____. Don't you think so?

Claire: But there are _____ dangerous animals in the jungle, Jinho.

Jinho: I know. But the jungle is _____ of adventure. I wish I _____ _____ there.

Claire: What _____ you do if you _____ in the jungle?

Jinho: I would _____ it. Maybe I could make some animal friends.

Claire: Then _____ would you sleep? In a _____?

Jinho: No, I would stay in a tree house. _____ I would be safe from _____ _____.

Claire: That _____ sense.

Real Life Communication B

A: I wish I could _____ in a house on the water _____ my vacation.

B: What _____ you do if you _____ there?

A: I would go swimming _____ _____. I would also go _____.

B: That _____ fun.

Let's Check 1

B: _____ is my dream house. _____ do you think, Alice?

G: Oh, it's in the deep sea. It looks so _____. So, what would you do if you _____ in that house?

B: I have an _____ in _____ _____ animals. So I would _____ the deep sea and find some _____ sea animals.

G: _____ sounds cool!

Let's Check 2

A: What's the _____?

B: My computer is so slow. I wish I could _____ a new computer.

[01~02] 다음 대화를 읽고 물음에 답하시오.

> G: Have you heard from Julia? She's traveling in Turkey, right?
> B: Yes, she sent me some pictures. Do you want to see them?
> G: Yes, please.
> B: Okay, take a look.
> G: Oh, look at those cave houses! They look so unique, don't they? (A) 난 그곳에서 살아 보면 좋을 텐데. (try)
> B: I like those balloons. They look so beautiful!
> G: I think Turkey is a wonderful place to visit. I hope to visit there some day.
> B: Me too!

01 위 대화의 밑줄 친 (A)의 우리말을 주어진 단어를 이용하여 영작하시오. (7 words)

➡ _____

02 위 대화를 읽고 대답할 수 없는 것은?
① Who is traveling in Turkey?
② Who received photos from Julia?
③ What kind of houses are there in Turkey?
④ When is G planning to visit Turkey?
⑤ Who wants to visit Turkey?

[03~04] 다음 대화를 읽고 물음에 답하시오.

> A: Look at these houses. They look very natural.
> B: Wow, _____(A)_____ try living here.
> A: Which house would you most like to live in?
> B: _____(B)_____ live in the stone house. It looks very strong.

03 위 대화의 빈칸 (A)와 (B)에 공통으로 들어갈 말을 쓰시오. (4 words)

➡ _____

04 What kind of house does B want most to live in? (9 words)

➡ _____

[01~03] 다음 대화를 읽고 물음에 답하시오.

G: Dohun, we need to start our project on our dream country ⓐto visit.

B: That's right. ⓑWhich country do you want to visit, Emma?

G: ⓒIn my case, I want to visit Spain.

B: (A) 네가 스페인을 방문한다면 뭘 할 거니?

G: I'm interested in buildings. So I ⓓwould go see La Sagrada Familia.

B: Isn't that the church Antoni Gaudí designed?

G: Yes, it is. It would be ⓔinterested to see how his design was inspired by nature.

B: Hmm... How about *Gaudí and Spain* as the title for our project?

G: I love it!

서답형
01 위 대화의 밑줄 친 ⓐ~ⓔ 중 흐름상 어색한 것을 찾아 바르게 고치시오.

➡ _____

서답형
02 위 대화의 밑줄 친 (A)를 영작하시오. (8 words)

➡ _____

서답형
03 위 대화에서 주어진 영영풀이가 가리키는 단어를 찾아 쓰시오.

> to give someone an idea for a book, film, product, etc.

➡ _____

[04~06] 다음 대화를 읽고 물음에 답하시오.

B: This is my dream house, Alice. What do you think?

G: Oh, the house has wheels! Is it a kind of car?

B: Yes, it can move like a car.

G: So what would you do if you (A)[lived / have lived] in that house?

B: I (B)[will travel / would travel] to many places with my family.

G: That sounds cool.

서답형
04 위 대화의 괄호 (A)와 (B)에서 알맞은 것을 고르시오.

➡ (A) _____ (B) _____

중요
05 위 대화를 읽고 대답할 수 없는 것은?

① What kind of house is B's dream house?
② What does B's dream house include?
③ What can B's dream house move like?
④ Where is the conversation taking place?
⑤ What does G think about B's dream house?

06 위 대화의 주제로 가장 적절한 것은?

① 꿈에 그리던 집에 대한 상상
② 자동차로 만든 집에 대한 상상
③ 가족과의 여행에 대한 상상
④ 특별한 바퀴가 달린 자동차에 대한 상상
⑤ 꿈 속에서 본 집에 대한 상상

[07~09] 다음 대화를 읽고 물음에 답하시오.

> Jinho: I think living in a jungle would be really exciting. Don't you think so?
>
> Claire: ① But there are some dangerous animals in the jungle, Jinho.
>
> Jinho: I know. ② But the jungle is full of adventure. ③ I wish I could live there.
>
> Claire: What would you do if you lived in the jungle?
>
> Jinho: ④ Maybe I could make some animal friends.
>
> Claire: Then where would you sleep? In a cave?
>
> Jinho: No, I would stay in a tree house. ⑤ (A) 그러면 나는 위험한 동물들로부터 안전할 거야.
>
> Claire: That makes sense.

07 위 대화의 ①~⑤ 중 주어진 문장이 들어가기에 가장 적절한 곳은?

> I would explore it.

①   ②   ③   ④   ⑤

08 위 대화의 내용과 일치하지 않는 것은?

① Jinho believes living in a jungle will be exciting.

② Claire thinks living in a jungle can be dangerous.

③ All jungles are full of exciting adventures.

④ Jinho thinks he could make some animal friends in the jungle.

⑤ Jinho would stay in a tree house for protection.

서답형

09 위 대화의 밑줄 친 (A)의 우리말을 영작하시오.

➡ _____

10 다음 중 짝지어진 대화가 어색한 것을 고르시오.

① A: What would you do if you visited Spain?

    B: I would go see La Sagrada Familia.

② A: What if you won a lottery?

    B: I'll travel all over the world.

③ A: What would you do if you had only a day left to live?

    B: I would visit my family and spend time with them.

④ A: What would you do if you lived in a desert?

    B: I would ride a camel.

⑤ A: What would you do if your friends told you their secrets?

    B: I would tell no one about it.

서답형

11 다음 대화의 밑줄 친 우리말에 맞게 주어진 단어를 바르게 나열하시오.

> A: 마법의 힘을 갖게 된다면 너는 뭘 할 거니?
> (could / a magical power / you / if / do / what / you / have / would)
>
> B: I would turn into a bird. Then I would be able to fly freely in the sky.

➡ _____

_____

[01~02] 다음 대화를 읽고 물음에 답하시오.

G: What would you do if you became a millionaire, Juwon?
B: (A)나는 나만의 집을 지을 거야.
G: What kind of house would you build?
B: I would build a house that is completely covered with mirrors.
G: Why?
B: The mirrors would make the house almost invisible. Wouldn't that be cool?
G: That would be cool!

01 위 대화의 밑줄 친 (A)의 우리말에 맞게 영작하시오.

➡ _____

02 What would B cover his dream house completely with? (9 words)

➡ _____
_____

03 다음 대화의 밑줄 친 우리말을 영작하시오. (8 words)

A: What's the matter?
B: My computer is so slow. 내가 새 컴퓨터를 갖고 있다면 좋을 텐데.

➡ _____

[04~05] 다음 대화를 읽고 물음에 답하시오.

A: I wish I could stay in a house on the water during my vacation.
B: (A)네가 거기에 있다면 무엇을 할 거니? (what, be)
A: I would go swimming every day. I would also go fishing.
B: That sounds fun.

04 위 대화의 밑줄 친 (A)의 우리말을 주어진 단어를 이용해 영어로 옮기시오.

➡ _____

05 What are the two things A would do in a house on the water? (7 words)

➡ _____

[06~07] 다음 대화를 읽고 물음에 답하시오.

G: Look. The house in this picture is upside down.
B: That's interesting. Does anybody live there?
G: No, it would not be easy to live there because the inside is also upside down.
B: Really? But I want to try living there.
G: What would you do if you lived in that house?
B: I would walk upside down like Spider-Man. I could also see things differently.

06 What are G and B talking about? (10 words)

➡ _____
_____

07 What would B do if he lived in the house that is upside down? (9 words)

➡ _____
_____

Grammar

교과서

1 가정법 과거: 'If+주어+동사 과거형 ~, 주어+would/could+동사원형 …'

> • **If** I **lived** in a pueblo, I **would climb** up a ladder to enter my house. 내가 만약 푸에블로에 산다면, 집에 들어가기 위해 사다리를 오를 텐데.
> • **If** I **lived** in a house with a garden, I **would plant** many flowers in it. 내가 정원이 있는 집에 산다면, 나는 정원에 많은 꽃을 심을 텐데.

■ 가정법 과거: 현재 사실을 반대로 가정 또는 실현 가능성이 없는 일을 가정할 때 쓰이며, '**If**+주어+**동사 과거형** ~, 주어+**would/could**+**동사원형** …' 형태로, '만약 ~라면 …할 텐데'의 뜻이다.

- **If** I **have** her number, I **will call** her. 내게 그녀의 전화번호가 있다면, 그녀에게 전화할 것이다. (조건문, 가능성이 유)
- **If** I **had** her number, I **would call** her. 내게 그녀의 전화번호가 있다면, 그녀에게 전화할 텐데. (가정법)
  = **As** I **don't have** her number, I **can't call** her. 내게 그녀의 전화번호가 없어서, 전화할 수 없다. (직설법)
- **If** Jane **were** here, she **would help** me. Jane이 여기 있다면, 그녀가 나를 도울 텐데.

■ 가정법 과거완료: 일어난 과거 사실을 반대로 가정할 때 쓰이며, '**If**+주어+**had**+**과거분사** ~, 주어+**would/could**+**have**+**과거분사** …'의 형태이다.

- **If** Peter **had played** the music, they **would have respected** him. Peter가 그 음악을 연주했더라면, 그들은 그를 존경했을 텐데.

■ '**I wish**' 가정법은 현재 사실에 반대되는 소망 또는 현재 사실에 대한 유감을 나타낸다.

- **I wish** I **were** a world famous director. 내가 세계적으로 유명한 감독이라면 좋을 텐데.
  = **I'm sorry that** I'**m not** a world famous director. (직설법)

■ 가정법의 다양한 표현들로 직설법의 의미를 나타낼 수 있다.

- **As** there **is** a gondola, we **can** go to school. 곤돌라가 있어서, 우리는 학교에 갈 수 있다. (직설법)
- → **If** there **were no** gondola, we **couldn't go** to school. 곤돌라가 없다면, 우리는 학교에 갈 수 없을 텐데. (가정법)
- → **Were** there **no** gondola, we **couldn't go** to school. (If 생략 후 도치)
- → **Without a** gondola, we **couldn't go** to school. (Without = But for)
- → **If it were not for** a gondola, we **couldn't go** to school.
- → **Were it not for** a gondola, we **couldn't go** to school. (If 생략 후 도치)

핵심 Check

> 1. 다음 우리말에 맞게 괄호 안의 어휘를 바르게 배열하여 빈칸을 채우시오.
>   (1) 내가 로봇이라면, 그녀의 말을 들을 텐데. (a robot, I, listen, were, would, her, to)
>   ➡ If I _____.
>   (2) 돈이 좀 있으면, 서울에 아파트를 살 텐데. (if, an apartment, money, buy, Seoul, would, had, some, I, in)
>   ➡ I _____.

② 5형식 동사 keep / make

- They would **keep me cool** in summer and **warm** in winter. 그것들은 나를 여름에는 시원하게, 겨울에는 따뜻하게 유지해 줄 것이다.
- Staying home all day **makes Tim and Julie bored**. 하루 종일 집에 있는 것이 Tim과 Julie를 지루하게 만든다.

■ 5형식 문장의 기본 형태(목적보어의 종류)
- Anthony **made** Tommy **an actor**. (명사) Anthony는 Tommy를 배우로 만들었다.
- The noise **made** our learning **difficult**. (형용사) 그 소음은 우리의 학습을 어렵게 만들었다.
- Your friends **want** you **to clean the room**. (to부정사) 네 친구들은 네가 방을 청소하길 원한다.
- The song **made** me **cry**. (원형부정사) 그 노래는 나를 울게 만들었다.
- They **saw** Mina **singing a song**. (현재분사) 그들은 Mina가 노래를 부르고 있는 것을 보았다.

■ 동사 keep과 make의 5형식 예문과 목적보어의 종류
- These gloves **keep** my hands **warm**. 이 장갑은 내 손을 따뜻하게 유지시킨다. (형용사)
- I **kept** Peter **waiting**. 나는 Peter를 계속 기다리게 했다. (현재분사: 능동)
- He **kept** his face **hidden**. 그는 자신의 얼굴을 숨긴 채로 있었다. (과거분사: 수동)
- Kate **made** her son **a lawyer**. Kate는 그녀의 아들을 변호사로 만들었다. (명사)
- The song always **makes** me **happy**. 그 노래는 항상 나를 행복하게 만든다. (형용사)
- Sad movies **make** me **cry**. 슬픈 영화는 나를 울게 한다. (원형부정사)

■ 그 외 5형식에 쓰는 동사들과 목적보어
(1) have, get
- The manager **had** the car **ready** by tomorrow. 매니저가 내일까지 차를 준비시켰다. (형용사)
- I **had** my brother **repair** my car. 나는 오빠에게 내 차를 수리하도록 부탁했다. (원형부정사)
- The professor **had** the report **printed**. 교수님이 보고서를 인쇄되도록 시켰다. (과거분사)
- I **got** Mike **to fix** the machine. 나는 Mike가 기계를 고치게 했다. (to부정사)
- Sumi **got** the car **washed**. 수미가 세차를 시켰다. (과거분사)

(2) leave, find
- Mike **left** the door **open**. Mike는 문을 열어 두었다. (형용사)
- You **left** the work half **done**. 당신은 일을 반만 해 놓았다. (과거분사)
- I **found** the water **run[running]**. 나는 물이 흐르는 것을 발견했다. (원형부정사/현재분사)

핵심 Check

2. 다음 괄호 안에서 알맞은 말을 고르시오.

(1) Jay kept her cat (walking / walk) across the garden.

(2) The neighbor kept the door (closing / closed) during her holiday.

01 다음 각 가정법 문장에서 어법상 <u>어색한</u> 단어를 한 개씩 찾아 고치시오.

(1) If I live in Venice, I could take a gondola.

_____ ➡ _____

(2) If the gondola had wings, we can fly in the sky.

_____ ➡ _____

(3) It would be nice if my neighbor calls me to come over for tea.

_____ ➡ _____

(4) I will be able to walk around if the town had raised walkways.

_____ ➡ _____

02 다음 중 어법상 <u>어색한</u> 문장을 고르시오.

① The show program made him a super star.
② The lady made her three sons politicians.
③ My grandparents called me of Puppy Ducky.
④ The participants found the experiment exciting.
⑤ Please keep your hands clean when you touch the tools.

03 다음 빈칸에 들어갈 말로 알맞은 것은?

> If there _____ *vaporetto*, a water bus, I would travel from island to island.

① can be   ② is   ③ have been
④ were   ⑤ has been

04 다음 각 문장의 빈칸에 공통으로 들어갈 말로 알맞은 것은?

> • The suspect _____ her face covered and hidden.
> • The dry weather and strong wind _____ the wildfire burning.
> • Your support _____ him from committing a crime.
> • The doctors always _____ their hands clean.

① got   ② let   ③ had
④ took   ⑤ kept

01 다음 문장의 빈칸 (A)~(C)에 들어갈 말로 가장 적절한 것은?

> • If I (A)_____ a lot of meney, I could buy the car.
> • If it were not for his advice, the president (B)_____ not win many votes.
> • If the movie (C)_____ earlier, Jim would come and get me out of the cinema.

	(A)	(B)	(C)
①	had	would	starts
②	have had	could	starts
③	have had	could	will start
④	had	would	started
⑤	have	could	started

02 다음 밑줄 친 부분과 쓰임이 같은 것을 <u>모두</u> 고르면?

> Going sledding in the snow <u>made</u> Tom and Sophie excited.

① The college students <u>made</u> a reading club and volunteered at the public library in the town.

② The wives of the coaches <u>made</u> the players a meal which was good for their health and athletic ability.

③ The vocal coaches and the producer at the competition show <u>made</u> the little girl a world famous singer.

④ Problems that seemed impossible to solve at that time <u>made</u> those people gathering at the square even stronger.

⑤ My father <u>made</u> a real cheeseburger for me and my best friend Jenny.

서답형
[03~06] 다음 우리말과 일치하도록 괄호 안에 주어진 단어들을 바르게 배열하시오.

03
> 그들은 침입자들로부터 자신을 안전하게 지키기 위해서 그곳에서 살기로 결정했다.
> → They decided to live there (invaders, from, to, themselves, safe, keep).

➡ They decided to live there _____
_____.

04
> 한 건물 안에서 함께 사는 것은 그들을 안전하게 지켜준다.
> → (them, safe, in, living, building, together, one, keeps).

➡ _____

05
> 비가 오면, 우리는 수영장에 갈 수 없을 텐데.
> → If (could, the swimming pool, go, we, it, to, rained, not).

➡ If _____.

06
> 토루에 산다면, 나는 항상 집에서 함께 놀 친구들이 있을 텐데.
> → If I lived in a tulou, I (with, would, have, to, always, friends, play) at home.

➡ If I lived in a tulou, I _____
_____ at home.

17 다음 중 같은 뜻을 가진 문장끼리 짝지어진 것은?

① She would invite me every weekend and enjoy swimming with me if she lived in a house with a swimming pool.
  = She didn't live in a house with a swimming pool, so she wouldn't invite me every weekend to enjoy swimming.

② Sean could write a letter to the director of the film if he knew her address in Seoul.
  = Sean can't write a letter to the director of the film though he knows her address in Seoul.

③ If my grandmother could walk faster than usual, she would arrive soon at the hospital.
  = My grandmother can't walk faster than usual, so she won't arrive at the hospital.

④ If it rained now, Jefferson would stay in his office.
  = It rains now, so Jefferson will stay in his office.

⑤ If the kids had seen the bus coming, they would not have got hurt in the accident.
  = The kids didn't see the bus coming, but they couldn't get hurt in the accident.

[08~09] 다음 우리말을 어법상 알맞게 영작한 것을 고르시오.

08

헬멧을 착용하는 것은 오토바이 운전자들을 안전하게 지켜준다.

① Wearing a helmet keeps motorbike drivers safely from accidents.
② Wearing a helmet keeps motorbike drivers safe from accidents.
③ Wearing helmets safely keep motorbike drivers from accidents.
④ Wearing helmets safely keeps motorbike drivers into accidents.
⑤ Wearing a helmet keeps safe for motorbike drivers from accidents.

09

겨울에 얇은 옷을 여러 겹으로 입는 것은 우리의 몸을 따뜻하게 유지해 주고, 우리가 활동하기 더 편하게 만들어 준다.

① Putting on layers of thin clothes in winter keep our bodies warm and makes us more active.
② Putting on thin layers of clothes in winter keeps our bodies warmly and makes us more active.
③ Putting on layers of thin clothes in winter keeps our bodies warm and makes us more actively.
④ Putting on layers of thin clothes in winter keeps our bodies warm and make us more active.
⑤ Putting on layers of thin clothes in winter keeps our bodies warm and makes us more active.

서답형
10 다음 가정법 과거 문장에서 어법상 어색한 부분을 찾아서 고치시오. (2곳)

If you lived in a desert and have no one to live with, what will you do?

➡ _____

[11~12] 다음 주어진 문장들 중 문장의 구조적 형식이 다른 하나는?

11
① People in that town always call the poor boy a fool.
② They left the baby alone in the forest where monkeys and wolves lived.
③ The physical education teacher made his students run faster.
④ The princess helped the maids wash the dishes used at the party.
⑤ The old woman in the country made them traditional Korean food.

12 중요
① He always keeps the door open.
② The way he proposed will keep your bag from getting stolen.
③ All the animals in the jungle saw Tarzan enter the cave.
④ The passenger got the porter to carry the baggage.
⑤ She found the man wearing black clothes disappearing into the dark.

[13~14] 다음은 각각 가정법 과거 형식의 문장들이다. 어법상 옳은 것을 고르시오.

13
① If Miranda has the ticket, she could take the bus on her way to New York.
② If I knew the truth, I would tell it to you.
③ I wish the new house will provide the comfort to the guests from Mexico.
④ If the tourists had seen the vaporetto, a water bus, they can travel on it.
⑤ I wish the villagers know the answer to the problem of the polluted river.

14
① If the lady is in Beijing, she could join her sister's graduation.
② If the robots had AI, they won't do the bad thing to human officers.
③ If it were not for the tie she bought me, I would not be able to pass the interview.
④ My younger brother could have got hurt, if the driver didn't pull up the bus immediately.
⑤ If the fish know the way to the river where they were born, they could go up against the stream.

 중요

다음 〈보기〉의 밑줄 친 부분과 쓰임이 다른 하나는?

보기
I could climb up a ladder to get in my house if I lived in a *pueblo* in New Mexico.

① I wish I could memorize as many poems as possible.
② The dogs and cats could get free lunch if the old lady bought their food at Ball Mart.
③ If the witnesses knew the motorbike's number, they could report to the judge.
④ Were it not for Sheryl's help, Peterson could not finish his science assignment.
⑤ Could you bring him a glass of apple juice after the game?

01 다음 각 가정법 문장에서 어법상 <u>어색한</u> 단어를 한 개씩 찾아 바르게 고치시오. (고친 부분은 두 단어라도 상관 없음.)

(1) Without a ladder, people won't be able to enter their *pueblos*.

➡ _____

(2) If your house has a flat roof, you could sometimes sleep up on the roof under the moon.

➡ _____

(3) I wish I will live in a different house in a different country.

➡ _____

(4) If it were not for the houses on the water, people in Venice will not be able to keep themselves safe from invaders.

➡ _____

(5) Suji would be late for the art class yesterday if her car had been broken.

➡ _____

(6) If the physics teacher were in the boy's situation, she will understand how urgently he should go to the restroom.

➡ _____

(7) I wish the round houses in China can house more than 50 families.

➡ _____

02 다음 우리말과 일치하도록 괄호 안에 주어진 단어들을 바르게 배열하여 문장을 완성하시오.

(1) 그 나무 기둥들이 지금까지 베니스를 지탱해 준다. (wooden, Venice, support, poles, those)

➡ _____ to this day.

(2) 그 두꺼운 벽들이 여름에는 사람들을 시원하게, 겨울에는 따뜻하게 유지해 줄 것이다. (warm, cool, keep, in summer, people, and, would, walls)

➡ The thick _____ in winter.

(3) 중국의 어떤 사람들은 커다란 둥근 건물을 그들의 집으로 만들었다. (building, a, house, made, their, huge, round)

➡ Some people in China _____.

(4) 수상 버스는 섬에서 섬으로 여행하는 것을 더욱 편하게 만들어 준다. (easier, makes, from, to, it, travel, island, water bus)

➡ A _____ to island.

03 다음 〈보기〉의 문장과 같은 뜻이 되도록 괄호 안에 주어진 조건에 맞게 빈칸을 채우시오.

> Without many wooden poles in the ground, Venice would be very different.

(1) _____ many wooden poles in the ground, Venice would be very different. (it, be동사 활용, 5 단어)

(2) _____ wooden poles in the ground, Venice would be very different. (there, no 활용, 4 단어)

(3) _____ many wooden poles in the ground, Venice would be very different. (it, be동사 활용, 4 단어)

(4) _____, Venice isn't very different. (직설법, there, 접속사 as 활용, 9 단어)

04 다음 주어진 문장과 뜻이 같도록 빈칸을 알맞게 채우시오. (11 단어)

> As Matthew doesn't live in a house with a soccer field, he can't invite his friends to play soccer after school.
> → If Matthew _____
> _____ his friends to play soccer after school.

05 다음 〈보기〉와 같이 우리말에 맞게 괄호 안에 주어진 단어들을 활용하여 빈칸에 들어갈 알맞은 말을 채워 넣으시오.

> ┤ 보기 ├
> They wanted to <u>keep themselves safe from</u> invaders. 그들은 침입자들로부터 자신들을 안전하게 지키기를 원했다. (safe, from, them)

(1) Staying home all day long _____
_____ _____. 하루 종일 집에 머물러 있는 것은 그들을 지루하게 만들었다. (bore)

(2) The visitors _____ _____ _____
_____ _____ in the woods. 그 방문객들은 숲에서 코알라들이 잎들을 먹고 있는 것을 보았다. (the koalas, see, leaf, eat)

(3) Brian and his friends _____
_____ _____ _____ their parents.
Brian과 그의 친구들은 그들의 부모님이 그들의 이름을 부르는 것을 들었다. (call, name, hear, by)

(4) The swampy surface _____ _____
_____ _____ _____
_____ their homes. 늪지 표면은 그들이 자기들의 집을 짓는 것을 어렵게 만들었다. (for, to, make, build)

[06~07] 다음 그림을 보고, 그림과 괄호 안에 주어진 단어를 활용하여 우리말에 맞게 빈칸을 채우시오.

06

stone house

> 내가 돌 집에 산다면, 태풍도 그 집을 흔들 수 없을 텐데. (the typhoon, shake)
> ➡ If _____
> _____.
> (가정법 과거, If 제외 총 11 단어)

07

My house is made of earth

> 흙으로 만든 집에 사는 것은 우리를 여름에 시원하게 유지해 준다. (keep, cool, make, live, earth)
> ➡ _____
> _____ in summer.
> (동명사 주어, 5형식 문장, in summer 제외 총 10 단어)

08 다음 직설법 문장을 가정법으로 고치시오.

(1) As there is no food left, the homeless man will work today.
➡ _____
_____

(2) Since he is not strong enough, he will exercise at the gym every day.
➡ _____
_____

Reading

If I Lived There

Different people live in different houses. Some use ladders to enter their houses. Others live in houses on the water. And others share their houses with many people. Imagine you live in one of these houses. How would that change your life?

Pueblos in New Mexico, USA

If I lived in a *pueblo*, I would climb up a ladder to enter my house. There's a hidden opening on top of the house. If unwelcome visitors appeared, I would pull the ladder up to stop them from entering. The thick walls are made of earth, straw, and water. They would keep me cool in summer and warm in winter. The house has a flat roof. I would sometimes sleep up on the roof under the moon and stars.

Houses on Water in Venice, Italy

If I lived in Venice, I would take a gondola to school every morning. Venice has 118 small islands. On weekends, I would travel from island to island by a *vaporetto*, a water bus. At high tide, the water from the Adriatic Sea often rises and leaves the streets full of water. However, I would be able to walk around the town through the raised walkways.

---

ladder: 사다리
enter: ~로 들어가다
unwelcome: 반갑지 않은
appear: 나타나다
pull up: 끌어올리다
earth: 흙
tide: 조수
walkway: 통로

확인문제

● 다음 문장이 본문의 내용과 일치하면 T, 일치하지 <u>않으면</u> F를 쓰시오.

1 By pulling the ladder up, people living in a *pueblo* protect themselves. ☐

2 The walkways in Venice are raised because the streets are always full of water. ☐

3 A gondola is a water bus in Venice. ☐

Venice is known as the "floating city." In Venice, there are many colorful houses on the water. You may wonder <u>how and why they built</u> <u>the houses on the water.</u> The old Venetians decided to live there to keep <u>themselves</u> safe from invaders. But <u>it</u> was not easy for <u>them to</u> <u>build</u> their homes on this swampy surface. So they installed more than 10 million wooden poles in the ground. <u>It is these wooden poles that</u> support Venice to this day.

Tulou in Fujian, China

If I lived in a *tulou*, a huge round house in Fujian, China, I would always have friends at home <u>to play with.</u> I would sometimes <u>hear my</u> <u>neighbor calling</u> me to come over for tea or dinner. In a *tulou*, there are usually three to five floors. The first floor <u>is used for</u> cooking and eating. And people store food and tools on the second floor. Do you wonder <u>where I would sleep?</u> My bedroom would be on the third or fourth floor.

A *tulou* is like a village. The people <u>living</u> in a *tulou* mostly have the same family name. Some large *tulou* can house <u>up to</u> 50 families. They work together and share many things. <u>Living together</u> in one building keeps them safe.

Homes are everywhere. But they are different all over the world. What is your home like?

invader: 침략자
swampy: 습지의
install: 설치하다, 장착하다
support: 지지하다, 지탱하다
come over: 들르다
store: 저장하다
family name: 성
house: 수용하다
up to: ~까지

● 다음 문장이 본문의 내용과 일치하면 T, 일치하지 <u>않으면</u> F를 쓰시오.

1 The old Venetians invaded the islands and kept living there. ☐

2 It was on the swampy surface that the old Venetians built their houses. ☐

3 More than 10 billion wooden poles are still in the ground. ☐

4 A *tulou* is a small house which can house up to about five families. ☐

5 A *tulou* has usually three to five floors. ☐

6 Friends gather together to live in a *tulou* so they have different family names. ☐

● 우리말을 참고하여 빈칸에 알맞은 말을 쓰시오.

1 Different people _____ _____ different houses.

2 Some _____ _____ _____ _____ _____ _____.
Others _____ _____ houses _____ the water.

3 And _____ _____ their houses _____ many people.

4 _____ you _____ _____ one of these houses. How would _____ _____ your life?

Pueblos in New Mexico, USA

5 If I _____ _____ a *pueblo*, I _____ _____ up a ladder _____ _____ _____ house.

6 There's a _____ _____ on top of the house.

7 _____ unwelcome visitors _____, I _____ _____ the ladder _____ _____ _____ them _____ entering.

8 The thick walls _____ _____ _____ earth, straw, and water.

9 They would _____ _____ _____ in summer and _____ in winter.

10 The house has _____ _____ _____. I would sometimes _____ _____ _____ _____ under the moon and stars.

Houses on Water in Venice, Italy

11 If I _____ _____ Venice, I _____ _____ _____ _____ to school every morning.

12 Venice _____ 118 small _____. _____ _____, I would travel _____ _____ _____ _____ by a *vaporetto*, a water bus.

13 At high tide, the water _____ the Adriatic Sea often _____ and _____ the streets _____ _____ _____.

14 _____, I would _____ the town through the raised walkways.

15 Venice _____ _____ _____ the " _____ city."

1 다양한 사람들이 다양한 집에서 살고 있습니다.

2 어떤 사람들은 집에 들어가기 위해 사다리를 이용합니다. 다른 사람들은 물 위에 있는 집에서 살고 있습니다.

3 그리고 또 다른 사람들은 많은 사람들과 함께 집을 공유합니다.

4 여러분이 이 집들 중 하나에 산다고 상상해 보세요. 여러분의 삶은 어떻게 바뀔까요?

푸에블로 – 미국 뉴멕시코
5 내가 만약 푸에블로에 산다면, 나는 집에 들어가기 위해 사다리를 오를 것이다.

6 집 꼭대기에는 숨겨진 구멍이 있다.

7 반갑지 않은 방문객이 나타난다면 나는 사다리를 끌어올려 그들이 들어오지 못하게 할 것이다.

8 두꺼운 벽은 흙, 지푸라기, 물로 만들어져 있다.

9 그것들은 여름에는 시원하게, 겨울에는 따뜻하게 유지시켜 준다.

10 집에는 평평한 지붕이 있다. 때때로 나는 달과 별들 아래의 지붕 위에서 잠을 잘 것이다.

물 위에 있는 집 – 이탈리아 베니스
11 내가 만약 베니스에 산다면, 나는 매일 아침 곤돌라를 타고 학교에 갈 것이다.

12 베니스는 **118**개의 작은 섬이 있다. 주말마다 나는 수상 버스인 바포레토를 타고 이 섬 저 섬을 여행할 것이다.

13 조수가 높을 때에는 아드리아 해의 물이 자주 범람하고 거리는 물로 가득 찬다.

14 그러나 나는 돌출되어 있는 통로로 도심 주변을 걸어다닐 수 있을 것이다.

15 베니스는 '떠다니는 도시'로 알려져 있다.

16 In Venice, _____ _____ many _____ _____ on the water.

17 You may wonder _____ and _____ _____ _____ _____ _____ _____ the water.

18 The old Venetians _____ _____ _____ _____ _____ to keep _____ _____ _____ invaders.

19 But it was not easy _____ _____ _____ _____ their homes on this _____ surface.

20 So they _____ more than 10 million _____ _____ in the ground.

21 It is these _____ _____ that _____ Venice _____ this day.

Tulou in Fujian, China

22 If I _____ in a *tulou*, a huge round house in Fujian, China, I _____ always _____ _____ at home _____ _____ _____.

23 I would sometimes _____ my neighbor _____ _____ _____ _____ _____ for tea or dinner.

24 In a *tulou*, there _____ usually _____ _____ _____.

25 The first floor _____ _____ _____ cooking and eating.

26 And people _____ _____ and _____ _____ the second floor.

27 Do you wonder _____ _____ _____ _____ _____? My bedroom _____ _____ _____ the third or fourth floor.

28 A *tulou* is _____ a village. The people _____ _____ a *tulou* mostly _____ the same family name.

29 Some large *tulou* _____ _____ _____ _____ 50 families. They _____ _____ and _____ many things.

30 _____ together in one building _____ _____ _____.

31 Homes are everywhere. But they are _____ _____ _____. _____ is your home _____?

16 베니스에는 물 위에 있는 색색의 건물들이 많다.

17 여러분은 어떻게, 그리고 왜 그들이 물 위에 집을 지었는지 궁금할 것이다.

18 옛 베니스 사람들은 침략자들로부터 자신들을 안전하게 지키기 위해 그곳에 살기로 결정했다.

19 하지만 그들이 이 습지 위에 집을 짓는 것은 쉽지가 않았다.

20 그래서 그들은 땅에 천만 개 이상의 나무 기둥을 설치했다.

21 이 나무 기둥들이 바로 지금까지 베니스를 지탱해 주고 있는 것이다.

토루 – 중국 푸젠

22 내가 만약 거대하고 둥그런 집인 중국 푸젠의 토루(tulou)에 산다면, 나는 항상 집에 함께 놀 친구들이 있을 것이다.

23 때때로 나의 이웃이 차를 마시거나 저녁 식사를 하러 집에 들르라고 나를 부르는 소리를 듣게 될 것이다.

24 토루는 대개 3층에서 5층으로 되어 있다.

25 1층은 요리하고 식사하는 데에 사용된다.

26 그리고 사람들은 2층에 식량과 도구를 보관한다.

27 내가 어디에서 잠을 잘지 궁금한가? 내 침실은 3층이나 4층에 있을 것이다.

28 토루는 마을과 같다. 토루에 사는 사람들은 대부분 같은 성(姓)을 가지고 있다.

29 몇몇 큰 토루는 50가구까지 수용할 수 있다. 그들은 함께 일하고 많은 것을 공유한다.

30 한 건물에 함께 사는 것은 그들을 안전하게 지켜 준다.

31 집은 어디에나 있습니다. 그러나 전 세계의 집은 모두 다릅니다. 여러분의 집은 어떤가요?

● 우리말을 참고하여 본문을 영작하시오.

1 다양한 사람들이 다양한 집에서 살고 있습니다.
➡ _____

2 어떤 사람들은 집에 들어가기 위해 사다리를 이용합니다. 다른 사람들은 물 위에 있는 집에서 살고 있습니다.
➡ _____

3 그리고 또 다른 사람들은 많은 사람들과 함께 집을 공유합니다.
➡ _____

4 여러분이 이 집들 중 하나에 산다고 상상해 보세요. 여러분의 삶은 어떻게 바뀔까요?
➡ _____

Pueblos in New Mexico, USA

5 내가 만약 푸에블로에 산다면, 나는 집에 들어가기 위해 사다리를 오를 것이다.
➡ _____

6 집 꼭대기에는 숨겨진 구멍이 있다.
➡ _____

7 반갑지 않은 방문객이 나타난다면 나는 사다리를 끌어올려 그들이 들어오지 못하게 할 것이다.
➡ _____

8 두꺼운 벽은 흙, 지푸라기, 물로 만들어져 있다.
➡ _____

9 그것들은 여름에는 시원하게, 겨울에는 따뜻하게 유지시켜 준다.
➡ _____

10 집에는 평평한 지붕이 있다. 때때로 나는 달과 별들 아래의 지붕 위에서 잠을 잘 것이다.
➡ _____

Houses on Water in Venice, Italy

11 내가 만약 베니스에 산다면, 나는 매일 아침 곤돌라를 타고 학교에 갈 것이다.
➡ _____

12 베니스는 118개의 작은 섬이 있다. 주말마다 나는 수상 버스인 바포레토를 타고 이 섬 저 섬을 여행할 것이다.
➡ _____

13 조수가 높을 때에는 아드리아 해의 물이 자주 범람하고 거리는 물로 가득 찬다.
➡ _____

14 그러나 나는 돌출되어 있는 통로로 도심 주변을 걸어다닐 수 있을 것이다.
➡ _____

15 베니스는 '떠다니는 도시'로 알려져 있다.
➡ _____

16 베니스에는 물 위에 있는 색색의 건물들이 많다.
➡ _____

17 여러분은 어떻게, 그리고 왜 그들이 물 위에 집을 지었는지 궁금할 것이다.
➡ _____

18 옛 베니스 사람들은 침략자들로부터 자신들을 안전하게 지키기 위해 그곳에 살기로 결정했다.
➡ _____

19 하지만 그들이 이 습지 위에 집을 짓는 것은 쉽지가 않았다.
➡ _____

20 그래서 그들은 땅에 천만 개 이상의 나무 기둥을 설치했다.
➡ _____

21 이 나무 기둥들이 바로 지금까지 베니스를 지탱해 주고 있는 것이다.
➡ _____

Tulou in Fujian, China

22 내가 만약 거대하고 둥그런 집인 중국 푸젠의 토루(tulou)에 산다면, 나는 항상 집에 함께 놀 친구들이 있을 것이다.
➡ _____
_____

23 때때로 나의 이웃이 차를 마시거나 저녁 식사를 하러 집에 들르라고 나를 부르는 소리를 듣게 될 것이다.
➡ _____

24 토루는 대개 3층에서 5층으로 되어 있다.
➡ _____

25 1층은 요리하고 식사하는 데에 사용된다.
➡ _____

26 그리고 사람들은 2층에 식량과 도구를 보관한다.
➡ _____

27 내가 어디에서 잠을 잘지 궁금한가? 내 침실은 3층이나 4층에 있을 것이다.
➡ _____

28 토루는 마을과 같다. 토루에 사는 사람들은 대부분 같은 성(姓)을 가지고 있다.
➡ _____

29 몇몇 큰 토루는 50가구까지 수용할 수 있다. 그들은 함께 일하고 많은 것을 공유한다.
➡ _____

30 한 건물에 함께 사는 것은 그들을 안전하게 지켜 준다.
➡ _____

31 집은 어디에나 있습니다. 그러나 전 세계의 집은 모두 다릅니다. 여러분의 집은 어떤가요?
➡ _____

[01~04] 다음 글을 읽고 물음에 답하시오.

(A)_____ Some use ladders to enter their houses. Others live in houses on the water. And others share their houses with many people. Imagine you live in one of these houses. How would that change your life?

***Pueblos* in New Mexico, USA**

If I lived in a *pueblo*, I would climb up a ladder to enter my house. (①) There's a hidden opening on top of the house. (②) If unwelcome visitors appeared, I would pull the ladder up to stop them from entering. (③) The thick walls are made of earth, straw, and water. (④) The house has a flat roof. (⑤) I would sometimes sleep up on the roof under the moon and stars.

01 다음 중 빈칸 (A)에 들어갈 말로 가장 적절한 것은?

① Different people live various lives.
② Different people live in different houses.
③ There are many kinds of people in the world.
④ People build their houses with various materials.
⑤ There are many people who own many houses.

02 ①~⑤ 중 주어진 문장이 들어가기에 가장 적절한 곳은?

They would keep me cool in summer and warm in winter.

①   ②   ③   ④   ⑤

03 Choose one that is TRUE.

① It is hard to find *pueblos* in New Mexico.
② People who live in *pueblos* enter the house through the door.
③ *Pueblos* have pointy roofs.
④ *Pueblos* have walls which are made of only earth.
⑤ By pulling up ladders, people living in *pueblos* can aviod unwanted guests.

서답형
04 What would the writer do on the roof of the house? Answer in English.

➡ _____

_____

[05~08] 다음 글을 읽고 물음에 답하시오.

Houses on Water in Venice, Italy

If I lived in Venice, I would take a gondola to school every morning. Venice has 118 small islands. On weekends, I would travel from island to island by a vaporetto, a water bus. At high tide, the water from the Adriatic Sea often rises and leaves the streets full of water. (A)_____, I would be able to walk around the town through the raised walkways.

Venice is known as the "floating city." In Venice, there are many colorful houses on the water. You may wonder how and why they built the houses on the water. The old Venetians decided to live there to keep themselves safe from invaders. But it was not easy for them to build their homes on this swampy surface. So they installed more than 10 million wooden poles in the ground. It is these wooden poles that support Venice to this day.

05 빈칸 (A)에 들어갈 말로 가장 적절한 것은?

① For instance   ② However

③ That is   ④ Therefore

⑤ In addition

06 다음과 같이 풀이되는 말을 위 글에서 찾아 쓰시오.

always very wet

➡ _____

07 When you are in Venice, what are there on the water? Answer in English.

➡ _____

08 다음 중 위 글을 읽고 답할 수 있는 것은?

① How long would it take to go to school by gondola?

② What happens in Venice when it is at low tide?

③ Who first invented a *vaporetto* in Venice?

④ Who named Venice "floating city?"

⑤ What supports Venice to this day?

[09~12] 다음 글을 읽고 물음에 답하시오.

Tulou in Fujian, China

If I lived in a *Tulou*, a huge round house in Fujian, China, I would always have friends at home to play with. I would sometimes hear my neighbor calling me to come over for tea or dinner. In a *Tulou*, there are usually three to five floors. The first floor is used for cooking and eating. And people store food and tools on the second floor. Do you wonder where I would sleep? My bedroom would be on the third or fourth floor.

A *tulou* is like (A)_____. The people living in a *tulou* mostly have the same family name. Some large *tulou* can house up to 50 families. They work together and share many things. Living together in one building keeps them safe.

Homes are everywhere. But they are different all over the world. What is your home like?

09 글의 흐름상 빈칸 (A)에 들어갈 말로 가장 적절한 것은?

① a city   ② a church

③ a village   ④ a tomb

⑤ a bedroom

10 What is a *tulou*? Answer in English with a full sentence.

➡ _____

11 What is TRUE about a *tulou*?

① It has only one floor.

② It houses only five families.

③ It can't store food.

④ It can't keep people safe.

⑤ People living there share many things.

12 If the writer lived in a tulou, where would he or she sleep? Answer in English with a full sentence.

➡ _____

[13~16] 다음 글을 읽고 물음에 답하시오.

Different people live in ①different houses. Some use ladders to enter their houses. Others live in houses on the water. And others share their houses with many people. Imagine you live in one of these houses. How would (A) that change your life?

***Pueblos* in New Mexico, USA**

If I lived in a *pueblo*, I would ②climb up a ladder to enter my house. There's a hidden opening on top of the house. If ③welcome visitors appeared, I would pull the ladder up to stop them from entering. The thick walls are made of earth, straw, and water. They would keep me ④cool in summer and warm in winter. The house has a ⑤flat roof. I would sometimes sleep up on the roof under the moon and stars.

13 ①~⑤ 중 글의 흐름상 어색한 것은?

① ② ③ ④ ⑤

14 다음 중 밑줄 친 (A)의 의미로 가장 적절한 것은?

① building different houses
② sharing a house with many people
③ leaving your house to live your life on your own
④ living in one of the houses mentioned above
⑤ living in a *pueblo* to live a different life from yours

15 What is there on top of a *pueblo*? Answer in English.

➡ _____

16 다음 중 푸에블로를 바르게 소개하고 있는 사람은?

① Semin: You can enjoy the house because it has a beautiful garden leading to the house.
② Yena: You'd better learn how to use a rope to enter the house.
③ Penny: You can experience the house only in Mexico.
④ David: Sleep up on the roof and enjoy the fantastic moon and stars.
⑤ Emma: The structure of the house welcome anyone who wants to come in.

[17~21] 다음 글을 읽고 물음에 답하시오.

Houses on Water in Venice, Italy

If I lived in Venice, I would take a gondola to school every morning. Venice has 118 small islands. On weekends, I would travel from island to island by a *vaporetto*, a water bus. At high tide, the water from the Adriatic Sea often rises and leaves the streets full of water. However, I would be able to walk around the town through the raised walkways.

(A) But it was not easy for them to build their homes on this swampy surface.

(B) Venice is known as the "floating city." In Venice, there are many colorful houses on the water.

(C) So they installed more than 10 million wooden poles in the ground. It is these wooden poles that support Venice to this day.

(D) You may wonder how and why they built the houses on the water. The old Venetians decided to live there to keep ⓐthemselves safe from invaders.

17 자연스러운 글이 되도록 (A)~(D)를 바르게 나열하시오.

➡ _____

서답형

18 What is a *vaporetto*? Answer in English with a full sentence.

➡ _____

서답형

19 다음 중 글의 내용과 일치하지 <u>않는</u> 부분을 찾아 바르게 고쳐 쓰시오.

> Building their homes on wetland was not an easy work to do for the old Venetians. But they made many poles made of steel and had them support Venice.

➡ _____

중요

20 Why are the streets full of water at high tide?

① Because of many water buses
② Due to lots of visitors
③ Owing to swampy land
④ Due to lowered walkways
⑤ Because at high tide, the water from the Adriatic Sea often rises

21 밑줄 친 ⓐ와 쓰임이 같은 것은?

① The man made the pasta <u>himself</u>.
② Please seat <u>yourself</u> on the chair.
③ The mayor <u>herself</u> attended the meeting.
④ He showed the picture to me <u>himself</u>.
⑤ Did they take the pictures <u>themselves</u>?

[22~25] 다음 글을 읽고 물음에 답하시오.

***Tulou* in Fujian, China**

If I lived in a *tulou*, a huge round house in Fujian, China, I would always have friends at home to play with. (①) I would sometimes hear my neighbor (A)_____ me to come over for tea or dinner. (②) In a *tulou*, there are usually three to five floors. (③) The first floor is used for cooking and eating. (④) And people store food and tools on the second floor. (⑤) My bedroom would be on the third or fourth floor.

A *tulou* is like a village. The people living in a *tulou* mostly have the same family name. Some large *tulou* can house up to 50 families. They work together and share many things. Living together in one building keeps them safe.

Homes are everywhere. But they are different all over the world. What is your home like?

22 동사 call을 어법에 맞게 빈칸 (A)에 쓰시오.

➡ _____

중요

23 ①~⑤ 중 주어진 문장이 들어가기에 가장 적절한 곳은?

> Do you wonder where I would sleep?

①　　　②　　　③　　　④　　　⑤

중요

24 Choose one that is TRUE.

① A *tulou* is a small square house.
② A *tulou* is one of traditional houses in China.
③ It is almost impossible to hear someone call your name in a *tulou*.
④ A *tulou* has up to five floors.
⑤ You have to cook outside when living in a *tulou*.

서답형

25 How many families can some large *tulous* house? Answer in English with a full sentence.

➡ _____

[01~05] 다음 글을 읽고 물음에 답하시오.

Different people live in different houses. Some use ladders to enter their houses. Others live in houses on the water. And others share their houses with many people. Imagine you live in one of these houses. How would that change your life?

***Pueblos* in New Mexico, USA**

If I lived in a *pueblo*, I would climb up a ladder to enter my house. There's a hidden opening on top of the house. If unwelcome visitors appeared, I would pull the ladder up to stop them from entering. The thick walls are made of earth, straw, and water. They would keep me cool in summer and warm in winter. The house has a flat roof. I would sometimes sleep up on the roof under the moon and stars.

01 What do some people have to use to enter their houses? Answer in English.

➡ _____

_____

02 What would the writer do if unwelcome visitors appeared? Answer in English with a full sentence.

➡ _____

_____

03 What are the thick walls made of? Answer in English.

➡ _____

_____

04 Why is it possible to sleep on the roof of the house, *pueblo*? Answer in English and use the word 'because.'

➡ _____

_____

05 다음과 같이 풀이되는 말을 위 글에서 찾아 쓰시오.

> a device used for climbing that has two long pieces of wood, metal, or rope with a series of steps between them

➡ _____

[06~09] 다음 글을 읽고 물음에 답하시오.

Houses on Water in Venice, Italy

If I (A)_____ in Venice, I would take a gondola to school every morning. Venice has 118 small islands. On weekends, I would travel from island to island by a va poretto, a water bus. At high tide, the water from the Adriatic Sea often rises and leaves the streets full of water. However, I would be able to walk around the town through the raised walkways.

Venice is known as the "floating city." In Venice, there are many colorful houses on the water. You may wonder how and why they built the houses on the water. The old Venetians decided to live there to keep themselves safe from invaders. But it was not easy for them to build their homes on this swampy surface. So they installed more than 10 million wooden poles in the ground. It is these wooden poles that support Venice to this day.

06 빈칸 (A)에 동사 live를 어법에 맞게 쓰시오.

➡ _____

07 What would the writer do on weekends? Answer in English.

➡ _____
_____

08 What is Venice known as? Answer in English with a full sentence.

➡ _____

09 다음 중 위 글의 내용과 일치하지 <u>않는</u> 곳을 한 군데 찾아 바르게 고쳐 쓰시오.

> Venice is the city which was built on a swampy surface. The old Venetians wanted to be safe from themselves, so they made the city with lots of wooden poles.

➡ _____

[10~12] 다음 글을 읽고 물음에 답하시오.

Tulou in Fujian, China

If I lived in a *tulou*, a huge round house in Fujian, China, I would always have friends at home to play with. I would sometimes hear my neighbor calling me to come over for tea or dinner. In a *tulou*, there are usually three to five floors. The first floor is used for cooking and eating. And people store food and tools on the second floor. (A)<u>내가 어디에서 잠을 잘지 궁금한가</u>? My bedroom would be on the third or fourth floor.

A *tulou* is like a village. The people living in a *tulou* mostly have the same family

name. Some large *tulou* can house up to 50 families. They work together and share many things. Living together in one building keeps them safe.

Homes are everywhere. But (B)<u>they</u> are different all over the world. What is your home like?

10 주어진 단어를 바르게 나열하여 밑줄 친 우리말 (A)를 영어로 쓰시오.

> (wonder / sleep / do / would / where / you / I)

➡ _____

11 밑줄 친 (B)가 가리키는 것을 우리말로 쓰시오.

➡ _____

12 위 글을 바탕으로 중국의 토루를 소개하는 글을 완성하시오.

> Do you want to share your house with many people? Why don't you visit a *tulou* in Fujian, China? In a *tulou*, people with _____ live in one building together. They work together and _____. There are usually three to five floors. The first floor is for _____. The second floor is used to _____. The third or fourth floor is used for _____.

Let's Write

When you visit Korea, you might wonder where you can stay. Why don't you
간접의문문(의문사+주어+동사) Why don't you 동사 ~?: 권유 표현
stay in a *hanok*? A *hanok* is a traditional Korean house.

If you stayed in a *hanok*, you would sleep on the floor because there are no
가정법 과거(현재와 반대) 조동사 과거형+원형 there are+복수 주어
beds. *Hanok* houses are mostly built with natural materials such as wood,
부사(주로) be built with 재료 = like
stone, straw, paper, and earth. These materials help you keep your skin
help+목적어+목적보어((to) 동사원형)
healthy. In the cold winter, the warm *ondol* floors heat your body. The doors in
hanok are covered with thin paper. They help keep you cool in summer.
= help to keep you cool

구문해설 • **natural material**: 천연 재료 • **straw**: 밀짚, 지푸라기

여러분이 한국을 방문할 때, 어디에서 머물지 궁금할 것입니다. 한옥에서 머물러 보면 어떨까요? 한옥은 한국의 전통 가옥입니다. 만약 여러분이 한옥에서 지낸다면, 여러분은 침대가 없기 때문에 바닥에서 잠을 자게 될 것입니다. 한옥 집은 대개 나무, 돌, 지푸라기, 종이, 흙과 같은 천연 재료로 지어져 있습니다. 이 재료들은 여러분의 피부를 건강하게 유지하도록 도와줍니다. 추운 겨울에는 따뜻한 온돌 바닥이 여러분의 몸을 데워줍니다. 한옥 문들은 얇은 종이로 덮여 있습니다. 그 문들은 여름에 여러분이 시원하게 지내도록 도와줍니다.

Culture & Life

If you walked down a street in the village of the Ndebele in South Africa, you
가정법 과거 (If+주어+과거동사, 주어+조동사의 과거형+동사원형)
would see houses with many unique patterns and styles. Each house tells a
each+단수 명사: 단수 취급
different story. Some stories might be about neighbors' babies. Others express
personal opinions. A long time ago, the Ndebele were at war with the Boers.
be at war: 전쟁을 치르다
When the Boers invaded their land, the Ndebele painted their houses with many
colorful symbols. So, their enemies couldn't understand what they were secretly
관계대명사(the thing which)
communicating to each other. The symbols expressed feelings such as sadness.
Those symbols were handed down from mothers to daughters. And they have kept
from A to B: A에서 B로 5형식 동사(keep+목적어+목적격보어)
their traditions alive.

구문해설 • **unique**: 독특한, 고유한 • **express**: 표현하다 • **opinion**: 의견 • **invade**: 침범하다
• **communicate**: 의사소통하다

남아프리카 은데벨레족 마을의 거리를 걸어가다 보면, 많은 독특한 모양과 양식의 집들을 보게 될 것이다. 각각의 집들은 서로 다른 이야기를 한다. 어떤 이야기들은 이웃 아이들에 관한 것일지 모른다. 또 다른 이야기들은 개인적인 의견을 표현한다. 오래전, 은데벨레족은 보어인과 전쟁을 치렀다. 보어인들이 그들의 땅을 침략했을 때, 은데벨레족은 여러 색의 상징으로 집을 칠했다. 그래서 적들은 그들이 비밀리에 주고받는 의사소통을 이해하지 못했다. 이러한 상징들은 슬픔과 같은 감정들을 표현했다. 그 상징들은 엄마들에게서 딸들에게로 전해져 왔다. 그리고 그들은 자신들의 전통이 계속 살아 있도록 유지해 왔다.

Words & Expressions

01 다음 짝지어진 단어의 관계가 〈보기〉와 같도록 빈칸에 알맞은 말을 쓰시오.

┌─ 보기 ├─────────────────────┐
│   │
│   light – heavy   │
│   │
└────────────────────────────────┘

(1) welcome – _____

(2) visible – _____

02 다음 중 밑줄 친 부분의 뜻풀이가 바르지 않은 것은?

① There is a narrow <u>walkway</u> next to the school. (통로)

② <u>Travel</u> expenses will be paid by the company. (여행하다, 이동하다)

③ You cannot make bricks without <u>straw</u>. (짚, 지푸라기)

④ When water levels <u>rise</u>, flooding results. (오르다, 올라가다)

⑤ The country has been regarded as an <u>invader</u> in the Middle East. (침략자)

03 다음 주어진 문장의 밑줄 친 take와 같은 의미로 쓰인 것은?

┌────────────────────────────────┐
│ I used to <u>take</u> a cab every morning not to │
│ be late for school.   │
└────────────────────────────────┘

① When did you <u>take</u> your driving test?

② Virginia is planning to <u>take</u> a computer course.

③ Can I <u>take</u> a bus going to City Hall from here?

④ Most hotels are willing to <u>take</u> credit cards.

⑤ Getting a paper cut doesn't <u>take</u> a long time to heal.

04 다음 우리말을 주어진 어구를 이용하여 영작하시오.

┌────────────────────────────────┐
│ 당신이 하는 말은 비논리적이다. (what, make │
│ sense, 7 words)   │
└────────────────────────────────┘

➡ _____

Conversation

[05~06] 다음 대화를 읽고 물음에 답하시오.

A: (A)I wish I could stay in a house on the water during my vacation.

B: _____ (B) _____ if you were there?

A: I would go swimming every day. I would also go fishing.

B: That sounds fun.

05 위 대화의 밑줄 친 (A)의 의도로 가장 적절한 것은?

① 상상력 표현하기   ② 소원 표현하기

③ 감정 표현하기   ④ 의견 표현하기

⑤ 선호 표현하기

06 위 대화의 빈칸 (B)에 들어갈 말로 가장 적절한 것은?

① What would you do

② Which would you do

③ What could you do

④ Which could you do

⑤ What will you do

[07~08] 다음 대화를 읽고 물음에 답하시오.

> B: This is my dream house. What do you think, Alice?
> (A) That sounds cool!
> (B) Oh, it's in the deep sea. It looks so unique. So, what would you do if you lived in that house?
> (C) I have an interest in deep sea animals. So I would explore the deep sea and find some unique sea animals.

07 위 대화가 자연스럽게 이어지도록 (A)~(C)의 순서를 배열하시오.

➡ _____

08 다음 중 위 대화를 읽고 대답할 수 있는 질문은?

① Why did B make the dream house?
② In what country is B's dream house located?
③ How was B's dream house built?
④ When is B planning to go to the dream house?
⑤ What would B find around the dream house?

[09~11] 다음 대화를 읽고 물음에 답하시오.

> Jinho: I think living in a jungle would be really exciting. Don't you think so?
> Claire: But there are some dangerous animals in the jungle, Jinho.
> Jinho: I know. (A)그렇지만 정글은 모험으로 가득 차 있잖아. I wish I could live there.
> Claire: (B)What would you do if you lived in the jungle?
> Jinho: I would explore (C)it. Maybe I could make some animal friends.

09 위 대화의 밑줄 친 (A)의 우리말을 영작하시오.

➡ _____

10 다음 중 위 대화의 밑줄 친 (B)와 바꿔 쓸 수 있는 것은?

① I should say you live in the jungle.
② What if you lived in the jungle?
③ Why don't you live in the jungle?
④ What about living in the jungle?
⑤ Have you ever imagined that you lived in the jungle?

11 위 대화의 밑줄 친 (B)it이 가리키는 것을 찾아 쓰시오.

➡ _____

Grammar

12 다음 주어진 문장과 가장 가까운 의미를 가진 문장을 고르시오.

> Living together in one building keeps us safe from invaders or thieves.

① When we lived together in one building, we were safe from invaders or thieves.
② We live together in one building, which makes us safe from invaders or thieves.
③ If we lived together in one building, we would be safe from invaders or thieves.
④ We live together in one building to feel safe from invaders or thieves.
⑤ We live together in one building because of the threat from invaders or thieves.

[13~14] 다음 가정법으로 주어진 우리말에 맞게 괄호 안에 주어진 어구를 어법상 적절한 형태로 바꿔 배열하고, 직설법 문장으로도 바꾸시오.

13

수영장이 있는 집에 산다면, 나는 매일 수영을 즐길 텐데. (in, with, a swimming pool, a house, I, I, live, will, enjoy)

➡ (1) If _____
   _____ swimming every day.
   (2) 직설법: As _____
   _____
   swimming every day.

14

땅 속에 이 나무 기둥들을 설치하지 않았더라면, 그들은 베니스에서 살 수 없었을 텐데. (in the ground, can't, install, this, live, not, have, wooden poles, they)

➡ (1) If they _____
   _____
   in Venice.
   (2) 직설법: As _____
   _____
   in Venice.

[15~16] 다음 중 어법상 어색한 문장을 고르시오.

15 ① If Junsik told what his friends did to the teacher, they would be punished.
② If Mina put that dress on, she would not look like a poor girl.
③ If Inho got up earlier, he could get there on time.

④ If my neighbor didn't fail to catch the bus that morning, he would not have been late for work.
⑤ If Smith were the boss, he could change the company's policy.

16 ① The housewives at the meeting made their husbands impressed by the gifts.
② The audience at the preview found the movie very touching.
③ The teacher kept the noisy boys raised their hands until the end of class.
④ Studying mathematics alone made me feel disappointed with myself.
⑤ The ice box helped keep the vegetables fresh longer than I thought.

17 다음 우리말을 영작할 때, 어법상 옳지 <u>않은</u> 문장을 <u>모두</u> 고르시오.

나무 기둥들이 없다면, 그 도시는 사람이 살 수 없을 텐데.

① Without wooden poles, people couldn't have lived in the city.
② If there were no wooden poles, people could not live in the city.
③ If it were not for wooden poles, people could not live in the city.
④ Were it not for wooden poles, people could not live in the city.
⑤ If there are no wooden poles, people could not live in the city.

[18~20] 다음 글을 읽고 물음에 답하시오.

Different people live ①in different houses. Some use ladders ②to enter into their houses. Others live in houses ③on the water. And others share their houses with many people. Imagine you live in one of these houses. How would that change your life?

***Pueblos* in New Mexico, USA**

If I lived in a *pueblo*, I would climb up a ladder to enter my house. There's a hidden opening on top of the house. If unwelcome visitors appeared, I would pull the ladder up to stop them from entering. The thick walls ④are made of earth, straw, and water. They would keep me cool in summer and warm in winter. The house has a flat roof. I ⑤would sometimes sleep up on the roof under the moon and stars.

18 ①~⑤ 중 어법상 바르지 <u>않은</u> 것은?

①   ②   ③   ④   ⑤

19 What is the passage mainly talking about?

① different people living different lives
② different ways to build houses
③ various houses in the world
④ how to get to an agreement among people
⑤ the special building method in the world

20 According to the passage, what does a *pueblo* have on top of the house?

➡ _____

_____

[21~24] 다음 글을 읽고 물음에 답하시오.

Houses on Water in Venice, Italy

If I lived in Venice, I would take a gondola to school every morning. Venice has 118 small islands. On weekends, I would travel from island to island by a vaporetto, a water bus. At high tide, the water from the Adriatic Sea often rises and leaves the streets full of water. However, I would be able to walk around the town through the raised walkways.

Venice is known (A)_____ the "floating city." (①) In Venice, there are many colorful houses on the water. (②) The old Venetians decided to live there to keep themselves safe from invaders. (③) But it was not easy for them to build their homes on this swampy surface. (④) So they installed more than 10 million wooden poles in the ground. (⑤) It is these wooden poles that support Venice to this day.

21 다음 중 빈칸 (A)에 들어갈 말과 같은 말이 들어가는 것은?

① I'm not in the mood _____ watching a movie.
② You should be ashamed _____ what you said to her.
③ Using chopsticks is related _____ their culture.
④ We regarded her _____ our leader.
⑤ Why was she absent _____ school the other day?

22 ①∼⑤ 중 주어진 문장이 들어가기에 가장 적절한 곳은?

> You may wonder how and why they built the houses on the water.

①   ②   ③   ④   ⑤

23 위 글의 내용을 바르게 이해한 사람은?

① A: It must be really fun to take a gondola to work every morning.

② B: I didn't know that Venice has so many big islands.

③ C: It is really amazing that people built many colorful houses under the water.

④ D: It is shameful that there is no water bus in Venice.

⑤ E: It is surprising that over ten million poles that support Venice to this day was made of wood.

24 What would make it possible for the writer to walk around the town at high tide? Answer in English.

➡ _____

_____

[25~27] 다음 글을 읽고 물음에 답하시오.

When you visit Korea, you might wonder where you can stay. Why don't you stay in a *hanok*? A *hanok* is a traditional Korean house. If you stayed in a *hanok*, you would sleep on the floor because there are no beds. *Hanok* houses are mostly built with natural materials such as wood, stone, straw, paper, and earth. These materials help you keep your skin healthy. In the cold winter, the warm *ondol* floors heat your body. The doors in *hanok* are covered with thin paper. They help keep you cool in summer.

25 Write the reason why you would sleep on the floor if you stayed in a *hanok*. Answer in English.

➡ _____

26 According to the passage, what heats your body in the cold winter? Answer in English.

➡ _____

_____

27 다음 중 위 글을 읽고 답할 수 있는 것은?

① How long did it take to build a *hanok*?

② What are traditional clothes of Korea?

③ How many people are needed to build a *hanok*?

④ With what are *hanok* houses mostly built?

⑤ With what are floors inside *hanok* covered?

출제율 90%

01 다음 영영풀이가 가리키는 것을 고르시오.

> to provide a place for somebody to live

① appear   ② house
③ enter   ④ install
⑤ relax

출제율 100%

02 다음 〈보기〉에서 알맞은 단어를 골라 문장을 완성하시오.

┌─ 보기 ─┐
for a while / live in / on weekends / up to
/ take a look

(1) Now forget the details and _____ at the big picture.
(2) I am so exhausted because I have to work even _____.
(3) We lived on the outskirts of New York _____.

[03~05] 다음 대화를 읽고 물음에 답하시오.

B: Will it snow today?
G: I have no idea. Why are you waiting for snow, Taeho?
B: I got a new sled for my birthday.   (A)
G: Let me check the weather. Umm, there will be no snow for a while.
B: I wish I could live in Alaska. Then I could go sledding all day!
G: No kidding! Alaska is a very cold place.
B: I think it would be fun. I want to build a snow house and stay there on vacation.
G: Living in a snow house sounds fun!

출제율 95%

03 위 대화의 빈칸 (A)에 들어갈 말로 가장 적절한 것은?

① I can't wait to receive another present.
② I can't wait to test it out.
③ I can't wait to make a sled for myself.
④ I can't wait to clean it up.
⑤ I can't wait to check the weather.

출제율 90%

04 What would B do if he lived in Alaska? (11 words)

➡ _____

_____

출제율 100%

05 다음 중 위 대화의 내용과 일치하지 <u>않는</u> 것은?

① G does not know whether it will snow or not today.
② A snow sled was given to B as a birthday gift.
③ It will snow for a while today.
④ B wants to live in Alaska and go sledding.
⑤ G thinks it's exciting to live in a snow house.

[06~07] 다음 대화를 읽고 물음에 답하시오.

G: Have you heard from Julia? She's traveling in Turkey, right? (①)
B: Yes, she sent me some pictures. Do you want to see (A)them? (②)
G: Yes, please.
B: Okay, take a look. (③)
G: Oh, look at those cave houses! (B)They look so unique, don't they? (④) I wish I could try living there.
B: I like those balloons. (⑤)
G: I think Turkey is a wonderful place to visit. I hope to visit (C)there someday.
B: Me too!

06 위 대화의 ①~⑤ 중 다음 주어진 문장이 들어갈 가장 적절한 곳은?

> They look so beautiful!

①   ②   ③   ④   ⑤

출제율 90%

07 위 대화의 밑줄 친 (A)~(C)가 가리키는 것을 영어로 쓰시오.

➡ (A) _____

   (B) _____

   (C) _____

출제율 100%

08 다음 가정법 문장들 중 어법상 옳은 것을 고르시오.

① If the lady were not so hungry, she can share her lunch with the man.

② April will feel sad if her boyfriend left her alone in the cinema.

③ All the students in her school would feel proud if Yuna wins the gold medal in the Olympics.

④ What would they do if they lived in a huge building as one family?

⑤ If it had not been for the thick walls, the people living in the pueblo would feel cold in winter.

출제율 100%

09 다음 각 빈칸에 공통으로 들어갈 단어 중 나머지 넷과 성격이 다른 하나는?

① Dancing with the puppies _____ the girl so happy that she couldn't believe it was real.

② Karl _____ his mother upset as he forgot to lock the door.

③ Jordan _____ the government take action about the pollution of the river.

④ The heating system _____ the people inside the building feel warm and cozy.

⑤ The author _____ an impressive story that everybody loved.

[10~11] 다음 주어진 우리말을 어법에 맞게 바르게 영작한 것은?

출제율 100%

10

> 어머니가 아프지 않으셔서 우리들과 함께 제주도로 여행을 가실 수 있으면 좋을 텐데. (그러나 어머니가 아프시다.)

① I wish we were not sick and could go to the Jeju island with my mom.

② I wish my mom were not sick and could go to the Jeju island with us.

③ I wish my mom were not sick and couldn't go to the Jeju island with us.

④ My mom wishes we were not sick and could go to the Jeju island with us.

⑤ I wish my mom is not sick and can go to the Jeju island with us.

출제율 95%

11

> 비가 심하게 오지 않았다면, 강물이 넘치지 않았을 텐데. (그러나 비가 너무 심하게 왔다).

① If it had not rained heavily, the river wouldn't have overflowed.

② If it had not rained heavily, the river wouldn't overflow.

③ Had it not rained heavily, the river would not overflow.

④ Didn't it rain heavily, the river would not be overflowed.

⑤ If it rained not heavily, the river would not have overflowed.

[12~13] 다음 문장의 밑줄 친 부분이 어법상 **어색한** 것은?

출제율 100%

12 ① The smile on the baby boy made his parents happy and <u>relieved</u>.

② My sisters always keep their room <u>clean</u>.

③ The movie we saw last night made almost all the people <u>sleep</u>.

④ The police officers kept the little girl <u>safely</u> from the gangsters.

⑤ These clothes would keep the poor kids in the village <u>warm</u>.

출제율 95%

13 ① The medicine that the doctor in the clinic prescribed will make you <u>sleepy</u>.

② The kittens I saw at the animal hospital made me <u>excited</u>.

③ The new refrigerator her father brought home can't keep the fruit <u>fresh</u>.

④ Each of the birds on the trees is keeping their eggs <u>warm</u>.

⑤ The collections in this museum make the visitors <u>interesting</u> in ancient Korean arts.

출제율 95%

14 다음 우리말을 괄호 안에 주어진 어구를 활용하여 조건에 맞게 영작하시오.

> 반갑지 않은 방문객이 나타난다면, 나는 사다리를 끌어올려 그들이 들어오지 못하게 할 텐데.
> (appear, pull up, stop, will, enter, the ladder, unwelcome visitors, from. If로 시작하는 가정법, 단어 변형 가능, 총 15 단어로 할 것.)

➡ _____

_____

출제율 95%

15 다음 중 각 문장의 밑줄 친 부분의 쓰임이 같은 것끼리 묶인 것을 고르시오.

> ⓐ The star chef, Mr. Baek, <u>made</u> the kids special food to encourage their lives.
> ⓑ Please do your best not to <u>make</u> your loved ones disappointed.
> ⓒ The principal <u>made</u> the teachers clean the way to the school.
> ⓓ The ladies in the club wanted to <u>make</u> the singer world famous.
> ⓔ Susan persuaded Jack to <u>make</u> a decision to help them.
> ⓕ My grandmother used to <u>make</u> me and my brother the sweet potato pizza.
> ⓖ Generally speaking, the cloudy weather <u>makes</u> people depressed.

① ⓐ, ⓒ, ⓓ, ⓔ   ② ⓐ, ⓒ, ⓕ, ⓖ
③ ⓐ, ⓔ, ⓕ, ⓖ   ④ ⓑ, ⓒ, ⓓ, ⓖ
⑤ ⓑ, ⓒ, ⓔ, ⓖ

[16~19] 다음 글을 읽고 물음에 답하시오.

Tulou in Fujian, China

If I ①<u>lived</u> in a *tulou*, a huge round house in Fujian, China, I would always have friends at home ②<u>to play</u>. I would sometimes hear my neighbor calling me ③<u>to come</u> over for tea or dinner. In a *tulou*, there are usually three to five floors. The first floor is used for cooking and eating. And people store food and tools on the second floor. Do you wonder where I would sleep? My bedroom would be on the third or fourth floor.

A *tulou* is like a village. The people ④<u>living</u> in a *tulou* mostly have the same family name. Some large *tulou* can house ⑤<u>up to</u> 50 families. They work together and share many things. Living together in one building keeps them safe.

16

출제율 100%

위 글의 제목으로 가장 적절한 것은?

① A *Tulou*: the Only Traditional House in China
② A Single-person House for Chinese People
③ A *Tulou*: A Community House in Fujian
④ A *Tulou*: A Huge Royal House in Fujian
⑤ The World's Famous House: *Tulous*

17

출제율 95%

①~⑤ 중 어법상 바르지 <u>않은</u> 것은?

①　　②　　③　　④　　⑤

18

출제율 100%

Choose one that is TRUE.

① *Tulous* are found everywhere in China.
② It would be hard to find friends in a *tulou*.
③ Sleeping rooms are on the same floor as a cooking room in a *tulou*.
④ To store food and tools in a *tulou* would not be easy.
⑤ It would be easy to hear neighbors call someone's name in a *tulou*.

19

출제율 90%

How many floors does a *tulou* usually have? Answer in English with a full sentence.

➡ _____

[20~23] 다음 글을 읽고 물음에 답하시오.

If you (A)_____ down a street in the village of the Ndebele in South Africa, you would see houses with many unique patterns and styles. Each house tells a different story. Some stories might be about neighbors' babies. Others express personal opinions.

A long time ago, the Ndebele were at war with the Boers. When the Boers invaded their land, the Ndebele painted their houses with many colorful symbols. So, their enemies couldn't understand what they were secretly communicating to each other. The symbols expressed feelings such as sadness. Those symbols were handed down from mothers to daughters. And they have kept their traditions alive.

20

출제율 95%

빈칸 (A)에 들어갈 말로 가장 적절한 것은?

① walk　　　　② will walk
③ have walked　④ walked
⑤ had walked

21

출제율 90%

Write the reason why the Boers couldn't understand what the Ndebele were secretly communicating to each other. Use the phrase 'It was because.'

➡ _____
_____
_____

22

출제율 90%

What did the symbols express? Answer in English.

➡ _____

23

출제율 100%

Choose one that is NOT true.

① The passage is about the stories of the Ndebele and their houses.
② The village of the Ndebele can be found in South Africa.
③ The houses in the village have many ordinary patterns and styles.
④ Each house in the village has their own stories.
⑤ Some houses in the village express personal opinions.

[01~02] 다음 대화를 읽고 물음에 답하시오.

> B: This is my dream house, Alice. What do you think?
> G: Oh, the house has wheels! Is it a kind of car?
> B: Yes, it can move like a car.
> G: So what would you do if you lived in that house?
> B: I would travel to many places with my family.
> G: That sounds cool.

01 Describe B's dream house in English. (Include two features.)

➡ _____

02 What would B do if he lived in his dream house? (9 words)

➡ _____

03 다음 그림을 보고 자연스러운 문장이 되도록 괄호 안에 주어진 단어를 바르게 배열하여 빈칸을 완성하시오.

(1)

➡ Living together in one _____ _____ comfortable. (the people, building, and, safe, keeps)

(2)

➡ The old Venetians installed more than 10 million wooden _____ _____. (make, support, poles, to, Venice, them)

04 다음 중에서 틀린 문장을 찾아 기호를 쓰고, 바르게 고쳐 문장을 다시 쓰시오.

① If the scientists were awarded for the discovery, their books would be sold even better.

② If the engineer made the flying taxi, I would use it as I go to work.

③ If the girl got up earlier, she wouldn't miss the bus.

④ If the officer knew the driver, he won't give her a ticket.

⑤ If the patient had put on the sunscreen, his skin would not have burned.

➡ _____
_____
_____

[05~06] 아래 각 두 문장을 가정법의 한 문장으로 합치되, 주어진 단어로 시작하시오.

05

> • Andrew doesn't know the title of the song.
> • He can't sing it at the school festival.

➡ If _____
_____.

- I'm sorry that my sisters are not nice.
- I want them to be as nice as Abigail.

➡ I _____ .

[07~08] 다음 글을 읽고 물음에 답하시오.

Different people live in different houses. Some use ladders to enter their houses. (A) The others live in houses on the water. And others share their houses with many people. (B)여러분이 이 집들 중 하나에 산다고 상상해 보세요. How would that change your life?

07 밑줄 친 (A)에서 어법상 틀린 것을 바르게 고쳐 다시 쓰시오.

➡ _____

주어진 단어를 바르게 나열하여 밑줄 친 우리말 (B)를 영어로 쓰시오.

(these / you / one / imagine / of / in / houses / live)

➡ _____

[09~10] 다음 글을 읽고 물음에 답하시오.

Tulou in Fujian, China

If I lived in a *tulou*, a huge round house in Fujian, China, I would always have friends at home to play with. I would sometimes hear my neighbor calling me to come over for tea or dinner. In a *tulou*, there are usually three to five floors. The first floor is used for cooking and eating. And people store food and tools on the second floor. Do you wonder where I would sleep? My bedroom would be on the third or fourth floor.

A *tulou* is like a village. The people living in a *tulou* mostly have the same family name. Some large *tulou* can house up to 50 families. They work together and share many things. Living together in one building keeps them safe.

09 According to the passage, what would the writer hear if she or he lived in a *tulou*? Answer in English.

➡ _____
_____

10 What do the people living in a *tulou* mostly have? Answer in English.

➡ _____
_____

01 다음 그림을 보고, 바다 속의 집에서 살면 무엇을 하고 싶은지 자유롭게 가정법 과거 시제를 사용하여 빈칸을 채우시오.

(1) If I lived in a house under the sea, _____.

(2) If I lived in a house under the sea, _____.

(3) If I lived in a house under the sea, _____.

02 다음 대화를 읽고 Juwon의 일기를 완성하시오.

G: What would you do if you became a millionaire, Juwon?

B: I would build my own house.

G: What kind of house would you build?

B: I would build a house that is completely covered with mirrors.

G: Why?

B: The mirrors would make the house almost invisible. Wouldn't that be cool?

G: That would be cool!

Recently, I was having a chat with my friend. She asked me what I _____ if I became a millionaire. I told her that I _____ my own house that is completely _____ mirrors. I've always thought that the mirrors would make the house almost _____, and I think it's really cool.

단원별 모의고사

01 다음 영영풀이가 가리키는 것은?

> the regular upward and downward movement of the level of the ocean that is caused by the pull of the sun and the moon on Earth

① surface   ② stream   ③ wave
④ earth   ⑤ tide

02 다음 빈칸에 알맞은 단어를 고르시오.

> happy : happily = high : _____

① high   ② highly
③ highness   ④ higher
⑤ highest

03 다음 우리말에 맞게 빈칸에 알맞은 말을 쓰시오.

> 교실에서 컴퓨터들은 게임을 위해 사용되어서는 안 된다.
>
> ➡ In the classroom, the computers should not _____ games.

[04~05] 다음 대화를 읽고 물음에 답하시오.

B: ⓐWill it snow today?
G: I have no idea. Why are you ⓑwaiting for snow, Taeho?
B: I got a new sled for my birthday. I can't wait to ⓒtest out it.
G: Let me ⓓcheck the weather. Umm, there will be no snow for a while.
B: (A)알래스카에 살 수 있다면 좋을 텐데! Then I could go sledding all day!
G: No kidding! Alaska is a very cold place.

B: I think it ⓔwould be fun. I want to build a snow house and stay there on vacation.
G: Living in a snow house sounds fun!

04 위 대화의 밑줄 친 (A)의 우리말을 주어진 단어를 사용하여 영작하시오. (wish, 7 words)

➡ _____

05 위 대화의 밑줄 친 ⓐ~ⓔ 중 어법상 어색한 것을 골라 바르게 고치시오.

➡ _____

[06~07] 다음 대화를 읽고 물음에 답하시오.

G: Look. ①The house in this picture is upside down.
B: That's interesting. ②Does anybody live there?
G: ③No, it would not be easy to live there because the inside is also upside down.
B: Really? But I want to try living there. ④I have wanted to live alone.
G: What (A)[would / could] you do if you (B)[lived / have lived] in that house?
B: I would walk upside down like Spider-Man. ⑤I could also see things differently.

06 밑줄 친 문장 ①~⑤ 중에서 전체 흐름과 관계 없는 문장은?

①   ②   ③   ④   ⑤

07 위 대화의 괄호 (A)와 (B)에서 알맞은 말을 고르시오.

➡ (A) _____ (B) _____

08 다음 대화의 밑줄 친 부분의 의도로 가장 적절한 것은?

> A: What's the matter?
> B: My computer is so slow. I wish I could have a new computer.

① 질문하기   ② 불만 토로하기
③ 의견 묻기   ④ 바람 표현하기
⑤ 상상력 표현하기

[09~11] 다음 대화를 읽고 물음에 답하시오.

> G: Dohun, we need to start our project on our dream country to visit.
> B: That's right. Which country do you want to visit, Emma?
> G: In my case, I want to visit Spain.
> B: What would you do if you visited Spain?
> G: I'm interested in buildings. (A)그래서 난 La Sagrada Familia를 보러 갈 거야.
> B: Isn't that the church Antoni Gaudí designed?
> G: Yes, it is. (B)It would be interesting to see how his design was inspired by nature.
> B: Hmm… How about *Gaudi and Spain* ___(C)___ the title for our project?
> G: I love it!

09 위 대화의 밑줄 친 (A)의 우리말을 주어진 단어를 이용하여 영작하시오. (go, 8 words)

➡ _____

10 위 대화의 밑줄 친 (B)瓜이 가리키는 것을 찾아 쓰시오.

➡ _____

위 대화의 빈칸 (C)에 적절한 것은?

① as   ② for
③ from   ④ at
⑤ with

12 다음 대화를 읽고 빈칸에 알맞은 말을 쓰시오.

> A: _____ you could have a magical power?
> B: I would turn into a bird. Then I would be able to fly freely in the sky.
> A: That's cool.

[13~15] 다음 중 밑줄 친 부분의 쓰임이 나머지와 다른 것은?

13
① The staff and makeup artists will <u>make</u> them look like the real idol singers.
② The teacher majoring in literature will <u>make</u> your report better for the review.
③ The drummer at the concert will <u>make</u> their songs more rhythmical for the beat.
④ The students at the cooking class will <u>make</u> you delicious bread.
⑤ Will the researchers <u>make</u> me nervous by asking some embarrassing requests?

14 ① Thomas had no idea <u>if</u> the rumor about the war would turn out true.

② <u>If</u> he were not ill, he would come to Ann's birthday party.

③ The employees in the company wouldn't go out to have lunch <u>if</u> it started raining.

④ The little girl would call her mom <u>if</u> she needed any help.

⑤ The athlete would get a full scholarship to the college <u>if</u> he won the championship medal.

15 ① The new clothes that his mother bought him <u>made</u> him look great.

② The smiles on my daughters' faces <u>make</u> me a superman.

③ The music with touching lyrics always <u>make</u> her encouraged to carry on.

④ My uncle in the college lab <u>made</u> me a fantastic figure of a dinosaur.

⑤ Eating too much junk food can <u>make</u> the little kids sick.

[16~17] 다음 중 〈보기〉의 밑줄 친 단어와 쓰임이 같은 것은?

16

| 보기 |

Dennis <u>would</u> meet the girl from Canada if his friend Sean asked him to guide her.

① My parents <u>would</u> go on a picnic to the park when I wasn't born.

② The members of the soccer club <u>would</u> like to have the steak for the party.

③ The CEO of the company <u>would</u> hire the person if she improved her skills.

④ <u>Would</u> you find me the ring I had been wearing before I took a shower?

⑤ The English teacher said that I <u>would</u> get the scholarship next year.

17

| 보기 |

The old Venetians decided to live in Venice to <u>keep</u> themselves safe from invaders.

① Please send out the photocopies and <u>keep</u> the original with you.

② You should <u>keep</u> your answers as simple as possible.

③ The poor family could not <u>keep</u> up the monthly payment for their house.

④ The politicians have failed to <u>keep</u> their election promises.

⑤ The museum has <u>kept</u> the visitors from taking pictures of its pictures.

18 다음 중 〈보기〉의 문장과 의미가 가장 가까운 것을 고르시오.

| 보기 |

If Choo were in good condition, he would make twice as many home runs as any other players

① As Choo was in good condition, he made twice as many home runs as any other player.

② As Choo isn't in good condition, he didn't make twice as many home runs as any other player.

③ Though Choo was not in good condition, he made twice as many home runs as any other player.

④ As Choo is not in good condition, he doesn't make twice as many home runs as any other player.

⑤ As Choo was not in good condition, he didn't make twice as many home runs as any other player.

19 다음 중 내용상 〈보기〉의 밑줄 친 부분과 바꿔 쓸 수 <u>없는</u> 것은?

> ┤ 보기 ├
>
> <u>If it were not for a gondola</u>, the Venetians could not go around as freely as they want.

① Were it not for a gondola,

② Without a gondola,

③ Had it not been for a gondola,

④ But for a gondola,

⑤ If there were no gondola,

20 다음 〈보기〉의 문장들 중에서 어법상 <u>어색한</u> 것을 <u>모두</u> 고르면?

> ┤ 보기 ├
>
> ⓐ The thick walls made of earth, straw, and water would keep me cool in summer and warm in winter.
>
> ⓑ The flat roof which a *pueblo* has makes it possible for me to sleep up on the roof under the moon and stars.
>
> ⓒ The raised walkways in Venice keep me walk around the town every day.
>
> ⓓ The old Venetians decided to live in Venice to keep themselves safely from invaders.
>
> ⓔ Those wooden poles that they installed have kept Venice to stand strong to this day.
>
> ⓕ Living in a huge round building makes me able to hear my neighbor calling me to come over for tea or dinner.
>
> ⓖ At high tide, the water from the Adriatic Sea often rises and leaves the streets full of water.
>
> ⓗ Living together in one building allows them be safe from the outsiders.

① ⓐ, ⓑ, ⓕ, ⓖ   ② ⓐ, ⓒ, ⓓ, ⓖ

③ ⓒ, ⓓ, ⓔ, ⓗ   ④ ⓑ, ⓒ, ⓔ, ⓖ

⑤ ⓒ, ⓓ, ⓕ, ⓗ

21 다음 우리말을 주어진 조건에 맞게 영작하시오.

> 내가 오직 사다리를 사용해야 집에 들어갈 수 있다면, 그것은 재미있을 텐데.
> (can, will, use, ladders, a house, enter, by, fun. If로 시작, 어휘 변형 가능, 총 14 단어로 할 것)

➡ _____

_____

[22~27] 다음 글을 읽고 물음에 답하시오.

> **Houses on Water in Venice, Italy**
>
> If I lived in Venice, I would take a gondola to school every morning. Venice has 118 small islands. On weekends, I would travel from island to island by a vaporetto, a water bus. At high tide, the water from the Adriatic Sea often rises and leaves the streets full of water. However, I would be able to walk around the town through the raised walkways.
>
> Venice is known as the "(A)_____." (①) In Venice, there are many colorful houses on the water. (②) You may wonder how and why they built the houses on the water. (③) The old Venetians decided to live there to keep themselves safe from invaders. (④) But it was not easy for them to build their homes on this swampy surface. (⑤) (B)<u>It is these wooden poles that support Venice to this day</u>

22 글의 흐름상 빈칸 (A)에 들어갈 말로 가장 적절한 것은?

① drowning boat   ② forgotten city

③ man-made tower   ④ floating city

⑤ city of the conqueror

23 ①~⑤ 중 주어진 문장이 들어가기에 가장 적절한 곳은?

> So they installed more than 10 million wooden poles in the ground.

①   ②   ③   ④   ⑤

24 What happens in Venice when it is at high tide? Answer in English.

➡ _____

_____

25 Choose one that is NOT true.

① A gondola is taken in order to go to school in Venice.
② Thanks to a water bus called a *vaporetto*, it is possible to travel between islands.
③ There are over 118 small islands in Venice.
④ The raised walkways make it possible for people in Venice to walk around.
⑤ The things that support Venice to this day are the wooden poles made by the old Venetians.

26 Write the reason why the old Venetians decided to live in Venice. Answer in English.

➡ _____

_____

27 다음 중 밑줄 친 (B)의 문법적 특징과 다른 하나는?

① It was in the library that I saw him.
② It was her husband that stole the money.
③ It is my car that is parked in front of the restaurant.
④ It is surprising that she didn't mention about the issue.
⑤ It is New York that I want to live in.

[28~29] 다음 글을 읽고 물음에 답하시오.

> *Tulou* in Fujian, China
>
> If I lived in a *tulou*, a huge round house in Fujian, China, I would always have friends at home to play with. I would sometimes hear my neighbor calling me to come over for tea or dinner. In a *tulou*, there are usually three ___ⓐ___ five floors. The first floor is used ___ⓑ___ cooking and eating. And people store food and tools on the second floor. Do you wonder where I would sleep? My bedroom would be on the third or fourth floor.
>
> A *tulou* is like a village. The people living in a *tulou* mostly have the same family name. Some large *tulou* can house up to 50 families. They work together and share many things. Living together in one building keeps them safe.

28 위 글의 ⓐ, ⓑ에 들어갈 전치사를 쓰시오.

➡ ⓐ _____, ⓑ _____

29 What keeps people living in a *tulou* safe? Answer in English.

➡ _____

_____

MEMO

Lesson 8

Behind the Numbers

🎙️ **의사소통 기능**

- 상술하기
  Five out of twenty-five students don't have pets.
  Over sixty percent of the students voted for her.
- 이해 점검하기
  Do you see what I mean?

🎙️ **언어 형식**

- too ～ to ...
  It's **too** hard **to** read and draw graphs.

- No one ...
  No one needs graphs in real life.

Words & Expressions

Key Words

- **adventure**[ədvéntʃər] 명 모험
- **anyway**[éniwèi] 부 게다가, 어쨌든
- **arrow**[ǽrou] 명 화살
- **article**[ɑ́:rtikl] 명 글, 기사
- **break**[breik] 동 고장 내다
- **celebrate**[séləbrèit] 동 기념하다
- **chase**[tʃeis] 동 뒤쫓다
- **claim**[kleim] 동 주장하다
- **class president** 학급 반장
- **count**[kaunt] 동 (수를) 세다
- **courageous**[kəréidʒəs] 형 용감한
- **election**[ilékʃən] 명 선거
- **enough**[inʌ́f] 형 충분한
- **equal**[í:kwəl] 동 같다
- **facial**[féiʃəl] 형 얼굴의
- **favorite**[féivərit] 형 매우 좋아하는
- **graph**[græf] 명 그래프
- **greedy**[grí:di] 형 탐욕스러운, 욕심 많은
- **helpful**[hélpfəl] 형 도움이 되는
- **importance**[impɔ́:rtəns] 명 중요성
- **lastly**[lǽstli] 부 마지막으로
- **leaf**[li:f] 명 잎, 나뭇잎, 풀잎
- **lucky**[lʌ́ki] 형 행운의
- **match**[mætʃ] 동 일치하다
- **matter**[mǽtər] 동 중요하다
- **midnight**[mídnait] 명 자정
- **minus**[máinəs] 전 ~을 뺀

- **muscle**[mʌ́sl] 명 근육
- **noon**[nu:n] 명 정오
- **novel**[nɑ́vəl] 명 소설
- **percent**[pərsént] 명 퍼센트, 백분
- **picnic**[píknik] 명 소풍
- **pie chart** 원 그래프
- **poisonous**[pɔ́izənəs] 형 독이 있는
- **realize**[rí:əlàiz] 동 깨닫다
- **reason**[rí:zn] 명 이유
- **repeat**[ripí:t] 동 반복하다, 따라 말하다
- **represent**[rèprizént] 동 나타내다
- **result**[rizʌ́lt] 명 결과
- **salty**[sɔ́:lti] 형 짭짤한
- **science-fiction** 형 공상과학의
- **snack**[snæk] 명 간식
- **shout**[ʃaut] 동 외치다, 소리치다
- **soldier**[sóuldʒər] 명 군인, 병사
- **solution**[səlú:ʃən] 명 해결책
- **struggle**[strʌ́gl] 동 투쟁하다, 분투하다
- **suddenly**[sʌ́dnli] 부 갑자기
- **sum**[sʌm] 명 계산, 총계
- **survey**[sərvéi] 동 설문조사하다
- **tax**[tæks] 명 세금
- **typewriter**[táipraitər] 명 타자기
- **vote**[vout] 동 투표하다
- **wave**[weiv] 동 손을 흔들다
- **weather report** 일기 예보

Key Expressions

- **be about to** 막 ~하려고 하다
- **be proud of** ~을 자랑스러워하다
- **be regarded as** ~로 여겨지다
- **be related to** ~와 연관되어 있다
- **be worried about** ~에 대해 걱정하다
- **between A and B** A와 B 사이에
- **get back** 되찾다
- **get inside** 들어가다
- **get off** 내리다
- **hide up** 잠복하다
- **in other words** 다시 말하면

- **look back** 뒤돌아보다
- **look up** 올려보다
- **not ~ anymore** 더 이상 ~ 않다
- **one by one** 하나씩
- **pick up** 집어들다
- **pull A onto B** A를 B로 끌어올리다
- **put down** 내려놓다
- **read oneself to sleep** 읽다가 잠들다
- **run for** 출마하다
- **take A to B** A를 B에 데려가다
- **walk out** 걸어나가다

Word Power

※ 서로 비슷한 뜻을 가진 어휘

- □ **chase** 뒤쫓다 – **pursue** 추적하다
- □ **equal** 같다 – **match** 일치하다
- □ **poisonous** 독이 있는 – **toxic** 유독성의
- □ **struggle** 고군분투하다 – **strive** 애쓰다

- □ **claim** 주장하다 – **insist** 주장하다
- □ **novel** 소설 – **fiction** 소설
- □ **represent** 나타내다 – **express** 나타내다
- □ **tax** 세금 – **duty** 세금, 의무

※ 서로 반대의 뜻을 가진 어휘

- □ **courageous** 용감한 ↔ **cowardly** 겁이 많은
- □ **lastly** 마지막으로 ↔ **firstly** 첫째로
- □ **midnight** 자정 ↔ **midday** 정오

- □ **greedy** 탐욕스러운, 욕심 많은 ↔ **generous** 아끼지 않는, 후한
- □ **lucky** 행운의 ↔ **unlucky** 불행의

※ 접미사 –tion. 동사+tion

- □ **act** + **-tion** → **action** 행동
- □ **compete** + **-tion** → **competition** 경쟁
- □ **educate** + **-tion** → **education** 교육
- □ **infect** + **-tion** → **infection** 감염, 전염병
- □ **situate** + **-tion** → **situation** 상황

- □ **calculate** + **-tion** → **calculation** 계산
- □ **correct** + **-tion** → **correction** 정정, 수정
- □ **examinate** + **-tion** → **examination** 시험, 검토
- □ **inform** + **-tion** → **information** 정보
- □ **solve** + **-tion** → **solution** 해결책

※ 접미사 –y. 명사+y

- □ **blood** + **-y** → **bloody** 피투성이의
- □ **fun** + **-y** → **funny** 재미있는
- □ **risk** + **-y** → **risky** 위험한
- □ **shine** + **-y** → **shiny** 빛나는

- □ **dust** + **-y** → **dusty** 먼지투성이인
- □ **greed** + **-y** → **greedy** 탐욕스러운
- □ **salt** + **-y** → **salty** 짭짤한
- □ **thirst** + **-y** → **thirsty** 갈증이 나는

English Dictionary

- □ **article** 글, 기사
  → a piece of writing appearing in a newspaper
  신문에 나오는 글
- □ **celebrate** 기념하다
  → to take part in special enjoyable activities in order to show that a particular occasion is important
  특정한 행사가 중요하다는 것을 보여주기 위해 특별하고 즐거운 활동에 참여하다
- □ **greedy** 탐욕스러운, 욕심 많은
  → wanting a lot more food, money, etc. than you need
  필요한 것보다 더 많은 돈이나 음식 등을 원하는
- □ **novel** 소설
  → a long written story about characters and events that have been invented by the writer
  작가에 의해 지어진 등장인물과 사건에 대한 긴 이야기
- □ **poisonous** 독이 있는
  → containing poison
  독을 가지고 있는

- □ **realize** 깨닫다
  → to understand clearly
  명확하게 이해하다
- □ **represent** 나타내다
  → to express by some symbol or character
  어떤 상징이나 특징으로 표현하다
- □ **sum** 총계, 계산
  → the total of two or more numbers or quantities, determined by mathematical process
  수학적 과정에 의해 결정되는 둘 또는 그 이상의 숫자 혹은 수량의 전체
- □ **tax** 세금
  → an amount of money that you have to pay to the government so that it can pay for public services
  정부가 공공 서비스에 대한 지불을 하도록 정부에 내야 하는 돈
- □ **wave** 손을 흔들다
  → to signal in greeting, by raising the hand and moving the fingers
  손을 들고 손가락을 움직여 인사로 신호하다

01 문장의 빈칸에 공통으로 들어갈 말로 가장 알맞은 것은?

> • Did you read the _____ about the plastic island?
> • Plastic _____s, like shampoo bottles, can be recycled, but they must be clean.

① object　　　　② result
③ poem　　　　④ article
⑤ novel

02 주어진 〈영영풀이〉를 읽고 빈칸에 알맞은 단어를 쓰시오.

> Each theme _____ the history and culture of the Joseon era.

> to express by some symbol or character

03 다음 빈칸에 들어갈 말이 바르게 짝지어진 것은?

> (A) I'm writing an article about students' favorite snacks. I'm _____ their health.
> (B) I will _____ the President in the election next year.

	(A)	(B)
①	related to	run for
②	related to	put down
③	worried about	run for
④	worried about	get back
⑤	put down	get back

04 다음 중 짝지어진 단어의 관계가 <u>다른</u> 것은?

① claim – insist
② equal – match
③ struggle – strive
④ novel – fiction
⑤ courageous – cowardly

[05~06] 다음 설명에 해당하는 단어를 고르시오.

05

> an amount of money that you have to pay to the government so that it can pay for public services

① tax　　　　② sum
③ fee　　　　④ cost
⑤ fare

06

> a long written story about characters and events that have been invented by the writer

① election　　　　② novel
③ typewriter　　　④ graph
⑤ science-fiction

07 다음 우리말에 맞게 주어진 단어를 활용하여 세 단어를 쓰시오.

> Jane은 이 반짝이는 장식품들을 하나씩 만듭니다. (one)

➡ Jane makes these shiny ornaments _____.

01 다음 빈칸에 들어갈 말을 〈보기〉에서 찾아 쓰시오. (필요하면 어형을 변화시킬 것)

┤ 보기 ├

adventure   celebrate   elect   face

(1) Chimpanzees can express its feelings through _____ expressions and sounds.

(2) In fact, Valentine's Day is _____ in most parts of the world.

(3) We just had an _____ for class presidents at school.

(4) These sports give people a chance to feel thrills from high speeds or _____.

02 다음 문장의 빈칸에 공통으로 들어갈 단어를 철자 s로 시작하여 쓰시오.

- Government is the best _____ for giving money to people who need it.
- They added different herbs and flowers to scent the _____.
- We need to find a better _____ to the conflict.

03 다음 우리말과 같은 표현이 되도록 문장의 빈칸을 채우시오.

(1) 참가자들은 단어를 듣고 그 단어를 반복했습니다.
➡ Participants listened to the words and then _____ the words back.

(2) 영화 속에서, 몇몇 계약직 노동자들은 그들의 인권을 지키려고 고군분투한다.
➡ In the movie, some contract workers _____ to preserve their human rights.

(3) 돈은 종종 사람들을 탐욕스럽고 이기적으로 만든다.
➡ Money often makes people _____ and selfish.

(4) 서로의 차이가 정말 중요하긴 하지만 서로가 같은 인간이라는 점이 더 중요하다.
➡ Our differences do _____, but our common humanity _____ more.

04 영영풀이에 해당하는 단어를 〈보기〉에서 찾아 첫 번째 빈칸에 쓰고, 두 번째 빈칸에는 우리말 뜻을 쓰시오.

┤ 보기 ├

wave   greedy   celebrate   sum

(1) _____: to take part in special enjoyable activities in order to show that a particular occasion is important: _____

(2) _____: to signal in greeting, by raising the hand and moving the fingers: _____

(3) _____: the total of two or more numbers or quantities, determined by mathematical process: _____

(4) _____: wanting a lot more food, money, etc. than you need: _____

Conversation

① 상술하기

> • **Five out of twenty students chose science-fiction books.** 20명의 학생들 중 5명이 공상과학 책을 선택했다.
>
> • **Two out of twenty students chose history books.** 20명의 학생들 중 2명이 역사책을 선택했다.

■ 'X out of Y'는 'Y 중에 X'라는 뜻으로 전체 Y 중에 X가 차지하는 비중을 나타낼 때 쓰는 표현이며, X와 Y는 숫자를 가리킨다. 전체 중 일부가 차지하는 비율을 나타낼 때는 퍼센트(percent)를 사용하여 나타낼 수도 있다.

• **A:** What can you tell from the pie chart? (원그래프에서 무엇을 알 수 있니?)

B: Five out of twenty students like action movies. That is twenty-five percent of total.
(20명의 학생들 중 5명이 액션 영화를 좋아해. 그것의 전체의 25%야.)

핵심 Check

1. 다음 빈칸에 공통으로 알맞은 어구를 쓰시오.

> **A:** What is this graph about?
> **B:** I did a survey on the kinds of pets my classmates have.
> **A:** What were the results?
> **B:** Twenty _____ twenty-five students have pets. Only five _____ twenty-five students don't have pets.

2 이해 점검하기

• **Do you see what I mean?** 내 말이 무슨 뜻인지 알겠어?

■ 'Do you see what I mean?'은 '내 말이 무슨 뜻인지 알겠어?'라는 뜻으로 상대방에게 어떤 상황에 대해 그것을 이해했는지 묻는 표현이다.

■ 같은 표현으로는 'Do you get what I mean?', 'Do you understand?', 'Do you follow me?' 등으로 바꿔서 표현할 수 있으며, 이에 대해 'Yes, I get it.', 'No, I don't understand.' 등으로 대답할 수 있다.

A: I surveyed 100 students and the results show that eighty percent of the students liked pizza and fried chicken for snacks. Do you see what I mean? (100명의 학생들을 조사했는데, 80%의 학생들이 간식으로 피자와 후라이드 치킨을 좋아한다는 결과가 나왔어. 내 말이 무슨 뜻인지 알겠어?)

B: Students really like fast food. What else did they like? (학생들이 정말 패스트푸드를 좋아하는구나. 그리고 또 뭘 좋아했는데?)

A: Twelve percent of the students chose chocolate cake as their favorite. (12%의 학생들이 초콜릿 케이크를 가장 좋아한다고 뽑았어.)

B: Wow, students should really try to eat healthier snacks! (우와, 학생들은 더 건강한 간식을 먹어야겠다!)

핵심 Check

2. 다음 우리말을 주어진 단어를 이용하여 영작하시오.

> **B:** My brother broke my computer. I'm so angry.
>
> **G:** Well, It takes a lot of muscles to look angry, but only a few to smile. Do you see what I mean?
>
> **B:** 응, 이해했어.(get) I guess it's not good to stay angry for a long time.
>
> **G:** That's right. Remember, it's always better to smile.

➡  _____

Listen & Speak 1 A

B: Minju, ❶what is this graph about?

G: I did a survey on the kinds of pets ❷my classmates have.

B: What were the results?

G: ❸Eighty percent of the students have pets. ❹Only five out of twenty-five students don't have pets.

B: What kind of pets do they have?

G: Well, ten students have dogs and three students have cats.

B: ❺What about the rest?

G: Seven students have fish.

B: 민주야, 이 그래프는 무엇에 관한 거야?

G: 나는 우리 반 친구들이 가지고 있는 애완동물의 종류에 대해 설문 조사했어.

B: 결과가 어땠어?

G: 학생들의 80%가 애완동물을 가지고 있어. 25명의 학생들 중 5명만 애완동물이 없어.

B: 그들은 어떤 종류의 애완동물을 가지고 있니?

G: 음. 10명은 개, 3명은 고양이를 가지고 있어.

B: 나머지는?

G: 7명은 물고기를 가지고 있어.

❶ 'what ~ about?'은 '~는 무엇에 관한 거니?'로 해석한다.
❷ 목적격 관계대명사 'that/which'가 생략되어 있는 관계대명사절로 선행사 'pets'를 수식하는 역할을 한다.
❸ 주어가 'percent'일 때는 'of' 뒤의 명사에 동사 수를 일치시킨다. 'the students'가 복수 명사이므로 동사는 'have'를 사용한다.
❹ 'X out of Y'는 'Y 중에 X'라는 뜻으로 전체 Y 중에 X가 차지하는 비중을 나타낼 때 쓰는 표현이다.
❺ 'What about+명사?'는 '~은 어때?'라는 표현이고, 'the rest'는 '나머지'의 뜻이다. 'rest'가 '휴식'을 의미할 때는 'the'를 사용하지 않는다.

Check(√) True or False

(1) Minju surveyed on the kinds of pets her classmates have.　　T ☐ F ☐

(2) Only eight out of twenty-five students don't have pets.　　T ☐ F ☐

Listen & Speak 2 A

B: Emma, ❶can you help me with this math problem?

G: Sure, what is it?

B: You have to move one stick ❷to make this sum right. How could four minus five equal six?

G: Oh, it's simple. You need to move one of the sticks in number four to make it eleven. ❸Do you see what I mean?

B: Yes, now I see what you mean. Eleven minus five equals six. How clever!

G: ❹Thinking outside the box can be helpful sometimes.

B: Emma, 이 수학 문제 좀 도와줄래?

G: 물론이지, 뭔데?

B: 이 계산이 맞도록 너는 한 개의 막대기를 옮겨야 해. 어떻게 4빼기 5가 6이 되지?

G: 오, 이건 간단해. 너는 숫자 4를 11로 만들기 위해 막대기 하나를 옮기면 돼. 무슨 말인지 알겠니?

B: 응, 이제 네 말이 무슨 뜻인지 알겠어. 11 빼기 5는 6이지. 너 정말 똑똑하구나!

G: 틀 밖에서 생각하는 것은 때때로 도움이 될 수 있지.

❶ 'help A with B'는 'A가 B하는 것을 돕다'라는 의미이다.
❷ 부정사의 부사적 용법 중 '목적'을 나타내는 용법으로 'in order to, so as to'로 바꾸어 쓸 수 있다.
❸ 'Do you see what I mean?'은 '내 말이 무슨 뜻인지 알겠어?'라는 뜻으로 상대방에게 어떤 상황에 대해 그것을 이해했는지 묻는 표현이다. 'Do you get what I mean?', 'Do you understand?' 등으로 바꿔서 표현할 수 있다.
❹ 'Thinking'은 동명사 주어로 사용되었다. 'think outside the box'는 '새로운 사고를 하다, 틀에서 벗어나 생각하다'라는 의미이다.

Check(√) True or False

(3) They need to move a stick to make the number four into eleven.　　T ☐ F ☐

(4) The boy thinks Emma is very clever.　　T ☐ F ☐

Listen & Speak 1 B

M: Mason, how was the election?

B: It was bad. I didn't win.

M: ❶How come?

B: Yura won. Over sixty percent of the students ❷voted for her.

M: Well, ❸you tried your best and that's what matters.

B: I guess so. I have learned many things ❹ while running for class president.

M: I'm really proud of you.

B: Thanks, Dad.

❶ 왜(Why?)'의 의미를 가진다. 'How come you didn't win?'의 줄임말이다.
❷ 'vote for'는 '~에게 투표하다'의 의미이다.
❸ 'try one's best'는 '최선을 다하다'라는 의미이고, 'what matters'는 보어 자리에 사용된 명사절로 'what'은 '관계대명사'로 '~인 것'의 의미이다.
❹ 'while+-ing'는 '~하는 동안'의 의미이다.

Listen & Speak 2 B

B: Jian, ❶what's the matter? You look upset.

G: My brother broke my computer. I'm so angry.

B: ❷I'm sorry to hear that, but your facial muscles must be tired.

G: What do you mean?

B: Well, ❸it takes a lot of muscles to look angry, but ❹only a few to smile. Do you see what I mean?

G: Oh, I get it. I guess ❺it's not good to stay angry for a long time.

B: That's right. Remember, ❻it's always better to smile!

❶ 상대방이 뭔가에 불만족하거나 실망하고 있는 것을 보고 그 이유를 물을 때 사용하는 표현이다.
❷ 유감이나 동정을 표현하는 말로 '안 됐구나.'의 의미이다.
❸ 'It takes+목적어+to부정사 ~' 형태로 '~하는 데 …을 필요로 하다'라는 의미이다.
❹ '(it takes) only a few muscles to smile.'에서 중복되는 말을 생략한 형태이다.
❺ 가주어(it) ~ 진주어(to stay angry) 구문이다.
❻ 가주어(it) ~ 진주어(to smile) 구문이다.

Real Life Communication

Mina: Henry, what are you doing?

Henry: I'm writing an article about students' favorite snacks. ❶I'm worried about their health.

Mina: Why?

Henry: Well, I surveyed 100 students and the results show ❷that eighty percent of the students liked pizza and fried chicken for snacks. ❸Do you see what I mean?

Mina: Oh, ❹I get it. Students really like fast food. ❺What else did they like?

Henry: Twelve percent of the students chose chocolate cake ❻as their favorite.

Mina: Wow, students should really try to eat healthier snacks!

❶ 'be worried about ~'은 '~에 관해 걱정하다'라는 의미이다.
❷ 'that'은 동사 'show'의 목적어를 이끄는 접속사이다.
❸ 'Do you see[know] what I mean?'은 '내 말이 무슨 뜻인지 알겠어?'라는 뜻으로 상대방에게 어떤 상황에 대해 그것을 이해했는지 묻는 표현이다.
❹ '이해했다'라는 뜻으로 'I understand.'와 같은 표현이다.
❺ 'else'는 '그 밖의, 다른'의 뜻을 가진 부사로 의문대명사 뒤에 위치한다.
❻ 'as'는 '전치사로 사용되었다.

Let's Check ❶

B: These days, you don't need paper tickets ❶ to watch a movie or go to a concert. You just need to store your ticket in your cell phone. Then show the ticket on your phone's screen before you go in. ❷You don't need to go through the trouble of printing out tickets. Do you see what I mean?

❶ to부정사의 부사적 용법 중 '목적'으로 '~하기 위해'의 의미로 사용되었다.
❷ 'don't need to V'는 '~할 필요없다'라는 의미로 'don't have to', 'need not'으로 바꾸어 쓸 수 있다.

● 다음 우리말과 일치하도록 빈칸에 알맞은 말을 쓰시오.

Listen & Speak 1 A

B: Minju, what is this _____ about?

G: I did a _____ on the _____ of pets my classmates have.

B: What were the _____?

G: Eighty _____ of the students have pets. Only five _____ _____ twenty-five students don't have pets.

B: _____ _____ _____ pets do they have?

G: Well, ten students have dogs and three students have cats.

B: What about _____ _____?

G: Seven students have _____.

해석

B: 민주야, 이 그래프는 무엇에 관한 거야?

G: 나는 우리 반 친구들이 가지고 있는 애완동물의 종류에 대해 설문 조사했어.

B: 결과가 어땠어?

G: 학생들의 80%가 애완동물을 가지고 있었어. 25명의 학생들 중 5명만 이 애완동물이 없었어.

B: 그들은 어떤 종류의 애완동물을 가지고 있니?

G: 음. 10명은 개, 3명은 고양이를 가지고 있어.

B: 나머지는?

G: 7명은 물고기를 가지고 있어.

Listen & Speak 1 B

M: Mason, how was the _____?

B: It was _____. I didn't _____.

M: _____ _____?

B: Yura won. _____ sixty percent of the students voted for her.

M: Well, you tried _____ _____ and that's _____ _____.

B: I _____ so. I have learned many things while _____ _____ class _____.

M: I'm really _____ _____ you.

B: Thanks, Dad.

M: Mason, 선거는 어땠니?

B: 안 좋았어요. 저는 이기지 못했어요.

M: 어째서?

B: 유라가 이겼어요. 학생들의 60% 이상이 그녀에게 투표했어요.

M: 음, 너는 최선을 다했고, 그게 중요한 거란다.

B: 저도 그렇게 생각해요. 반장 선거에 출마한 동안 많은 것을 배웠어요.

M: 나는 네가 정말 자랑스럽구나.

B: 고마워요, 아빠.

Listen & Speak 2 A

B: Emma, can you _____ me _____ this math problem?

G: Sure, what is it?

B: You _____ _____ move one stick _____ _____ this _____ right. _____ could four _____ five _____ six?

G: Oh, it's simple. You _____ _____ move one of the _____ in number four _____ _____ it eleven. Do you see _____ _____ _____?

B: Yes, now I see _____ you mean. Eleven _____ five equals six. _____ clever!

G: _____ _____ _____ _____ _____ can be _____ sometimes.

B: Emma, 이 수학 문제 좀 도와줄래?

G: 물론이지, 뭔데?

B: 이 계산이 맞도록 너는 한 개의 막대기를 옮겨야 해. 어떻게 4빼기 5가 6이 되지?

G: 오, 이건 간단해. 너는 숫자 4를 11로 만들기 위해 막대기 하나를 옮기면 돼. 무슨 말인지 알겠니?

B: 응, 이제 네 말이 무슨 뜻인지 알겠어. 11 빼기 5는 6이지. 너 정말 똑똑하구나!

G: 틀 밖에서 생각하는 것은 때때로 도움이 될 수 있지.

Listen & Speak 2 B

B: Jian, what's _____ _____? You _____ _____.

G: My brother _____ my computer. I'm so angry.

B: _____ _____ _____ _____ that, but your _____ muscles must _____ _____.

G: _____ _____ _____ _____ _____?

B: Well, it _____ a lot of _____ _____ _____ angry, but only _____ _____ to smile. Do you see _____ I mean?

G: Oh, I _____ it. I guess it's not good _____ _____ angry _____ _____ _____ _____.

B: That's right. Remember, _____ always better _____ _____!

Real Life Communication

Mina: Henry, what are you doing?

Henry: I'm writing an _____ about students' _____ _____. I'_____ _____ _____ their health.

Mina: Why?

Henry: Well, I _____ 100 students and the _____ show that _____ _____ of the students liked pizza and fried chicken for snacks. _____ _____ _____ what I mean?

Mina: Oh, _____ _____ _____. Students really like fast food. _____ _____ did they like?

Henry: _____ _____ of the students _____ chocolate cake as their _____.

Mina: Wow, students should really _____ _____ eat _____ snacks!

Let's Check

B: _____ _____, you don't need _____ _____ to watch a movie or go to a concert. You just need to _____ your ticket _____ your cell phone. Then _____ the ticket on your phone's _____ before you _____ _____. You _____ _____ _____ the _____ of _____ out tickets. Do you see _____ _____ _____?

해석

B: 지안아, 무슨 문제 있니? 너 속상해 보여.

G: 내 남동생이 내 컴퓨터를 고장 냈어. 정말 화나.

B: 그렇다니 유감이지만, 너의 얼굴 근육은 피곤할 거야.

G: 무슨 뜻이니?

B: 음, 화난 표정을 지을 때는 많은 근육이 필요하지만, 웃을 때는 몇 개의 근육만 필요하거든. 무슨 말인지 알겠어?

G: 오, 이해했어. 오랫동안 화난 상태로 있으면 좋지 않겠구나.

B: 맞아. 기억해, 웃는 게 항상 더 낫다는 것을 말이야!

미나: Henry, 너 뭐 하고 있니?

Henry: 난 학생들이 가장 좋아하는 간식에 관한 기사를 쓰고 있어. 나는 그들의 건강이 걱정 돼.

미나: 왜?

Henry: 음, 난 100명의 학생들에게 설문 조사를 했고, 학생들의 80%가 간식으로 피자나 프라이드치킨을 좋아한다는 결과가 나왔어. 무슨 뜻인지 알겠니?

미나: 아, 알겠어. 학생들은 패스트푸드를 정말 좋아하지. 그들은 또 어떤 것을 좋아했니?

Henry: 학생들의 12%가 가장 좋아하는 것으로 초콜릿 케이크를 골랐어.

미나: 와우, 학생들은 더 건강한 간식을 먹도록 정말로 노력해야겠다!

B: 요즘에, 당신은 영화를 보거나 공연장에 가기 위해 종이 티켓이 필요하지 않습니다. 당신은 단지 당신의 휴대전화에 티켓을 저장하면 됩니다. 그리고 나서 입장하기 전에 휴대전화 화면 위의 티켓을 보여줍니다. 당신은 번거롭게 티켓을 출력할 필요가 없습니다. 무슨 뜻인지 아시겠어요?

01 우리말에 맞도록 주어진 단어를 이용하여 영어로 쓰시오.

> 내 말이 무슨 뜻인지 알겠어? (see / what)

➡ _____

02 다음 대화의 빈칸에 들어갈 말로 알맞지 <u>않은</u> 것은?

> A: How could five plus three equal six?
> B: Why don't you move the stick in number five to make it three? _____
> A: Do you mean the one on the top left?
> B: That's right.

① Do you get what I mean?
② Do you understand?
③ Do you get it?
④ Did you move the stick?
⑤ Do you get the point?

03 다음 대화의 빈칸에 들어갈 말로 알맞은 것은?

> M: Mason, how was the election?
> B: It was bad. I didn't win.
> M: _____
> B: Yura won. Over sixty percent of the students voted for her.
> M: Well, you tried your best and that's what matters.
> B: I guess so.

① What about you?
② How come?
③ What do you think of the result of the election?
④ Are you satisfied with the result of the election?
⑤ How do you like the election?

[01~02] 다음 대화를 읽고 물음에 답하시오.

Mina: Henry, what are you doing?

Henry: I'm writing an article about students' favorite snacks. (A)_____

Mina: Why?

Henry: Well, I surveyed 100 students and the results show that eighty percent of the students liked pizza and fried chicken for snacks. Do you see what I mean?

Mina: Oh, I get it. Students really like fast food. What else did they like?

Henry: Twelve percent of the students chose chocolate cake as their favorite.

Mina: Wow, students should really try to eat healthier snacks!

01 위 대화의 빈칸 (A)에 들어갈 말로 알맞은 것을 고르시오.

① I had trouble writing the article.

② I'm happy with the result of the survey.

③ I'm worried about their health.

④ I'm not satisfied with the article.

⑤ I think most students are more worried about their health than any other thing.

02 위 대화의 내용과 일치하지 <u>않는</u> 것은?

① Henry is writing an article about students' favorite snacks.

② The results show that 80 percent of the students liked pizza and fried chicken for snacks.

③ Most students like fast food.

④ Twelve students surveyed liked chocolate cake.

⑤ We can know most students eat healthier snacks.

03 다음 두 사람의 대화가 <u>어색한</u> 것은?

① A: What is your favorite type of movie?
   B: My favorite type of movie is a romance movie.

② A: We should have more tennis classes for after-school classes.
   B: What makes you say that?

③ A: Do you think we can go on a picnic on Wednesday?
   B: I don't think so. Wednesday will be too cold to go on a picnic.

④ A: Do you see what I mean?
   B: Oh, I've seen it before.

⑤ A: What can you tell from the chart?
   B: Forty percent of the students liked red.

04 다음 대화의 밑줄 친 (a)~(e) 중 어휘의 쓰임이 <u>어색한</u> 것은?

B: Jian, what's the matter? You (a)<u>look upset</u>.

G: My brother broke my computer. I'm so angry.

B: I'm (b)<u>sorry</u> to hear that, but your facial muscles must be (c)<u>relaxed</u>.

G: What do you mean?

B: Well, it takes (d)<u>a lot of muscles</u> to look angry, but only a few to smile. Do you see what I mean?

G: Oh, I get it. I guess it's not good (e)<u>to stay angry</u> for a long time.

B: That's right. Remember, it's always better to smile!

① (a) ② (b) ③ (c) ④ (d) ⑤ (e)

15 대화의 ①~⑤ 중 도표의 내용과 일치하지 <u>않는</u> 것은?

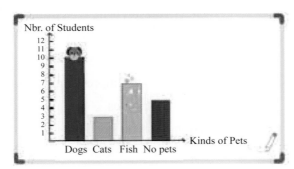

B: Minju, what is this graph about?

G: ①I did a survey on the kinds of pets my classmates have.

B: What were the results?

G: ②Eighty percent of the students don't have pets. ③Only five out of twenty-five students don't have pets.

B: What kind of pets do they have?

G: Well, ④ten students have dogs and three students have cats.

B: What about the rest?

G: ⑤Seven students have fish.

　① 　　② 　　③ 　　④ 　　⑤

06 다음 대화의 (A)~(D)를 알맞은 순서로 배열한 것은?

(A) Look at the pie chart. Seventy percent of the students said that they wanted to learn tennis. Do you see what I mean?

(B) Oh, I see.

(C) We should have more tennis classes for after-school classes.

(D) What makes you say that?

① (A)–(C)–(B)–(D)　② (B)–(A)–(D)–(C)

③ (C)–(B)–(A)–(D)　④ (C)–(D)–(A)–(B)

⑤ (D)–(C)–(A)–(B)

[07~08] 다음 대화를 읽고 물음에 답하시오.

B: Emma, can you help me with this math problem?

G: Sure, what is it?

B: You have to move one stick to make this sum right. (a)<u>어떻게 4빼기 5가 6이 되지?</u> (minus / how / four / five / six / could / equal)

G: Oh, it's simple. You need to move one of the sticks in number four (A)＿＿＿＿＿. Do you see what I mean?

B: Yes, now I see what you mean. Eleven minus five equals six. How clever!

G: Thinking outside the box can be helpful sometimes.

07 위 대화의 빈칸 (A)에 들어갈 말로 알맞은 것은?

① to equal six

② to make it eleven

③ to help me with this math problem

④ to make it five

⑤ to think outside the box

08 위 대화의 밑줄 친 우리말 (a)에 맞게 주어진 단어를 알맞은 순서로 배열하시오.

➡ ＿＿＿＿＿＿＿＿＿＿＿＿＿＿＿

09 다음 글의 밑줄 친 (a)~(e) 중 어휘의 쓰임이 <u>어색한</u> 것은?

These days, you don't need (a)<u>paper tickets</u> to watch a movie or go to a concert. You just need to (b)<u>store</u> your ticket in your cell phone. Then show the ticket (c)<u>on your phone's screen</u> before you go in. You (d)<u>need to</u> go through the trouble of printing out tickets. Do you see (e)<u>what I mean</u>?

① (a)　② (b)　③ (c)　④ (d)　⑤ (e)

[01~02] 다음 대화를 읽고 물음에 답하시오.

Mina: Henry, what are you doing?

Henry: I'm writing an article about students' favorite snacks. I'm worried about their health.

Mina: Why?

Henry: Well, I surveyed 100 students and the results show that eighty percent of the students liked pizza and fried chicken for snacks. (A)_____

Mina: Oh, I get it. Students really like fast food. What else did they like?

Henry: Twelve percent of the students chose chocolate cake as their favorite.

Mina: Wow, students should really try to eat healthier snacks!

01 위 대화를 읽고 다음 질문에 대한 답을 조건에 맞게 영어로 쓰시오.

┌─ 조건 ─┐
- 대명사 'them'을 이용할 것.
- 4 단어로 쓸 것.

Q: How many students liked pizza and fried chicken for snacks?

➡ _____

02 위 대화의 흐름상 빈칸 (A)에 들어갈 말을 〈조건〉에 맞게 영어로 쓰시오.

┌─ 조건 ─┐
- 이해했는지 확인하는 표현을 쓸 것.
- 'see'와 'what'을 이용할 것.

➡ _____

03 다음 원 그래프에 맞게 대화의 빈칸을 완성하시오.

Favorite Type of Movie

Other: 3 (15%) / Scary: 2 (10%) / Romance: 6 (30%) / Comedy: 4 (20%) / Action: 5 (25%)

Total number of students: 20

A: What can you tell from the pie chart?

B: Six _____ twenty students like _____. That is _____ the total. And _____ twenty students like scary movies. That is _____ of the total.

04 다음 그림을 참고하여 대화의 흐름상 의미가 통하도록 주어진 단어를 알맞은 순서대로 빈칸에 배열하시오.

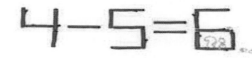

B: Emma, can you help me with this math problem?

G: Sure, what is it?

B: You have to move one stick to make this sum right. How could four minus five equal six?

G: Oh, it's simple. _____ Do you get what I mean?

B: Yes, now I see what you mean. Eleven minus five equals six. How clever!

(move / one of / eleven / the / in number / sticks / four / to make / it)

➡ You need to _____

_____.

Grammar

1 too 형용사/부사 to 동사원형

• It's **too** hard **to read** and **draw** graphs. 그래프를 읽고 그리는 것은 너무 어려워.

■ 'too 형용사/부사 to부정사'의 형태로 '너무 ~해서 …할 수 없다'로 해석하고 'so 형용사/부사 that 주어 can't.'로 바꿔 쓸 수 있다.

• The house looked **too** scary for me **to go** in. 그 집은 너무 무서워 보여서 나는 들어갈 수 없었다.
= The house looked **so** scary **that** I **couldn't** go in.

■ to부정사의 의미상 주어는 'for+목적격'의 형태로 따로 나타내 주어야 한다.

• The bed is too heavy **for me** to lift. 그 침대는 내가 들기에 너무 무겁다.
• The problem is too difficult **for me** to solve. 그 문제는 너무 어려워서 나는 풀지 못한다.

■ 'too ~ to …' 구문에서 주어와 to부정사의 목적어가 일치하는 경우, 목적어를 쓰지 않는다.

• The soup is too hot to eat it. (✕)
→ The soup is too hot to eat. 그 수프는 먹기에 너무 뜨겁다.

cf. 'too ~ to …' 구문을 'so ~ that …' 구문으로 바꿀 경우, 생략된 목적어를 that절에 명시해야 한다.

• The laptop was **too** expensive for me **to buy**. 그 노트북은 너무 비싸서 내가 살 수가 없었다.
→ The laptop was **so** expensive **that** I couldn't buy **it**. 그 노트북은 너무 비싸서 나는 그것을 살 수 없었다.

■ '형용사/부사 enough to 부정사(= so 형/부 that 주어 can 동사원형)'는 '~할 만큼 충분히 …하다'라는 뜻을 갖는다.

• She is tall **enough to** be a volleyball player. 그녀는 배구 선수가 되기에 충분히 키가 크다.
= She is **so** tall **that** she can be a volleyball player.

*'enough 명사 to동사원형'은 '~할 만큼 충분한 명사'로 해석한다.

ex. We don't have **enough** time **to do** that. 우리는 그것을 할 충분한 시간을 가지고 있지 않다.

핵심 Check

1. 다음 괄호 안에서 알맞은 말을 고르시오.

(1) The weather is (to / too / so) cold (to / too / that) go for a swim.

(2) There are (too / enough) chairs to sit on.

(3) It is too late (to / for) him to get the operation.

(4) I was stupid (too / enough) to believe him.

② No one ...

> • **No one** needs graphs in real life. 아무도 실제 생활에서는 그래프가 필요하지 않아.

- ■ 'No one ...'은 문장의 시제가 현재인 경우 'No one + 단수동사' 형태로 쓰고 '아무도 ... 않다'라는 의미이다.
  - • **No one** goes out in this hot weather. 아무도 이 더운 날씨에 나가지 않는다.
  - • **No one** was outside the building when it rained. 비가 왔을 때 아무도 건물 밖에 있지 않았다.

- ■ 'No one ...'은 none, nobody, nothing 등과 같이 문장 전체를 부정한다.
  - • **No one** wears a uniform outside of school. 학교 밖에서 어느 누구도 교복을 입지 않는다.
    = **Nobody** wears a uniform outside of school.
  - • **None** of us is entirely blameless in this matter. 우리들 중 이 문제에 대해 전적으로 떳떳한 사람은 아무도 없어.
  *none of 단수명사+단수 동사
  *none of 복수명사+단수/복수 동사
  - • **Nothing** could weaken his resolve to continue. 그 무엇도 계속하겠다는 그의 결심을 약화시키지 못했다.

- ■ 문장 앞에 Not이 붙는 경우는 전체 부정이 아니라 부분 부정이다.
  - • **Not** every man can sing well. (부분 부정) 모든 사람이 노래를 잘할 수 있는 것은 아니다.
  - • **No** man can sing well. (전체 부정) 노래를 잘할 수 있는 사람이 없습니다.

- ■ none, nothing이 but과 함께 쓰이면(nothing but) '오직'이란 뜻이 된다.
  - • **Nothing but** a miracle can save her now. 이제 오직 기적만이 그녀를 구할 수 있다.

핵심 Check

2. 다음 괄호 안에서 알맞은 단어를 고르시오.

   (1) No one (is / are) cooking in the kitchen.

   (2) No one (comes / come) to a party without a present.

3. 다음 문장과 같은 의미가 되도록 빈칸에 알맞은 말을 한 단어로 쓰시오.

> No one can replace you. = _____ can replace you.

01 다음 문장에서 어법상 <u>어색한</u> 부분을 바르게 고쳐 쓰시오. 어색한 부분이 없으면 '없음'으로 쓰시오.

(1) None of the teachers has pointed that out to the students.

＿＿＿＿＿＿＿ ➡ ＿＿＿＿＿＿＿

(2) Not everyone believe fortunetellers.

＿＿＿＿＿＿＿ ➡ ＿＿＿＿＿＿＿

(3) I'm too tired to studying.

＿＿＿＿＿＿＿ ➡ ＿＿＿＿＿＿＿

(4) The bread is too dry to eat it.

＿＿＿＿＿＿＿ ➡ ＿＿＿＿＿＿＿

02 괄호 안의 단어를 활용하여 빈칸에 어법상 알맞게 쓰시오.

None of my advice ＿＿＿＿＿＿＿(seem) to have penetrated his thick skull.

*penetrate 관통하다

03 다음 밑줄 친 ①～⑤ 중 어법상 <u>어색한</u> 것을 고르시오.

The dishwasher is ①<u>too</u> heavy ②<u>for</u> ③<u>me</u> ④<u>to</u> lift ⑤<u>it</u>.

04 다음 문장과 같은 뜻이 되도록 괄호 안의 단어를 활용하여 다시 쓰시오.

(1) I slept too late to get up early. (so)

➡ ＿＿＿＿＿＿＿＿＿＿＿＿＿

(2) He was wise enough to accept the offer. (so)

➡ ＿＿＿＿＿＿＿＿＿＿＿＿＿

(3) The box was too heavy for me to lift. (so)

➡ ＿＿＿＿＿＿＿＿＿＿＿＿＿

(4) The problem was so difficult that I couldn't solve it. (too)

➡ ＿＿＿＿＿＿＿＿＿＿＿＿＿

(5) She was so lucky that she could be chosen for the team.

➡ ＿＿＿＿＿＿＿＿＿＿＿＿＿

01 다음 문장에서 어법상 틀린 부분을 찾아 바르게 고쳐 쓰시오.

> The tea is so hot for me to drink.

_____ ➡ _____

02 다음 빈칸에 들어갈 말로 알맞은 것을 고르시오.

> The car is too expensive _____ him to buy.

① to ② for ③ of
④ that ⑤ so

03 다음 문장에서 어법상 어색한 것을 고르시오.

> Fortunately, ①no one ②were in the house ③when ④the fire ⑤broke out.

① no one ② were
③ when ④ the fire
⑤ broke out

04 우리말에 맞게 영작할 때 빈칸에 들어갈 어휘로 알맞은 것을 고르시오.

> 공자는 "모든 것이 저만의 아름다움을 지니고 있으나 모든 이가 그것을 볼 수는 없다."고 말했다.
> → Confucius said, "Everything has its beauty but _____ everyone sees it."

① not ② no
③ none ④ all
⑤ some

05 우리말에 맞게 영작할 때, 빈칸에 들어갈 말로 바르게 짝지어진 것을 고르시오.

> • 여기에서는 한 번도 무슨 일이 생기는 법이 없다.
> → ___(A)___ ever happens here.
> • 모든 사람들이 그 게들을 못마땅하게 여기지는 않습니다.
> → ___(B)___ is angry about the crabs.
> • 주변에 다른 사람은 아무도 없었다.
> → There ___(C)___ no one else around.

	(A)	(B)	(C)
①	Not everyone	None of you	were
②	No one	None of you	was
③	Nothing	None of you	were
④	Nothing	Not everyone	was
⑤	Nothing	Not everyone	were

06 다음 빈칸에 들어갈 알맞은 말을 모두 고르시오.

> None of the passengers _____ badly hurt.

① to be ② being ③ be
④ are ⑤ were

07 다음 빈칸에 들어갈 말로 적절하지 않은 것을 고르시오.

> This book is too difficult for _____ to read.

① you ② him ③ me
④ her ⑤ I

08 다음 중 어법상 <u>어색한</u> 것을 고르시오.

> ①The joke ②is ③too rude ④to repeat ⑤ it.

① The joke   ② is
③ too   ④ to repeat
⑤ it

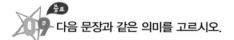 다음 문장과 같은 의미를 고르시오.

> None of the groups knew each other.

① Everyone in the groups knew each other.
② Not everyone in the groups knew each other.
③ Some in the groups knew each other, and the others in the groups didn't know each other.
④ No one in the groups knew each other.
⑤ Some in the groups knew each other, others in the groups didn't know each other, and still others were new members.

서답형
10 두 문장이 같은 뜻이 되도록 빈칸에 알맞은 말을 쓰시오.

> These shoes are too small for me to wear.
> = These shoes are _____ small _____
>   I can't wear _____ .

11 다음 우리말을 옮긴 것으로 알맞은 것을 고르시오.

> 네 환상을 깨고 싶진 않지만 모든 사람들이 너처럼 정직하지는 않아.

① I hate to break your fantasy, but not everyone is as honest as you.
② I hate to break your fantasy, but no one is as honest as you.
③ I don't want to break your fantasy, but no one is as honest as you.
④ I want to break your fantasy, but not everyone is as honest as you.
⑤ I want to break your fantasy, but no one is as honest as you.

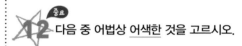 다음 중 어법상 <u>어색한</u> 것을 고르시오.

> She was ①too ②shy ③to ④asking anyone ⑤for help.

① too   ② shy   ③ to
④ asking   ⑤ for

13 다음 문장과 같은 의미를 갖는 문장을 고르시오.

> It's warm enough for us to eat outside.

① It's so warm that we can't eat outside.
② It's warm but we can't eat outside.
③ It's not warm enough to eat outside.
④ It's so cool that we can eat outside.
⑤ It's so warm that we can eat outside.

14 우리말을 참고하여 빈칸에 들어갈 어휘끼리 짝지어진 것을 고르시오.

전선이 소켓에 닿을 정도로 긴가요?
→ _____ the cable long _____ reach the socket?

① Is, so that
② Is, enough to
③ Are, so that
④ Are, enough to
⑤ Is, so as to

15 다음 중 어법상 어색한 것을 고르시오.

① We were amazed to find that no one were hurt.
② No one ever died of a broken heart.
③ No one has ever questioned her judgement.
④ No one has yet been chosen for the main role.
⑤ It soon became apparent that no one was going to come.

16 빈칸에 들어갈 적절한 말을 고르시오.

Not everyone _____ that this new trend is good for Asian cinema.

① thought
② think
③ thinks
④ thinking
⑤ to think

17 빈칸에 들어갈 적절한 말을 고르시오.

Make sure that no one _____ about this.

① finds out
② founds
③ founded
④ discovered
⑤ discover

18 우리말에 맞게 괄호 안의 단어를 활용하여 영작할 때,

(1) 3번째 단어를 쓰시오.
• 내 일에 신경쓰지 마. (it, none, business)
➡ _____

(2) 1번째 단어를 쓰시오.
• 모든 사람이 똑같이 생각하는 것은 아니다. (everyone, alike)
➡ _____

(3) 6번째 단어를 쓰시오.
• 눈이 너무 많이 쌓여 그는 걸을 수가 없었다. (deep, to walk)
➡ _____

19 다음 중 어법상 어색한 것을 모두 고르시오.

① Is it too much to ask for being a little quiet?
② Is it too late to cancel my order?
③ It is too late of them to put it off now.
④ It was too stormy to sail that night.
⑤ The sale prices were too good to miss them.

20 빈칸에 들어갈 알맞은 단어끼리 짝지어진 것을 고르시오.

Death is more universal than life; __(A)__ dies but __(B)__ lives.

	(A)	(B)
①	not everyone	everyone
②	no one	not everyone
③	everyone	no one
④	no one	everyone
⑤	everyone	not everyone

★01 다음 문장에서 어법상 <u>어색한</u> 것을 찾아 바르게 고쳐 다시 쓰시오.

> No one were supposed to know about it.

➡ _____

02 다음 (A) 문장을 (B)처럼 고쳤을 때 어법상 <u>어색한</u> 부분을 찾아 바르게 고치시오.

> (A) I'm too frightened to ask him now.
> (B) I'm so frightened that he can't ask me now.

➡ _____

03 주어진 철자로 시작하여 빈칸에 들어갈 알맞은 말을 순서대로 쓰시오.

> (1) Korea will be too small f_____ you to work.
> 당신에게 한국은 활동하는 데 너무 좁습니다.
> (2) N_____ one knows for sure what happened.
> 무슨 일이 있었는지 아무도 확실히 모른다.

★04 다음 우리말에 맞게 괄호 안의 단어를 활용하여 영작하시오.

(1) 그 기계는 너무 위험해서 사람들이 다룰 수 없다.
➡ (so, handle) _____

_____

(2) 그 상점은 사람들이 너무 많아서 둘러볼 수 없다. (too, around, crowded)
➡ _____

05 〈보기〉에 주어진 어휘를 이용하여 영작하시오.

> ┤ 보기 ├
> • could have predicted
> • it   • final   • lately
> • outcome   • be well   • enough
> • has been • well

(1) 어느 누구도 그 최종 결과를 예측할 수 없었을 것이다.
➡ _____

(2) 모든 사람이 그 최종 결과를 예측할 수는 없었을 것이다.
➡ _____

_____

(3) 그녀는 최근에 외출을 할 정도로 몸이 좋아졌다.
➡ _____

(4) 그녀가 여행을 할 정도로 건강한가요?
➡ _____

06 우리말에 맞게 괄호의 단어를 활용하여 영작하시오.

(1) 그는 자동차 한 대를 충분히 들어올릴 정도로 힘이 세요. (lift, enough)

➡ _____

(2) 그 음식은 그의 공복을 채우기에 충분하지 못했다. (hunger, enough)

➡ _____

(3) 그녀는 책장 꼭대기까지 닿을 수 있을 정도로 키가 크다. (reach, so)

➡ _____

_____

07 ^{중요} 다음 각 문장과 같은 의미가 되도록 괄호 안의 단어를 활용하여 문장을 다시 쓰시오.

(1) No one parked their car in the garage. (nobody)

(2) Not everyone parked their car in the garage. (some, others)

➡ (1) _____

(2) _____

_____

08 <보기>의 단어 중 하나를 제외하고 모두 활용하여 우리말에 맞게 영작하시오.

┌─ 보기 ─────────────────────────┐
문이 너무 뻑뻑해서 열리지 않는다.
(it, door, is, the, too, to, open, stiff)
└──────────────────────────────┘

➡ _____

09 ^{고난이도} 빈칸에 공통으로 들어갈 2 단어를 쓰시오.

(1) 자본주의를 싫어하는 사람도 있고 PC를 싫어하는 사람도 있다. 그러나 PC를 좋아하는 사람 중에 마이크로소프트 사를 싫어하는 사람은 없다.

➡ There are people who don't like capitalism, and people who don't like PCs. But there's _____ who likes the PC who doesn't like Microsoft. (Bill Gates)

(2) 모두가 비슷한 생각을 한다는 것은, 아무도 생각하고 있지 않다는 말이다.

➡ When all think alike, _____ thinks very much. (Albert Einstein)

10 우리말을 참고하여 빈칸에 들어갈 알맞은 말을 쓰시오.

┌──────────────────────────────┐
• 너무 어두워서 나는 책을 읽을 수가 없다.
➡ It is too dark for me to _____ books.
└──────────────────────────────┘

11 ^{중요} 다음 문장을 괄호 안의 단어를 활용하여 영작할 때 빈칸을 알맞게 채우시오.

(1) 거리에는 한 사람도 보이지 않았다. (no)

➡ _____ seen on the street.

(2) 나는 케이크를 만들기에 충분한 설탕이 없다. (enough)

➡ I don't have _____ a cake.

(3) 우리는 쇼핑을 가기에 충분한 시간이 없다. (enough)

➡ There isn't _____ go shopping.

(4) 그는 너무 피곤해서 올라갈 수 없었다. (so, climb up)

➡ He was _____.

Do Graphs Matter, Pascal?

Pascal was doing his math homework in his room. He was struggling
= He had hard time with graphs.

with graphs.

"It's too hard to read and draw graphs. Why do I need these anyway?
too ~ to V: 너무 ~해서 V할 수 없다

No one needs graphs in real life." He put down his pen and picked
No one ~: 아무도 ~ 않는   과거시제(put-put-put)

up his favorite book, *Robin Hood*. He decided to read himself to sleep.
When he was about to open the book, he heard a voice. He looked up
be about to V: 막 V하려고 하다

from the book to see who was talking. He couldn't believe his eyes. It
to부정사의 부사적 용법(~하기 위해서) 간접의문문(의문사+주어+동사): see의 목적어

was his dog, Manny, who was talking!

"Close your eyes and repeat after me. *Cogito ergo sum*," said Manny.

"You can talk?"

"Just repeat! *Cogito ergo sum*."

Pascal closed his eyes and repeated the words. Suddenly, he heard
men shouting. When he opened his eyes, he saw soldiers on horses.
지각동사+목적어+Ving: 목적어가 V하는 것을 듣다

They were chasing a man with arrows in his hand. The man saw Pascal
and shouted.

"It's too dangerous for you to stand there. Come on." The man pulled
to부정사의 의미상 주어

Pascal onto his horse and rode into the woods.

When they arrived at a house, the man stopped and got off his horse.

"Hello, my name is Robin Hood."

"Wow! Are you the Robin Hood from the book?"

"No, I'm the Robin Hood of Sherwood Forest. Who are you and why
are you here?"

"My name is Pascal. I don't know why I'm here, but there must be a
간접의문문(의문사+주어+동사): know의 목적어   ~임에 틀림없다

reason. You saved me from the soldiers. Thank you so much. Is there

anything I can do for you?"

---

graph: 그래프, 도표
matter: 중요하다
struggle: 고군분투하다, 몸부림치다
read oneself to sleep: 읽다가 잠들다
repeat: 반복하다
shout: 소리치다
soldier: 병사, 군인
chase: 뒤쫓다, 추적하다
arrow: 화살
reason: 이유

📎 **확인문제**

● 다음 문장이 본문의 내용과 일치하면 T, 일치하지 <u>않으면</u> F를 쓰시오.

1 Pascal was fond of drawing graphs. ☐

2 Pascal wasn't surprised that Manny was talking to him. ☐

3 Robin wondered why Pascal was there. ☐

"Well, can you help us get back the money that the king took from the people? He taxed them too much. He is too greedy to share with the people, so they don't have enough money to buy food.

I want to help them get their money back. However, there are many soldiers in the tower, so no one can get inside."

"Hmm… I think I have a solution. But first, can you take me to the tower? I need to count the number of soldiers."

Robin and Pascal hid up in a tree and counted the soldiers one by one. "There are five soldiers from midnight to six in the morning. Next, there are three soldiers until noon, and then there are eight soldiers until six in the evening. Lastly, there are twelve soldiers until midnight. So, you should go inside between six in the morning and noon."

"What? I don't get it."

Pascal thought for a moment. 'Hmm… A graph might make this easier to understand.'

Pascal drew a graph and showed it to Robin.

"Look, the most dangerous time is between six in the evening and midnight. Four times more soldiers work at that time than from six in the morning until noon. Do you see what I mean?"

"Aha! I get it now. Thank you so much, Pascal!"

"You're welcome. Now I realize the importance of graphs. No one can say that we don't need them anymore."

Pascal walked out of the woods. When he looked back, he saw Robin Hood waving at him. Pascal waved back and said to himself, "It was a great adventure. How do I go back? Oh, I know. I should say the words *Cogito ergo sum!*"

---

get back: 되찾다
tax: 세금을 부과하다
greedy: 탐욕스러운
enough: 충분한
solution: 해결책
count: 수를 세다
one by one: 하나씩
midnight: 자정
noon: 정오
realize: 깨닫다
look back: 뒤돌아보다
wave: (손 등을) 흔들다
adventure: 모험

 **확인문제**

● 다음 문장이 본문의 내용과 일치하면 T, 일치하지 않으면 F를 쓰시오.

1 Pascal counted the soldiers in order to know when to go into the tower. ☐

2 The king taxed the people too much, so people didn't have enough money. ☐

● 우리말을 참고하여 빈칸에 알맞은 말을 쓰시오.

1 Pascal _____ _____ _____ _____ in his room. He was _____ _____ graphs.

2 "It's _____ _____ _____ _____ and _____ graphs. Why do I need _____ anyway? No one _____ _____ in real life."

3 He _____ _____ his pen and _____ his favorite book, *Robin Hood*.

4 He _____ _____ _____ _____ to sleep. When he _____ _____ _____ _____ the book, he heard a voice.

5 He _____ _____ _____ the book _____ _____ _____ _____ _____ .

6 He couldn't believe his eyes. It was his dog, Manny, _____ _____ talking!

7 "_____ your eyes and _____ _____ me. *Cogito ergo sum*," said Manny.

8 "_____ _____ _____ ?" "Just _____ ! *Cogito ergo sum*."

9 Pascal closed his eyes and _____ _____ _____ . Suddenly, he _____ men _____ .

10 _____ he opened his eyes, he saw soldiers _____ _____ .

11 They were _____ a man _____ _____ in his hand. The man saw Pascal and _____ .

12 "_____ too dangerous _____ _____ there. Come on."

13 The man _____ Pascal onto his horse and _____ into the woods.

14 When they _____ _____ a house, the man _____ and _____ _____ his horse.

15 "Hello, _____ _____ _____ Robin Hood."

16 "Wow! Are you _____ _____ _____ _____ the book?"

17 "No, I'm the Robin Hood of Sherwood Forest. _____ _____ and why _____ _____ here?"

18 "My name is Pascal. I don't know _____ _____ _____ , but there _____ _____ a reason. You _____ me _____ the soldiers. Thank you so much. _____ _____ _____ I can do _____ you?"

1	파스칼은 그의 방에서 수학 숙제를 하고 있었습니다. 그는 그래프 문제에 고군분투하고 있었습니다.
2	"그래프를 읽고 그리는 것은 너무 어려워. 게다가 내가 왜 그래프가 필요하겠어? 아무도 실제 생활에서는 그래프가 필요하지 않아."
3	그는 그의 펜을 내려놓고, 그가 가장 좋아하는 책, '로빈 후드'를 집어 들었습니다.
4	그는 책을 읽으며 잠들기로 했습니다. 그가 책을 펴려고 할 때, 그는 목소리를 들었습니다.
5	누가 말하고 있는지 보기 위해 그는 책에서 눈을 들어 올려다보았습니다.
6	그는 그의 눈을 믿을 수 없었습니다. 말하는 것은 바로 자신의 개, Manny였습니다!
7	"눈을 감고 내 말을 따라 말하세요. 코기토 에르고 숨." Manny가 말했습니다.
8	"너는 말할 수 있니?" "그냥 따라 하세요! 코기토 에르고 숨."
9	파스칼은 그의 눈을 감고 그 단어들을 따라 말했습니다. 갑자기 그는 남자들이 소리치는 것을 들었습니다.
10	그가 눈을 떴을 때, 그는 말을 탄 병사들을 보았습니다.
11	그들은 손에 화살을 든 남자를 뒤쫓고 있었습니다. 그 남자는 파스칼을 보고 소리쳤습니다.
12	"네가 거기 서 있는 것은 너무 위험해. 이리 와."
13	그 남자는 파스칼을 그의 말에 올려 태우고 숲으로 말을 몰았습니다.
14	그들이 한 집 앞에 이르렀을 때, 그 남자는 멈추고 말에서 내렸습니다.
15	"안녕, 내 이름은 로빈 후드야."
16	"와우! 당신이 책 속의 로빈 후드인가요?"
17	"아니, 나는 셔우드 숲의 로빈 후드야. 너는 누구이고 왜 여기에 있니?"
18	"제 이름은 파스칼이에요. 저는 제가 왜 여기 있는지 모르지만 이유가 분명 있을 거예요. 당신은 저를 병사들로부터 구해줬어요. 정말 감사드려요. 제가 당신을 위해 할 수 있는 것이 있을까요?"

19 "Well, can you help us _____ _____ the money _____ the king _____ from the people? He _____ _____ too much.

20 He is _____ _____ _____ with the people, so they don't have _____ _____ _____ _____ food.

21 I want to _____ _____ _____ their money _____. _____, there are many soldiers in the tower, so _____ _____ _____ _____ inside."

22 "Hmm... I think I have a solution. But first, can you _____ _____ _____ _____ _____? I need to _____ _____ _____ soldiers."

23 Robin and Pascal _____ _____ in a tree and _____ the soldiers _____ _____ _____.

24 "_____ _____ five soldiers _____ midnight _____ six in the morning.

25 Next, there are _____ _____ _____ _____, and then there are _____ _____ _____ six in the evening.

26 _____, there are twelve soldiers _____ midnight. So, you should _____ _____ _____ _____ six in the morning _____ _____."

27 "What? I _____ _____ _____ _____."

28 Pascal thought for a moment. 'Hmm... A graph _____ _____ _____ _____ understand.'

29 Pascal _____ a graph and _____ _____ to Robin.

30 "Look, _____ _____ _____ _____ is between six in the evening and midnight.

31 _____ _____ _____ _____ work at that time from six in the morning until noon. Do you see _____ _____ _____?"

32 "Aha! I _____ now. Thank you _____ _____, Pascal!"

33 "You're welcome. Now I _____ _____ _____ _____. No one can say _____ we don't need _____ anymore."

34 Pascal _____ _____ _____ the woods. When he _____ _____, he saw Robin Hood _____ at him.

35 Pascal _____ _____ and said to _____, "It was a great _____. How _____ _____ _____ _____? Oh, I know. I _____ _____ the words *Cogito ergo sum*!"

---

19 "음, 우리가 왕이 사람들에게서 가져간 돈을 되찾는 것을 도와 줄 수 있니? 그는 그들에게 세금을 너무 많이 부과했어.

20 그는 너무 탐욕스러워서 사람들과 나누지 않아. 그래서 그들은 음식을 살 충분한 돈이 없어.

21 나는 그들의 돈을 다시 찾을 수 있도록 돕고 싶어. 하지만 탑 안에 병사들이 많아서 아무도 들어갈 수 없어."

22 "흠… 제게 해결책이 있는 것 같아요. 그러나 우선 저를 탑에 데려가 주실 수 있나요? 저는 병사들의 수를 세야 해요."

23 로빈과 파스칼은 나무에 숨어서 병사들의 수를 한 명씩 세었습니다.

24 "자정부터 새벽 여섯 시까지는 다섯 명의 병사들이 있어요.

25 그다음, 정오까지는 세 명의 병사들이 있고, 오후 여섯 시까지는 여덟 명의 병사들이 있어요.

26 마지막으로, 자정까지는 열두 명의 병사들이 있어요. 그래서 당신은 새벽 여섯 시에서 정오 사이에 들어가야 해요."

27 "뭐라고? 나는 이해하지 못했어."

28 파스칼은 잠시 생각에 잠겼습니다. '흠…그래프가 이것을 이해하는 것을 쉽게 해 줄지도 몰라.'

29 파스칼은 그래프를 그려서 그것을 로빈에게 보여주었습니다.

30 "보세요, 가장 위험한 시간은 저녁 여섯 시에서 자정까지예요.

31 오전 여섯 시부터 정오까지보다 그 시간에 네 배나 더 많은 병사들이 일해요. 제 말이 무슨 뜻인지 아시겠어요?"

32 "아하! 이제 이해했어. 너무 고마워, 파스칼!"

33 "천만에요. 이제 저는 그래프의 중요성을 깨달았어요. 아무도 그래프가 더 이상 필요 없다고 말할 수 없을 거예요."

34 파스칼은 숲에서 걸어 나왔습니다. 그가 뒤돌아봤을 때, 그는 로빈 후드가 그에게 손을 흔들고 있는 것을 보았습니다.

35 파스칼은 손을 흔들어 답하고 혼잣말을 했습니다. "정말 멋진 모험이었어. 나는 어떻게 돌아가지? 오, 알겠어. 나는 코기토 에르고 숨이라는 말을 해야 해!"

● 우리말을 참고하여 본문을 영작하시오.

1 파스칼은 그의 방에서 수학 숙제를 하고 있었습니다. 그는 그래프 문제에 고군분투하고 있었습니다.
➡ _____

2 "그래프를 읽고 그리는 것은 너무 어려워. 게다가 내가 왜 그래프가 필요하겠어? 아무도 실제 생활에서는 그래프가 필요하지 않아."
➡ _____

3 그는 그의 펜을 내려놓고, 그가 가장 좋아하는 책, '로빈 후드'를 집어 들었습니다.
➡ _____

4 그는 책을 읽으며 잠들기로 했습니다. 그가 책을 펴려고 할 때, 그는 목소리를 들었습니다.
➡ _____

5 누가 말하고 있는지 보기 위해 그는 책에서 눈을 들어 올려다보았습니다.
➡ _____

6 그는 그의 눈을 믿을 수 없었습니다. 말하는 것은 바로 자신의 개, Manny였습니다!
➡ _____

7 "눈을 감고 내 말을 따라 말하세요. *코기토 에르고 숨.*" Manny가 말했습니다.
➡ _____

8 "너는 말할 수 있니?" "그냥 따라 하세요! *코기토 에르고 숨.*"
➡ _____

9 파스칼은 그의 눈을 감고 그 단어들을 따라 말했습니다. 갑자기 그는 남자들이 소리치는 것을 들었습니다.
➡ _____

10 그가 눈을 떴을 때, 그는 말을 탄 병사들을 보았습니다.
➡ _____

11 그들은 손에 화살을 든 남자를 뒤쫓고 있었습니다. 그 남자는 파스칼을 보고 소리쳤습니다.
➡ _____

12 "네가 거기 서 있는 것은 너무 위험해. 이리 와."
➡ _____

13 그 남자는 파스칼을 그의 말에 올려 태우고 숲으로 말을 몰았습니다.
➡ _____

14 그들이 한 집 앞에 이르렀을 때, 그 남자는 멈추고 말에서 내렸습니다.
➡ _____

15 "안녕, 내 이름은 로빈 후드야."
➡ _____

16 "와우! 당신이 책 속의 로빈 후드인가요?"
➡ _____

17 "아니, 나는 셔우드 숲의 로빈 후드야. 너는 누구이고 왜 여기에 있니?"
➡ _____

18 "제 이름은 파스칼이에요. 저는 제가 왜 여기 있는지 모르지만 이유가 분명 있을 거예요. 당신은 저를 병사들로부터 구해줬어요. 정말 감사드려요. 제가 당신을 위해 할 수 있는 것이 있을까요?"
➡ _____

19 "음, 우리가 왕이 사람들에게서 가져간 돈을 되찾는 것을 도와줄 수 있니? 그는 그들에게 세금을 너무 많이 부과했어.
➡ _____

20 그는 너무 탐욕스러워서 사람들과 나누지 않아. 그래서 그들은 음식을 살 충분한 돈이 없어.
➡ _____

21 나는 그들의 돈을 다시 찾을 수 있도록 돕고 싶어. 하지만 탑 안에 병사들이 많아서 아무도 들어갈 수 없어."
➡ _____

22 "흠… 제게 해결책이 있는 것 같아요. 그러나 우선 저를 탑에 데려가 주실 수 있나요? 저는 병사들의 수를 세야 해요."
➡ _____

23 로빈과 파스칼은 나무에 숨어서 병사들의 수를 한 명씩 세었습니다.
➡ _____

24 "자정부터 새벽 여섯 시까지는 다섯 명의 병사들이 있어요.
➡ _____

25 그다음, 정오까지는 세 명의 병사들이 있고, 오후 여섯 시까지는 여덟 명의 병사들이 있어요.
➡ _____

26 마지막으로, 자정까지는 열두 명의 병사들이 있어요. 그래서 당신은 새벽 여섯 시에서 정오 사이에 들어가야 해요."
➡ _____

27 "뭐라고? 나는 이해하지 못했어."
➡ _____

28 파스칼은 잠시 생각에 잠겼습니다. '흠… 그래프가 이것을 이해하는 것을 쉽게 해 줄지도 몰라.'
➡ _____

29 파스칼은 그래프를 그려서 그것을 로빈에게 보여주었습니다.
➡ _____

30 "보세요, 가장 위험한 시간은 저녁 여섯 시에서 자정까지예요.
➡ _____

31 오전 여섯 시부터 정오까지보다 그 시간에 네 배나 더 많은 병사들이 일해요. 제 말이 무슨 뜻인지 아시겠어요?"
➡ _____

32 "아하! 이제 이해했어. 너무 고마워, 파스칼!"
➡ _____

33 "천만에요. 이제 저는 그래프의 중요성을 깨달았어요. 아무도 그래프가 더 이상 필요 없다고 말할 수 없을 거예요."
➡ _____

34 파스칼은 숲에서 걸어 나왔습니다. 그가 뒤돌아봤을 때, 그는 로빈 후드가 그에게 손을 흔들고 있는 것을 보았습니다.
➡ _____

35 파스칼은 손을 흔들어 답하고 혼잣말을 했습니다. "정말 멋진 모험이었어. 나는 어떻게 돌아가지? 오, 알겠어. 나는 코기토 에르고 숨이라는 말을 해야 해!"
➡ _____

[01~03] 다음 글을 읽고 물음에 답하시오.

Pascal was doing his math homework in his room. He was struggling with graphs.

"It's too hard to read and draw graphs. Why do I need these anyway? No one needs graphs in real life." (①) He put down his pen and picked up his favorite book, *Robin Hood*. (②) He decided to read himself to sleep. (③) He looked up from the book to see who was talking. (④) He couldn't believe his eyes. It was his dog, Manny, who was talking! (⑤)

"Close your eyes and repeat after me. *Cogito ergo sum*," said Manny.

"You can talk?"

"Just repeat! *Cogito ergo sum*."

Pascal closed his eyes and repeated the words.

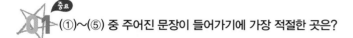

01 (①)~(⑤) 중 주어진 문장이 들어가기에 가장 적절한 곳은?

> When he was about to open the book, he heard a voice.

①   ②   ③   ④   ⑤

서답형
02 다음과 같이 풀이되는 말을 위 글에서 찾아 쓰시오.

> to say or write something again or more than once

➡ _____

03 다음 중 위 글을 읽고 답할 수 있는 것은?

① Why was Pascal studying math?
② How long did Pascal live with Manny?
③ Why does Pascal like *Robin Hood*?
④ What did Manny tell Pascal to do?
⑤ What does 'Cogito ergo sum' mean?

[04~06] 다음 글을 읽고 물음에 답하시오.

"No, I'm the Robin Hood of Sherwood Forest. (A)_____"

"My name is Pascal. I don't know why I'm here, but there must be a reason. You saved me from the soldiers. Thank you so much. Is there anything I can do for you?"

"Well, can you help us get back the money that the king took from the people? He taxed them too much. He is too greedy to share with the people, so they don't have enough money to buy food. I want to help them get their money back. (B)_____, there are many soldiers in the tower, so no one can get inside."

"Hmm... I think I have a solution. But first, can you take me to the tower? I need to count the number of soldiers."

04 빈칸 (A)에 들어갈 말로 가장 적절한 것은?

① What brings you here again?
② Who are you and when did you arrive?
③ How come you came alone?
④ What can I do for you here?
⑤ Who are you and why are you here?

05 빈칸 (B)에 들어갈 말로 가장 적절한 것은?

① Therefore   ② Nevertheless
③ As a result   ④ However
⑤ Moreover

서답형
06 To where does Pascal want Robin to take him? Answer in English.

➡ _____

[07~09] 다음 글을 읽고 물음에 답하시오.

Suddenly, Pascal heard men shouting. When ①he opened his eyes, ②he saw soldiers on horses. They were chasing a man with arrows in his hand. The man saw ③Pascal and shouted.

"It's too dangerous for ④you to stand there. Come on." The man pulled Pascal onto ⑤his horse and rode into the woods.

When they arrived at a house, the man stopped and got off his horse.

"Hello, my name is Robin Hood."

"Wow! Are you the Robin Hood from the book?"

07 밑줄 친 ①~⑤ 중 가리키는 대상이 다른 하나는?

①   ②   ③   ④   ⑤

08 다음 중 위 글에서 찾아볼 수 있는 장면은?

① Pascal with arrows in his hand
② Pascal shouting at some men
③ Soldiers chasing Pascal on horses
④ Robin Hood running out of the woods
⑤ Robin Hood being chased by soldiers

서답형
09 What did Robin Hood do when he arrived at a house with Pascal? Answer in English.

➡ _____

_____

[10~12] 다음 글을 읽고 물음에 답하시오.

Robin and Pascal hid up in a tree and counted the soldiers one by one.

"There are five soldiers from midnight to six in the morning. Next, there are three soldiers until noon, and then there are eight soldiers until six in the evening. Lastly, there are twelve soldiers until midnight. So, you should ①go inside between six in the morning and noon."

"What? I don't get it."

Pascal thought for a moment. 'Hmm... A graph might make this ②easier to understand.'

Pascal ③drew a graph and showed it to Robin.

"Look, ④the safest time is between six in the evening and midnight. Four times more soldiers work at that time than from six in the morning until noon. Do you see what I mean?"

"Aha! I get it now. Thank you so much, Pascal!"

"You're welcome. Now I realize the importance of graphs. No one can say that we ⑤don't need them anymore."

Pascal walked out of the woods. When he looked back, he saw Robin Hood waving at him. Pascal waved back and said to himself, "It was a great adventure. How do I go back? Oh, I know. I should say the words *Cogito ergo sum!*"

10 밑줄 친 ①~⑤ 중 글의 흐름상 어색한 것은?

①   ②   ③   ④   ⑤

11 위 글의 내용과 일치하는 것은?

① Robin understood what Pascal said at once.
② Pascal made Robin count the soldiers alone.
③ Pascal realized the importance of graphs.
④ Robin couldn't understand the graph.
⑤ Pascal couldn't figure out when to enter the tower.

서답형

12 When Pascal looked back, what did he see? Answer in English with seven words.

➡ _____

[13~15] 다음 글을 읽고 물음에 답하시오.

Pascal was doing his math homework in his room. He was struggling with graphs.

"It's too hard to read and draw graphs. Why do I need these anyway? No one needs graphs in real life." He put down his pen and picked up his favorite book, *Robin Hood*. He decided to read himself to sleep. When he was about to open the book, he heard a voice. He looked up from the book to see who was talking. He couldn't believe his eyes. It was his dog, Manny, who was talking!

"Close your eyes and repeat after me. *Cogito ergo sum*," said Manny.

"You can talk?"

"Just repeat! *Cogito ergo sum*."

Pascal closed his eyes and repeated the words.

서답형

13 What was Pascal doing in his room? Answer in English.

➡ _____

14 What did Pascal think about graphs?

① He thought they were very useful.

② He thought they were interesting.

③ He thought they made lives difficult.

④ He thought they were not necessary.

⑤ He thought they were informative.

중요

15 Choose one that is TRUE.

① Pascal drew graphs with ease.

② Pascal had a friend named Manny.

③ Pascal heard a voice while reading.

④ Pascal did what Manny told him to do.

⑤ Pascal wasn't interested in who was talking to him.

[16~19] 다음 글을 읽고 물음에 답하시오.

Suddenly, he heard men shouting. When he opened his eyes, he saw soldiers on horses. They were chasing a man with arrows in his hand. The man saw Pascal and shouted.

"It's too dangerous for you to stand there. Come on." The man pulled Pascal onto his horse and rode into the woods.

When they arrived at a house, the man stopped and got off his horse.

"Hello, my name is Robin Hood."

"Wow! Are you the Robin Hood from the book?"

"No, I'm the Robin Hood of Sherwood Forest. Who are you and why are you here?"

"My name is Pascal. I don't know why I'm here, but there ⓐmust be a reason. You saved me from the soldiers. Thank you so much. Is there anything I can do for you?"

"Well, can you help us get back the money that the king took from the people? He taxed them too much. He is too (A)_____ to share with the people, so they don't have enough money to buy food. I want to help them get their money back. However, there are many soldiers in the tower, so no one can get inside."

중요

위 글의 흐름상 빈칸 (A)에 들어갈 말로 가장 적절한 것은?

① generous   ② indifferent

③ anxious   ④ boring

⑤ greedy

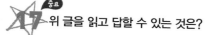 위 글을 읽고 답할 수 있는 것은?

① Why were the men chasing Robin?

② How long did it take to get to the house?

③ What made Pascal go there?

④ How many men were chasing Robin?

⑤ Why did Robin pull Pascal onto his horse?

18 밑줄 친 ⓐ와 쓰임이 같은 것은?

① His new novel is a <u>must</u> for them.

② All visitors <u>must</u> write their names.

③ You <u>must</u> read this book for yourself.

④ They <u>must</u> keep quiet in the library.

⑤ He <u>must</u> be brave to help you in that situation.

서답형
19 What does Robin want to do to help people? Answer in English.

➡ _____

[20~23] 다음 글을 읽고 물음에 답하시오.

"Hmm... I think I have a solution. But first, can you take me to the tower? I need to count the number of soldiers."

Robin and Pascal hid up in a tree and counted the soldiers one by one.

"There are five soldiers from midnight to six in the morning. Next, there are three soldiers until noon, and then there are eight soldiers until six in the evening. Lastly, there are twelve soldiers until midnight. So, you should go inside (A)_____."

"What? I don't get it."

Pascal thought for a moment. 'Hmm... A graph might make (B)<u>this</u> easier to understand.'

Pascal drew a graph and showed it to Robin.

"Look, the most dangerous time is between six in the evening and midnight. Four times more soldiers work at that time than from six in the morning until noon. Do you see what I mean?"

"Aha! I get it now. Thank you so much, Pascal!"

"You're welcome. Now I realize the importance of graphs. No one can say that we don't need them anymore."

Pascal walked out of the woods. When he looked back, he saw Robin Hood waving at him. Pascal waved back and said to himself, "It was a great adventure. How do I go back? Oh, I know. I should say the words *Cogito ergo sum*!"

20 위 글의 흐름상 빈칸 (A)에 들어갈 말로 가장 적절한 것은?

① anytime you want to go inside

② except six in the morning and noon

③ between noon and in the evening

④ between six in the morning and noon

⑤ between midnight and in the evening

서답형
21 밑줄 친 (B)의 의미를 우리말로 쓰시오.

➡ _____

서답형
22 What did Pascal realize? Answer in English.

➡ _____

23 Choose one that is TRUE.

① Pascal couldn't draw a graph for Robin.

② Five soldiers work after morning.

③ Pascal wasn't helpful for Robin.

④ Robin didn't know Pascal was leaving.

⑤ Pascal thought the experience adventurous.

[01~04] 다음 글을 읽고 물음에 답하시오.

Pascal was doing his math homework in his room. (A)He was struggling with graphs.

"It's too hard to read and draw graphs. Why do I need these anyway? No one needs graphs in real life." He put down his pen and picked up his favorite book, *Robin Hood*. He decided to read himself to sleep. When he was about to open the book, he heard a voice. He looked up from the book to see who was talking. He couldn't believe his eyes. It was his dog, Manny, who was talking!

"Close your eyes and repeat after me. *Cogito ergo sum*," said Manny.

"You can talk?"

"Just repeat! *Cogito ergo sum*."

Pascal closed his eyes and repeated the words.

01 주어진 어구를 활용하여 밑줄 친 (A)와 같은 의미의 문장을 쓰시오.

(have / hard time)

➡ _____

02 What did Pascal do after putting down his pen? Answer in English.

➡ _____

03 Write the reason why Pascal couldn't believe his eyes when he looked up from the book. Use the phrase 'It was because.'

➡ _____

04 When Pascal was about to open the book, what happened? Answer in English.

➡ _____
_____

[05~09] 다음 글을 읽고 물음에 답하시오.

Suddenly, Pascal heard men shouting. When he opened his eyes, he saw soldiers on horses. They were chasing a man with arrows in his hand. The man saw Pascal and shouted.

"It's too dangerous for you to stand there. Come on." The man pulled Pascal onto his horse and rode into the woods.

When they arrived at a house, the man stopped and got off his horse.

"Hello, my name is Robin Hood."

"Wow! Are you the Robin Hood from the book?"

"No, I'm the Robin Hood of Sherwood Forest. Who are you and why are you here?"

"My name is Pascal. I don't know why I'm here, but there must be a reason. You saved me from the soldiers. Thank you so much. Is there anything I can do for you?"

"Well, can you help us get back the money that the king took from the people? He taxed them too much. He is too greedy to share with the people, so they don't have enough money to buy food. I want to help them get their money back. However, there are many soldiers in the tower, so no one can get inside."

"Hmm... I think I have a solution. But first, can you take me to the tower? I need to count the number of soldiers."

05 What did Pascal see when he opened his eyes? Answer in English.

➡ _____

06 What did Robin have in his hand? Answer in English.

➡ _____

07 Write the reason why the people don't have enough money to buy food. Use the phrase 'It was because.'

➡ _____

_____

08 다음은 위 글의 내용을 요약한 것이다. 빈칸에 알맞은 말을 쓰시오.

> Robin Hood met Pascal in the middle of a chase from soldiers. He and Pascal rode into _____. After they got off at a safe place, Robin Hood explained to Pascal that the greedy king was overtaxing the people and asked Pascal to help him _____.

09 Write the reason why no one can get inside the tower. Use the phrase 'It was because.'

➡ _____

_____

[10~13] 다음 글을 읽고 물음에 답하시오.

Robin and Pascal hid up in a tree and counted the soldiers one by one.

"There are five soldiers from midnight to six in the morning. Next, there are three soldiers until noon, and then there are eight soldiers until six in the evening. Lastly, there are twelve soldiers until midnight. So, you should go inside between six in the morning and noon."

"What? I don't get it."

Pascal thought for a moment. 'Hmm... A graph might make this easier to understand.'

Pascal drew a graph and showed it to Robin.

"Look, the most dangerous time is between six in the evening and midnight. Four times more soldiers work at that time than from six in the morning until noon. Do you see what I mean?"

"Aha! I get it now. Thank you so much, Pascal!"

"You're welcome. Now I realize the importance of graphs. No one can say that we don't need them anymore."

Pascal walked out of the woods. When he looked back, he saw Robin Hood waving at him. Pascal waved back and said to himself, "It was a great adventure. How do I go back? Oh, I know. I should say the words *Cogito ergo sum*!"

10 What did Robin and Pascal do when hiding up in a tree? Answer in English.

➡ _____

11 How many soldiers are there from midnight to noon? Answer in English.

➡ _____

12 What did Pascal use to make Robin understood? Answer in English.

➡ _____

13 What did Pascal see when he looked back? Answer in English.

➡ _____

Communication Task

I did a survey on the books we want for our school library.
<small>'the books'를 선행사로 하는 목적격 관계대명사 that/which가 생략되어 있다.</small>

The result says that thirteen out of twenty students chose novels.
<small>'say'의 목적어를 이끄는 접속사   ~ 중에서</small>

That is sixty-five percent of the total. Five out of twenty students chose

science-fiction books. However, only two out of twenty students chose history

books. From this survey result, I think the school library should get more
<small>동사 'think'의 목적어를 이끄는 접속사 'that'이 생략되어 있다.</small>

novels. Do you see what I mean?

<small>**구문해설** • **survey**: 조사 • **result**: 결과 • **choose**: 선택하다 • **total**: 총계</small>

Before You Read B Look and Write

Book Club: Your Reviews

Title: *Robin Hood*

Topic of the book: It's about a man who struggles to help people from the
<small>선행사 주격 관계대명사   to부정사의 부사적 용법</small>

greedy king.

My favorite character: My favorite character is Robin Hood because he shoots
<small>이유를 나타내는 접속사 (절과 절을 연결)</small>

arrows better than soldiers.

My opinion of the book: It's bad to tax too much.
<small>명사적 용법</small>

After all, not money but people matter the most.
<small>not A but B A가 아니라 B   주어가 people이므로 복수 동사</small>

<small>**구문해설** • **struggle**: 분투하다, 투쟁하다 • **greedy**: 욕심 많은 • **tax**: 세금 • **after all**: 결국 • **matter**: 중요하다</small>

Let's Write

Look at the survey result on "Who is your favorite character?" Fifteen out of thirty
<small>~에 관한   out of: ~ 중에서</small>

students chose Hong Gildong. In other words, fifty percent of the students chose
<small>다시 말해서</small>

the character. I think it's because the character is courageous. Next, nine students
<small>it's because+이유</small>

chose Kongiwi and six students chose Robin Hood. No one chose Nolbu. Maybe

it's because the character is too greedy to be liked by others.
<small>too ~ to V: 너무 ~해서 V할 수 없는</small>

<small>**구문해설** • **survey**: 설문조사 • **result**: 결과 • **courageous**: 용기 있는</small>

해석

나는 우리 학교 도서관에 필요한 책들을 조사했다. 그 결과 20명 중 13명이 소설을 선택하였다. 이는 전체의 65퍼센트이다. 20명 중 5명은 공상 과학 책을 선택했다. 그러나 20명 중 2명만이 역사책을 선택했다. 이러한 조사 결과를 통해 학교 도서관은 더 많은 소설을 구해야 한다고 생각한다. 무슨 뜻인지 알겠니?

책 동아리: 너의 후기들
제목: 로빈 후드
책의 주제: 욕심 많은 왕으로부터 사람을 구하려 고군분투하는 한 남자의 이야기이다.
내가 가장 좋아하는 등장인물: 병사들보다 화살을 더 잘 쏘기 때문에 내가 가장 좋아하는 등장인물은 로빈 후드이다.
책에 대한 나의 논평: 세금을 너무 많이 부과하는 것은 나쁘다. 결국, 돈이 아니라 사람이 가장 중요하다.

'당신이 가장 좋아하는 등장인물은 누구입니까?'라는 설문 조사 결과를 보자. 30명의 학생들 중 15명이 홍길동을 선택했다. 다시 말하면, 학생들 중 50퍼센트가 그 등장인물을 선택했다. 내 생각에 그것은 그 등장인물이 용감하기 때문이다. 그다음에 9명의 학생들이 콩쥐를 선택했고, 6명의 학생들이 로빈 후드를 선택했다. 아무도 놀부를 선택하지 않았다. 아마도 그것은 그 등장인물이 다른 사람들이 좋아하기에 너무 탐욕스럽기 때문일 것이다

Words & Expressions

01 다음 주어진 두 단어의 관계가 같도록 빈칸에 알맞은 단어를 쓰시오.

> represent – express : fiction – _____

02 다음 문장의 빈칸 (A)와 (B)에 들어갈 어휘가 바르게 짝지어진 것은?

> • Nobel Prizes are (A)_____ the highest form of recognition in the world.
> • I was just (B)_____ ask you the same thing.

① worried about – about to
② worried about – due to
③ looked up – going to
④ regarded as – about to
⑤ regarded as – related to

[03~04] 다음 영영풀이에 해당하는 것을 고르시오.

03

> a piece of body tissue that helps you to move a particular part of the body

① picnic   ② muscle
③ result   ④ limb
⑤ cell

04

> a thin stick with a sharp point at one end, which is shot from a bow

① survey   ② shout
③ tax   ④ solution
⑤ arrow

05 문장의 흐름에 맞게 빈칸을 두 단어로 채우시오.

> Some people try to get on the subway before others _____.

06 다음 밑줄 친 부분의 뜻이 잘못된 것은?

① The child chased after the bird. (뒤쫓았다)
② Believe it or not, many people claim to have seen a UFO. (주장하다)
③ Can you count the eggs in the basket? (수를 세다)
④ These salty foods have become an indispensable part of our lives! (소금)
⑤ I realized how hard the work was. (깨달았다)

Conversation

07 다음 대화의 빈칸 (A)에 들어갈 말로 알맞은 것은?

> M: Mason, how was the election?
> B: It was bad. I didn't win.
> M: How come?
> B: Yura won. Over sixty percent of the students voted for her.
> M: Well, you tried your best and that's what matters.
> B: I guess so. I have learned many things (A)_____.
> M: I'm really proud of you.
> B: Thanks, Dad.

① while running with her
② while running the election
③ while running for class president
④ while running a race
⑤ while running for class

08 다음 그림에 맞게 대화의 빈칸에 문제의 해결 방법으로 알맞은 말을 고르시오.

Move one stick to make this sum right.

> A: How could six plus two equal eleven?
> B: Why don't you move the stick in number six to make it nine? Do you see what I mean?
> A: _____
> B: That's right.

① Do you mean the one on the bottom left?
② Do you mean the one on the top right?
③ Do you mean the one on the bottom right?
④ Do you mean the one on the top left?
⑤ Do you mean the one on the middle?

[09~10] 다음 대화를 읽고 물음에 답하시오.

> Mina: Henry, what are you doing?
> Henry: I'm writing an article about students' favorite snacks. (①) I'm worried about their health. (②)
> Mina: Why?
> Henry: Well, I surveyed 100 students and the results show that sixty percent of the students liked pizza and twenty percent of the students liked fried chicken for snacks. In other words, most students liked fried chicken more than any other snack. (③)
> Mina: Oh, I get it. Students really like fast food. What else did they like? (④)
> Henry: Twelve percent of the students chose chocolate cake as their favorite. (⑤)
> Mina: Wow, students should really try to eat healthier snacks!

09 위 대화에서 다음 도표와 다른 문장을 찾아 바르게 고치시오. (문장 전체를 바르게 고쳐 쓰시오.)

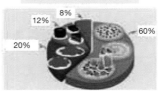

Favorite Snacks

➡ _____
_____

10 위 대화의 (①)~(⑤) 중 주어진 문장이 들어갈 위치로 알맞은 것은?

> Do you see what I mean?

①   ②   ③   ④   ⑤

11 다음 대화를 읽고 답할 수 없는 질문은?

> B: Jian, what's the matter? You look upset.
> G: My brother broke my computer. I'm so angry.
> B: I'm sorry to hear that, but your facial muscles must be tired.
> G: What do you mean?
> B: Well, it takes a lot of muscles to look angry, but only a few to smile. Do you see what I mean?
> G: Oh, I get it. I guess it's not good to stay angry for a long time.
> B: That's right. Remember, it's always better to smile!

① What made Jian angry?
② How did the boy feel about Jian's matter?
③ Why does it take only a few facial muscles to smile?
④ Does Jian see what the boy means?
⑤ Why is it always better to smile?

Grammar

12 우리말에 맞게 주어진 단어를 활용하여 영작하시오.

(1) 난 혼자 가기 너무 무서워. (scared, too, on my own)

➡ _____

(2) 난 바빠서 숨 돌릴 틈도 없다. (to, take a rest)

➡ _____

(3) 그는 너무 정직해서 거짓말을 못한다. (so, honest, tell)

➡ _____

(4) 승객과 승무원은 아무도 다치지 않았다. (none, injured)

➡ _____

13 각 문장과 같은 의미의 문장을 쓰시오.

(1) They were brave enough to face the strong enemy.

➡ _____
  _____

(2) He is clever enough to solve the riddle.

➡ _____

14 다음 중 어법상 올바른 문장을 고르시오.

① No one are wearing a uniform.
② No one swims in the sea.
③ No one were happy with the news.
④ No one carry a bag with them.
⑤ No one correct him when he is wrong.

15 다음 문장을 바꿔 쓸 때 <u>어색한</u> 것을 고르시오.

① It was warm enough for her children to play outside.
  → It was so warm that her children could play outside.
② I was too hungry to walk.
  → I was so hungry that I couldn't walk.
③ She is rich enough to help the poor.
  → She is so rich that she can help the poor.
④ The toy was so expensive that I couldn't buy it.
  → The toy was expensive enough for me to buy.
⑤ He behaved so kindly that I thanked him.
  → He behaved kindly enough for me to thank.

16 어법상 <u>어색한</u> 것을 바르게 고쳐 문장을 다시 쓰시오.

┌─────────────────────────────────────┐
│ This chance is too good to miss it. │
└─────────────────────────────────────┘

➡ _____

17 다음 중 문장 전환이 <u>어색한</u> 것을 고르시오.

① Minji is so short that she can't get on the ride.
  → Minji is too short to get on the ride.
② The cat is so old that she can't climb up the tree.
  → The cat is too old to climb up the tree.
③ The dog is too big to get inside the box.
  → The dog is so big that he can get inside the box.
④ Jake is too weak to lift the boxes.
  → Jake is so weak that he can't lift the boxes.
⑤ The problem was too difficult for me to write.
  → The problem was so difficult that I couldn't solve it.

[18~20] 다음 글을 읽고 물음에 답하시오.

Pascal was doing his math homework in his room. He was struggling (A)_____ graphs.

"It's too hard to read and draw graphs. (①) Why do I need these anyway? No one needs graphs in real life." (②) He put down his pen and picked up his favorite book, *Robin Hood*. (③) He decided to read himself to sleep. When he was about to open the book, he heard a voice. (④) He couldn't believe his eyes. (⑤) It was his dog, Manny, who was talking!

"Close your eyes and repeat after me. *Cogito ergo sum*," said Manny.

"You can talk?"

"Just repeat! *Cogito ergo sum*."

Pascal closed his eyes and repeated the words.

18 빈칸 (A)에 들어갈 말과 같은 말이 들어가는 것은?

① You may refer _____ your notes.
② Her job is mainly concerned _____ sales.
③ The book is well organized in terms _____ plot.
④ Drought may result _____ the shortened snow season.
⑤ Their goal is to bring _____ peace in people.

19 (①)~(⑤) 중 주어진 문장이 들어가기에 가장 적절한 곳은?

He looked up from the book to see who was talking.

①   ②   ③   ④   ⑤

20 Choose one that is not TRUE.

① Pascal had difficult time studying graphs.
② Pascal thought graphs were not needed in real life.
③ Pascal's favorite book was *Robin Hood*.
④ Pascal was surprised to see his dog talking to him.
⑤ Pascal repeated what Manny said with his eyes open.

[21~23] 다음 글을 읽고 물음에 답하시오.

When they arrived at a house, the man stopped and ①got off his horse.

"Hello, my name is Robin Hood."

"Wow! Are you the Robin Hood from the book?"

"No, I'm the Robin Hood of Sherwood Forest. Who are you and why are you here?"

"My name is Pascal. I don't know why I'm here, but there must be a reason. You ②saved me from the soldiers. Thank you so much. Is there anything I can do for you?"

"Well, can you help us ③get back the money that the king took from the people? He taxed them too much. He is too ④greedy to share with the people, so they don't have enough money (A)to buy food. I want to help them get their money back. However, there are many soldiers in the tower, so no one can get inside."

"Hmm... I think I have a solution. But first, can you take me to the tower? I need to count ⑤a number of soldiers."

21 밑줄 친 ①~⑤ 중 글의 흐름상 어색한 것은?

①   ②   ③   ④   ⑤

22 밑줄 친 (A)와 쓰임이 같은 것은?

① It was nice to talk with her.
② Is there any chance to meet him?
③ They kept running to escape.
④ He ordered me to get some water.
⑤ She must be upset to hear the news.

23 What did Robin ask Pascal? Answer in English and use the word 'if.'

➡ _____

_____

[24~26] 다음 글을 읽고 물음에 답하시오.

What kinds of numbers are thought to be lucky or unlucky? Do you think it is similar around the world?

Usually, the number 7 is a lucky number in countries like England, the USA, and France. However, a lucky number in one country can be unlucky in another. Chinese people think 7 is unlucky because July or "the seventh month" is often thought of as a month for ghosts.

Many people in Western countries don't like the number 13. There are even scary movies about Friday the 13th. However, in Italy, the number is related to a good person, St. Anthony. He prayed for lost things or people. Now, people celebrate the day he died, June 13th.

How about the number 4? In Germany, the number is regarded as lucky because it matches the number of leaves on a four-leaf clover. However, in China, the sound of the word for the number 4 is similar to (A)that of the Chinese word for death.

24 위 글의 제목으로 가장 적절한 것은?

① Seven: World's Common Lucky Number
② Various Meanings That Numbers Have in the World
③ The Meanings of Different Numbers in Different Cultures
④ What Makes People in the World Think Number Has Meanings?
⑤ The Meanings of Certain Numbers in Korea

25 밑줄 친 (A)가 의미하는 것을 위 글에서 찾아 쓰시오.

➡ _____

26 Choose one that is TRUE.

① The number 7 is considered a lucky number all around the world.
② There exists a day for ghosts in China.
③ People in Western don't like the number 13 including Italian.
④ St. Anthony prayed for lost things or people.
⑤ Chinese see the number 4 as a lucky number.

✏️ 출제율 90%

01 다음 짝지어진 단어의 관계가 같도록 빈칸에 알맞은 말을 쓰시오.

> greedy – generous : midday – _____

✏️ 출제율 90%

02 다음 영영풀이에 해당하는 단어는?

> a piece of writing appearing in a newspaper

① suggestion   ② lesson
③ novel   ④ article
⑤ cartoon

[03~04] 다음 대화를 읽고 물음에 답하시오.

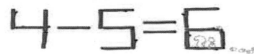

B: Emma, can you help me with this math problem?
G: Sure, what is it?
B: You have to (a)move one stick to make this sum (b)right. How could four minus five equal six?
G: Oh, it's simple. You need to move one of the sticks in number (c)five to make it eleven. Do you see what I mean?
B: Yes, now I see what you mean. Eleven minus five (d)equals six. How clever!
G: Thinking outside the box can be (e)helpful sometimes.

✏️ 출제율 100%

03 위 그림을 참고하여 대화의 밑줄 친 (a)~(e) 중, 어휘의 쓰임이 어색한 것은?

① (a)   ② (b)   ③ (c)   ④ (d)   ⑤ (e)

✏️ 출제율 100%

04 위 대화의 내용과 일치하지 않는 것은?

① The boy asks Emma to help him with the math problem.
② To make this sum right, Emma has to move one stick.
③ Emma thinks the solution of this math problem is simple.
④ The boy thinks Emma is very clever.
⑤ The boy doesn't understand what Emma means.

✏️ 출제율 95%

05 다음 대화의 밑줄 친 (a)~(e) 중, 어법상 어색한 것은?

> B: Minju, (a)what is this graph about?
> G: I did a survey on the kinds of (b)pets my classmates have.
> B: What were the results?
> G: Eighty percent of the students (c)have pets. Only five out of twenty-five students (d)doesn't have pets.
> B: What kind of pets do they have?
> G: Well, ten students have dogs and three students have cats.
> B: (e)What about the rest?
> G: Seven students have fish.

① (a)   ② (b)   ③ (c)   ④ (d)   ⑤ (e)

[06~07] 다음 대화를 읽고 물음에 답하시오.

M: Mason, how was the election?
B: It was bad. I didn't win.
M: (A)How come?
B: Yura won. Over sixty percent of the students voted for her.
M: Well, you tried your best and that's what matters.

B: I guess so. I have learned many things while running for class president.

M: I'm really proud of you.

B: Thanks, Dad.

출제율 90%

06 대화의 밑줄 친 (A)를 완전한 문장으로 쓰시오.

➡ _____

출제율 95%

07 위 대화에서 다음 〈영영풀이〉가 설명하는 단어를 찾아 쓰시오.

to compete as a candidate in an election

➡ _____

[08~09] 다음 대화를 읽고 물음에 답하시오.

Mina: Henry, what are you doing?

Henry: I'm writing an article about students' favorite snacks. I'm worried about their health.

Mina: Why?

Henry: Well, I surveyed 100 students and the results show that eighty percent of the students liked pizza and fried chicken for snacks. (A)Do you see what I mean?

Mina: Oh, I get it. Students really like fast food. What else did they like?

Henry: Twelve percent of the students chose chocolate cake as their favorite.

Mina: Wow, students should really try to eat healthier snacks!

출제율 100%

08 위 대화를 읽고 답할 수 <u>없는</u> 질문은?

① What are they talking about?

② How many students did Henry survey?

③ According to the survey, do the students often eat healthy snacks?

④ What percent of the students chose chocolate cake?

⑤ How many kinds of snacks can the students eat in this survey?

출제율 90%

09 위 대화의 밑줄 친 (A)와 같은 의미를 가진 문장이 되도록 get을 활용하여 영작하시오.

➡ _____

출제율 95%

10 다음 대화의 (A)와 (B)의 우리말에 맞게 주어진 단어를 이용하여 영작하시오.

B: Jian, what's the matter? You look upset.

G: My brother broke my computer. I'm so angry.

B: I'm sorry to hear that, but your facial muscles must be tired.

G: What do you mean?

B: Well, (A)화난 표정을 지을 때는 많은 근육이 필요해(take, a lot of, look), but only a few to smile. Do you see what I mean?

G: Oh, I get it. I guess (B)오랫동안 화난 상태로 있으면 좋지 않아(it, stay, for).

B: That's right. Remember, it's always better to smile!

➡ (A) _____

(B) _____

11 다음 도표를 보고 '~ percent of ...' 표현을 사용하여 아래 질문에 2가지 사실을 상술하는 답을 쓰시오.

Favorite Color

Q: What can you tell from the chart?

➡ (1) _____

(2) _____

12 빈칸에 공통으로 들어갈 두 단어를 쓰시오.

- _____ likes the same cars, clothes, or music. (모두가 같은 자동차, 옷, 음악을 좋아하는 것은 아니다.)
- _____ agrees with the use of CCTV in schools. (모든 사람이 학교에서의 CCTV 사용에 대해 찬성하는 것은 아니다.)
- _____ can afford to own their own apartment or house. (모든 사람이 자신의 아파트나 집을 장만할 수 있는 건 아니다.)

13 괄호 안에 주어진 어휘를 이용하여 다음 문장과 같은 의미를 지닌 문장을 쓰시오.

(1) Nobody was at home. (no)

➡ _____

(2) Nobody has told me about the new rules. (no)

➡ _____

(3) Some are able to join these active groups. Others aren't. (everyone)

➡ _____

(4) Some people seem to be happy. Others don't. (everyone)

➡ _____

14 다음 문장을 too를 이용하여 바꿔 쓰시오.

(1) He was so young that he can't understand it.

➡ _____

(2) Alex was so shy that he couldn't talk to her.

➡ _____

(3) The manual was so complicated that he couldn't understand it.

➡ _____
_____

[15~19] 다음 글을 읽고 물음에 답하시오.

Robin and Pascal hid up in a tree and counted the soldiers one by one.

"There are five soldiers from midnight to six in the morning. Next, there are three soldiers until noon, and then there are eight soldiers until six in the evening. Lastly, there are twelve soldiers until midnight. So, you should go inside between six in the morning and noon."

"What? (A)I don't get it."

Pascal thought for a moment. 'Hmm... A graph might make this easier to understand.'

Pascal drew a graph and showed it to Robin.

"Look, the most dangerous time is between six in the evening and midnight. Four times more soldiers work at that time than from six in the morning until noon. Do you see what I mean?"

"Aha! I get it now. Thank you so much, Pascal!"

"You're welcome. Now I realize the importance of graphs. No one can say that we don't need them anymore."

Pascal walked out of the woods. When he looked back, he saw Robin Hood ⓐ_____ at him. Pascal ⓑ_____ back and said to himself, "It was a great adventure. How do I go back? Oh, I know. I should say the words *Cogito ergo sum*!"

15 빈칸 ⓐ와 ⓑ에 동사 wave를 어법에 맞게 각각 쓰시오.

➡ ⓐ _____, ⓑ _____

16 밑줄 친 (A)를 대신하여 쓸 수 있는 것은?

① I don't know what to do.
② I don't understand what you say.
③ I can't believe what you said.
④ I want more information from you.
⑤ I don't make you understood.

17 How many soldiers work from six in the evening to midnight? Answer in English.

➡ _____

_____

18 When Pascal drew a graph and showed it to Robin, what happened?

① He needed more information.
② He drew it as Pascal did.
③ He kept asking about it.
④ He thought it was not helpful.
⑤ He understood it right away.

19 위 글을 읽고 답할 수 있는 것은?

① Why did Robin want to go inside?
② How many soldiers are there inside?
③ What does *Cogito ergo sum* mean?
④ Why did they count the soldiers?
⑤ How many hours did a soldier work a day?

[20~22] 다음 글을 읽고 물음에 답하시오.

Look at the survey result on "Who is your favorite character?" Fifteen out of thirty students chose Hong Gildong. (A)_____, fifty percent of the students chose the character. I think it's because the character is courageous. Next nine students chose Kongiwi and six students chose Robin Hood. No one chose Nolbu. Maybe it's because the character is too greedy to be liked by others.

20 빈칸 (A)에 들어갈 말로 가장 적절한 것은?

① For instance
② In other words
③ Nevertheless
④ On the other hand
⑤ However

21 How many characters were there for students to choose? Answer in English.

➡ _____

22 Choose one that is NOT true.

① Thirty students took part in the survey.
② Half of the students chose Hong Gildong as their favorite character.
③ Six students chose Robin Hood.
④ Kongiwi was chosen by thirty percent of students.
⑤ Nolbu was chosen due to his greediness.

01 다음 대화의 밑줄 친 부분에서 잘못된 것을 바르게 고쳐 쓰시오.

> Mina: Henry, what are you doing?
>
> Henry: I'm writing an article about students' favorite snacks. (A)I'm worry about their health.
>
> Mina: Why?
>
> Henry: Well, I surveyed 100 students and the results show that eighty percent of the students liked pizza and fried chicken for snacks. (B) Do you see that I mean?
>
> Mina: Oh, I get it. Students really like fast food. What else did they like?
>
> Henry: Twelve percent of the students chose chocolate cake as their favorite.
>
> Mina: Wow, students should really try to eat healthier snacks!

➡ (A) _____

(B) _____

02 다음 우리말에 맞게 괄호 안에 주어진 어휘를 활용하여 빈칸을 채우시오.

(1) 너의 옷은 나에게 맞을 만큼 충분히 크다. (big, fit)

➡ Your clothes are _____.

(2) 그들은 골고루 돌아갈 만큼 충분한 음식이 있다. (go)

➡ They have _____ around.

(3) 나에게 음료수를 사 줄 만큼 충분한 돈을 갖고 있니? (buy, a drink)

➡ Have you got _____
_____?

03 다음 도표를 보고 대화의 빈칸을 완성하시오.

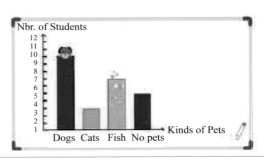

> B: Minju, what is this graph (1)_____?
>
> G: I did a survey on the kinds of (2)_____ my classmates have.
>
> B: What were the results?
>
> G: Eighty percent of the students have pets. Only (3)_____ twenty-five students don't have pets.
>
> B: What kind of pets do they have?
>
> G: Well, (4)_____ have dogs and three students have cats.
>
> B: What about the rest?
>
> G: Seven students have (5)_____.

04 우리말에 맞게 주어진 단어를 활용하여 알맞게 영작하시오.

(1) Covid-19에도 불구하고 모든 사람이 마스크를 쓰는 것은 아닙니다. (despite, everyone)

➡ _____

(2) 이번 장마철에는 폭우로 인해 거리를 걷는 사람이 없었습니다. (no, rainy season, due to)

➡ _____
_____

(3) 대유행(pandemic)이 너무 심해서 Berlin으로 여행할 수 없습니다. (severe)

[1] so, that 활용 ➡ _____

_____

[2] too, to 활용 ➡ _____

_____

Robin and Pascal hid up in a tree and counted the soldiers one by one.

"There are five soldiers from midnight to six in the morning. Next, there are three soldiers until noon, and then there are eight soldiers until six in the evening. Lastly, there are twelve soldiers until midnight. So, you should go inside between six in the morning and noon."

"What? I don't get it."

Pascal thought for a moment. 'Hmm... A graph might make this easier to understand.' Pascal drew a graph and showed it to Robin.

"Look, the most dangerous time is between six in the evening and midnight. Four times more soldiers work at that time than from six in the morning until noon. Do you see what I mean?"

"Aha! I get it now. Thank you so much, Pascal!"

"You're welcome. Now I realize the importance of graphs. No one can say that we don't need them anymore."

Pascal walked out of the woods. When he looked back, (A)_____. Pascal waved back and said to himself, "It was a great adventure. How do I go back? Oh, I know. I should say the words *Cogito ergo sum*!"

05 주어진 단어를 바르게 배열하여 빈칸 (A)에 들어갈 말을 쓰시오. 필요하다면 어형을 바꾸시오.

(he / him / Robin Hood / see / wave / at)

➡ _____

06 According to Pascal, when was the most dangerous time? Answer in English.

➡ _____

07 How many times more soldiers worked during the most dangerous time compared to six in the morning until noon? Answer in English with a full sentence.

➡ _____

_____

08 Why did Pascal draw a graph? Answer by using the words below.

(a graph / to / make / easier / for / to / understand)

➡ _____

_____

Look at the survey result on "Who is your favorite character?" Fifteen out of thirty students chose Hong Gildong. In other words, fifty percent of the students chose the character. I think it's because the character is courageous. Next nine students chose Kongiwi and six students chose Robin Hood. No one chose Nolbu. Maybe it's because (A)the character is too greedy to be liked by others.

09 주어진 단어를 사용하여 밑줄 친 문장 (A)와 같은 의미의 문장을 쓰시오.

(so / that)

➡ _____

_____

10 What percent of students chose Robin Hood? Answer in English.

➡ _____

창의사고력 서술형 문제

01 주어진 도표를 보고 'X out of Y'와 '~ percent of ...'를 이용하여 빈칸을 완성하시오.

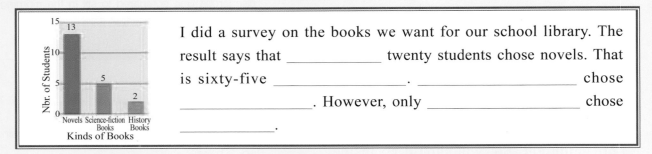

I did a survey on the books we want for our school library. The result says that _____ twenty students chose novels. That is sixty-five _____. _____ chose _____. However, only _____ chose _____.

02 다음 그래프를 참고하여 각 문항에 알맞은 퍼센트(%)를 계산한 후 가능한 문장을 쓰시오.

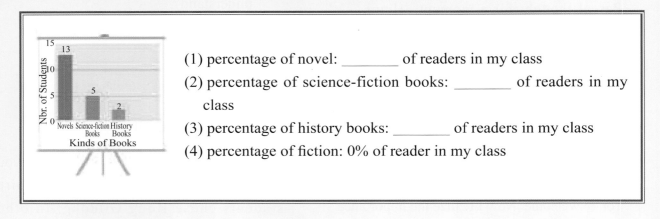

(1) percentage of novel: _____ of readers in my class

(2) percentage of science-fiction books: _____ of readers in my class

(3) percentage of history books: _____ of readers in my class

(4) percentage of fiction: 0% of reader in my class

03 다음 그래프를 보고 그래프를 설명하는 글을 완성하시오.

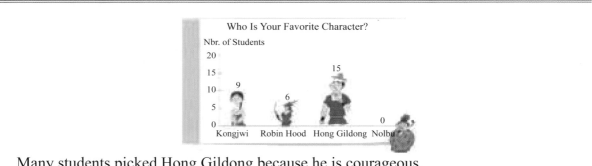

Many students picked Hong Gildong because he is courageous.
No one picked Nolbu. I think it's because he is too greedy.

Look at the survey result on "Who is your favorite character?" _____ out of thirty students chose _____. In other words, _____ percent of the students chose the character. I think it's because the character is _____. Next, _____ students chose _____ and _____ students chose _____. No one chose _____. Maybe it's because the character is _____ liked by others.

단원별 모의고사

01 다음 단어에 대한 영어 설명이 <u>어색한</u> 것은?

① realize: to understand or become aware of a particular fact or situation

② midnight: 12 o'clock at night

③ solution: a way of solving a problem or dealing with a difficult situation

④ count: to calculate the total number of people, things, etc.

⑤ greedy: having a lot of money or valuable possessions

02 다음 짝지어진 단어의 관계가 같도록 빈칸에 알맞은 말을 쓰시오.

lucky – unlucky : firstly – _____

03 다음 중 짝지어진 대화가 <u>어색한</u> 것은?

① A: Do you see what I mean?
   B: No, I don't understand.

② A: Can you help me with this math problem?
   B: Sure, what is it?

③ A: What's the matter? You look upset.
   B: I'm sorry to hear that.

④ A: What kind of pets do they have?
   B: Well, ten students have dogs and three students have cats.

⑤ A: We should have more tennis classes for after-school classes.
   B: What makes you say that?

04 다음 영영풀이에 해당하는 어구를 고르시오.

used to introduce an explanation that is simpler than the one given earlier

① therefore　　② moreover
③ in the end　　④ in other words
⑤ however

05 다음 대화의 밑줄 친 (a)~(e)에 대한 설명 중 <u>잘못된</u> 것은?

Mina: Henry, what are you doing?
Henry: I'm writing an article about students' favorite snacks. (a)I'm worried about their health.
Mina: (b)Why?
Henry: Well, I surveyed 100 students and the results show that (c)eighty percent of the students liked pizza and fried chicken for snacks. (d)Do you see what I mean?
Mina: Oh, I get it. Students really like fast food. What else did they like?
Henry: (e)Twelve percent of the students chose chocolate cake as their favorite.
Mina: Wow, students should really try to eat healthier snacks!

① (a): 그들의 건강에 대해 걱정한다는 의미이다.

② (b): 'How come?'이나 'What makes you say that?'으로 바꾸어 쓸 수 있다.

③ (c): 'eighty out of one hundred students'로 바꾸어 쓸 수 있다.

④ (d): '내 말이 무슨 뜻인지 알겠어?'라는 뜻으로 'What do you mean?'으로 바꾸어 쓸 수 있다.

⑤ (e): 그 학생들 중 12퍼센트라는 의미이다.

06 다음 대화의 우리말을 〈조건〉에 맞게 영작하시오.

> B: Emma, can you help me with this math problem?
>
> G: Sure, what is it?
>
> B: You have to move one stick to make this sum right. How could four minus five equal six?
>
> G: Oh, it's simple. You need to move one of the sticks in number four to make it eleven. Do you see what I mean?
>
> B: Yes, now I see what you mean. Eleven minus five equals six. How clever!
>
> G: 틀 밖에서 생각하는 것은 때때로 도움이 될 수 있지.

> ┤ 조건 ├
> • 동명사를 이용할 것.
> • 빈도부사는 문장 끝에 쓸 것.
> • 'outside, box, helpful'을 사용할 것.

➡ _____

[07~08] 다음 대화를 읽고 물음에 답하시오.

> B: Jian, what's the matter? You look upset.
>
> G: My brother broke my computer. I'm so angry.
>
> B: I'm sorry to hear that, but your facial muscles must be tired.
>
> G: What do you mean?
>
> B: Well, it takes a lot of muscles to look angry, but (A)only a few to smile. Do you see what I mean?
>
> G: Oh, I get it. I guess it's not good to stay angry for a long time.
>
> B: That's right. Remember, it's always better to smile!

07 밑줄 친 (A)를 생략되지 않은 문장으로 다시 쓰시오.

> ┤ 조건 ├
> 'muscles'를 추가하여 8 단어로 쓸 것.

➡ _____

08 위 대화를 읽고 다음 문장의 빈칸에 알맞은 말을 넣어 Jian 에게 조언하는 말을 완성하시오.

> It takes a lot of _____ to look angry, but you don't need a lot to _____. So don't stay _____ for a long time.

09 다음 글의 밑줄 친 어구의 뜻이 **잘못된** 것은?

> These days, you (a)don't need paper tickets to watch a movie or go to a concert. You just need to (b)store your ticket in your cell phone. Then show the ticket (c)on your phone's screen before you go in. You (d)don't need to (e)go through the trouble of printing out tickets. Do you see what I mean?

① (a): 종이 티켓이 필요하지 않다
② (b): 티켓을 저장하다
③ (c): 휴대전화 화면 위의
④ (d): ~해서는 안 된다
⑤ (e): 번거롭게 티켓을 출력하다

10 괄호 안의 단어를 활용하여 우리말에 맞게 영작하시오.

(1) 당신은 너무 커서 이 자전거를 탈 수 없어요. (too, big)

➡ _____

(2) John의 아들은 너무 똑똑해서 친구들과 어울릴 수 없어요. (smart, too, hang out with)

➡ _____

(3) 이 커피는 너무 써서 마실 수가 없어요. (bitter, too)

➡ _____

(4) 이 애플파이는 너무 맛있어서 사지 않을 수가 없어. (so, buy, stop, delicious)

➡ _____

_____

(5) 이 밧줄은 너무 두꺼워서 가위로 자를 수가 없습니다. (too, cut)

➡ _____

(3) 모든 사람이 그걸 살 여유가 되는 건 아니다.

→ Not everyone can afford it.

➡ _____

(4) 창문을 좀 닫아 주시겠어요?

→ Would you be kind enough closing the window?

➡ _____

11 다음 빈칸에 들어갈 어휘로 적절치 않은 것을 모두 고르시오.

It was too cold for us to _____ outside.

① go ② going
③ swim ④ swimming
⑤ do some activities

12 다음 중 어법상 어색한 것을 모두 고르시오.

① He had so much work that he could rest.
② The container was too heavy for him to lift it.
③ He is too slow to catch up with others.
④ His voice is too small to be heard.
⑤ The problem was too hard for her to solve.

13 다음 각 문장에서 어법상 어색한 곳을 바르게 고쳐 다시 쓰시오. (어색한 곳이 없을 경우, '없음'으로 쓸 것.)

(1) 신입 사원 중 사실 눈에 띄는 인물이 없다.

→ No one really stand out among new recruits.

➡ _____

(2) 따라서 아무도 그 고릴라들을 도울 수 없다.

→ Therefore, nobody are able to help the gorillas.

➡ _____

14 다음 그래프의 해석이 잘못된 것을 고르시오.

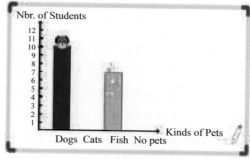

① Most students have dogs.
② Not everyone has pets.
③ No one has cats.
④ About 40% of my classmates raise fish.
⑤ Everyone has pets.

15 다음 각 문장을 괄호 안의 단어를 배열하여 문장을 완성할 때,

(1) 3번째 단어를 쓰시오.

• 모든 사람이 다 그렇게 생각하는 것은 아니다. (like, not, thinks, that, everyone)

➡ _____

(2) 6번째 단어를 쓰시오.

• 그녀는 상황이 자기가 견디기에 너무 힘들다고 말했다. (to, deal, situation, said, the, too, for, stressful, her, she, was)

➡ _____

(3) 7번째 단어를 쓰시오.
- 나는 너무 배가 불러서 더 이상 먹을 수 없다.
  (more, I, full, that, I, am, can't, so, eat)

➡ _____

(4) 10번째 단어를 쓰시오.
- 그 돌은 너무 무거워서 그가 그것을 옮길 수 없었다. (stone, heavy, couldn't, it, that, the, was, move, so, he)

➡ _____

[16~18] 다음 글을 읽고 물음에 답하시오.

> Pascal was doing his math homework in his room. He was ①struggling with graphs.
>
> (A) He looked up from the book to see ②who was talking. He couldn't believe his eyes. It was his dog, Manny, who ③was talking!
>
> (B) He put down his pen and picked up his favorite book, *Robin Hood*. He decided to read ④himself to sleep. When he was about to ⑤ opening the book, he heard a voice.
>
> (C) "It's too hard to read and draw graphs. Why do I need these anyway? No one needs graphs in real life."

16 자연스러운 글이 되도록 (A)~(C)를 바르게 나열하시오.

➡ _____

17 다음 중 위 글을 읽고 답할 수 없는 것은?

① What was Pascal's favorite book?
② When did Pascal hear a voice?
③ What was too hard for Pascal to do?
④ Why was Pascal surprised?
⑤ How long did Pascal do his homework?

18 밑줄 친 ①~⑤ 중 어법상 바르지 않은 것은?

①   ②   ③   ④   ⑤

[19~25] 다음 글을 읽고 물음에 답하시오.

> Suddenly, he heard men shouting. When he opened his eyes, he saw ①soldiers on horses. They were chasing a man with ②arrows in his hand. The man saw Pascal and shouted.
>
> "(A)네가 거기 서 있는 것은 너무 위험해. Come on." The man pulled Pascal onto his horse and rode into the woods.
>
> When they arrived at a house, the man stopped and got (B) his horse.
>
> "Hello, my name is Robin Hood."
>
> "Wow! Are you the Robin Hood from the book?"
>
> "No, I'm the Robin Hood of Sherwood Forest. Who are you and why are you here?"
>
> "My name is Pascal. I don't know why I'm here, but there must be a ③reason. You saved me from the soldiers. Thank you so much. Is there anything I can do for you?"
>
> "Well, can you help us get back the money that the king took from the people? He taxed them too much. He is too ④greedy to share with the people, so they don't have ⑤enough money to buy food. I want to help them get their money back. However, there are many soldiers in the tower, so no one can get inside."
>
> "Hmm... I think I have a solution. But first, can you take me to the tower? I need to count the number of soldiers."

19 밑줄 친 우리말 (A)를 다음 〈조건〉에 맞게 영어로 쓰시오.

┌─ 조건 ─┐
가주어 It과 진주어 to부정사를 이용할 것.

➡ _____

20 위 글의 빈칸 (B)에 알맞은 것은?

① on   ② off   ③ into
④ from   ⑤ with

21 What were the soldiers chasing? Answer in English.

➡ _____

_____

22 다음 중 ①~⑤에 해당하는 영영풀이가 아닌 것은?

① a member of an army, especially one who is not an officer
② a thin stick with a sharp point at one end, which is shot from a bow
③ an explanation for something that has happened or that somebody has done
④ giving more of something, especially money, than is usual or expected
⑤ as many or as much as somebody needs or wants

23 로빈의 성품을 잘 묘사하는 단어를 두 개 고르시오.

① just   ② mindless   ③ brave
④ cowardly   ⑤ thoughtless

24 Choose one that is NOT true.

① Robin Hood had arrows in his hand.
② Rohin Hood rode into the woods with Pascal.
③ The tower was protected by many soldiers.
④ The soldiers kept chasing Robin until they found him in the woods.
⑤ The king was greedy enough to tax people too much.

25 Write the reason why Pascal wanted Robin to take him to the tower. Use the phrase 'It was because.'

➡ _____

_____

MEMO

MEMO

MEMO

INSIGHT
on the textbook

교과서 파헤치기

※ 다음 영어를 우리말로 쓰시오.

01 flat _____

02 roof _____

03 hidden _____

04 cave _____

05 huge _____

06 mostly _____

07 colorful _____

08 walkway _____

09 unwelcome _____

10 install _____

11 tide _____

12 swampy _____

13 wooden _____

14 ladder _____

15 surface _____

16 straw _____

17 millionaire _____

18 invisible _____

19 opening _____

20 support _____

21 everywhere _____

22 floating _____

23 raised _____

24 house _____

25 appear _____

26 store _____

27 invader _____

28 thick _____

29 imagine _____

30 village _____

31 usually _____

32 however _____

33 rise _____

34 share _____

35 upside down _____

36 come over _____

37 be known as _____

38 hand down _____

39 walk around _____

40 for a while _____

41 full of _____

42 stop A from ~ing _____

43 be made up of _____

※ 다음 우리말을 영어로 쓰시오.

01 보통, 대개

02 흙

03 구멍

04 높이 올린

05 습지의

06 보이다, 나타나다

07 지붕

08 침략자

09 지탱하다, 떠받치다

10 반갑지 않은

11 설치하다

12 동굴

13 저장하다, 보관하다

14 형형색색의

15 상상하다

16 평평한

17 때때로, 가끔

18 숨겨진

19 표면, 지면, 수면

20 떠다니는

21 거대한, 굉장히 큰

22 두꺼운, 살찐

23 백만장자

24 수용하다

25 눈에 보이지 않는, 투명한

26 짚, 지푸라기

27 나무로 된

28 사다리

29 주로, 일반적으로

30 통로

31 오르다, 올라가다

32 조수, 흐름

33 모든 곳에, 어디나

34 공유하다

35 ~ 위에

36 하루 종일

37 ~을 물려주다

38 들르다

39 A가 ~하지 못하게 막다

40 ~로서 알려 지다

41 돌아다니다

42 A를 당겨 올리다

43 ~로 구성되다,
   ~로 만들어지다

※ 다음 영영풀이에 알맞은 단어를 <보기>에서 골라 쓴 후, 우리말 뜻을 쓰시오.

1 _____ : impossible to see: _____

2 _____ : level, with no high hills or other raised parts: _____

3 _____ : to provide a place for somebody to live: _____

4 _____ : the dry stems of wheat and other grain plants: _____

5 _____ : a large hole in the side of a hill or under the ground: _____

6 _____ : to fix equipment or furniture into position so that it can be used: _____

7 _____ : a space or hole that somebody or something can pass through: _____

8 _____ : a person who has a million pounds, dollars, etc.; a very rich person: _____

9 _____ : very wet or covered with water land in which plants, trees, etc. are growing: _____

10 _____ : to put something that is not being used in a place where it can be kept safely: _____

11 _____ : a passage or path for walking along, often outside and raised above the ground: _____

12 _____ : having a large distance between the top and bottom or front and back surfaces: _____

13 _____ : an army or a country that enters another country by force in order to take control of it: _____

14 _____ : to hold somebody or something in position; to prevent somebody or something from falling: _____

15 _____ : a device used for climbing that has two long pieces of wood, metal, or rope with a series of steps or rungs between them: _____

16 _____ : the regular upward and downward movement of the level of the ocean that is caused by the pull of the sun and the moon on Earth: _____

보기			
walkway	cave	swampy	flat
ladder	invisible	tide	opening
thick	millionaire	store	house
support	straw	invader	install

※ 다음 우리말과 일치하도록 빈칸에 알맞은 말을 쓰시오.

Listen and Speak 1 A

G: _____ you heard from Julia? She's _____ in Turkey, right?

B: Yes, she sent me some pictures. Do you _____ to _____ them?

G: Yes, please.

B: Okay, _____ a look.

G: Oh, look at those cave houses! They look so _____, don't they?
   I wish I could try _____ there.

B: I like _____ balloons. They look so _____!

G: I think Turkey is a wonderful place _____ visit. I _____ to visit there _____ _____ .

B: Me _____!

Listen and Speak 1 B

B: Will _____ snow today?

G: I have no idea. _____ are you _____ _____ snow, Taeho?

B: I got a new sled for my birthday. I can't _____ to test it _____ .

G: Let me _____ the weather. Umm, there will be no snow for a while.

B: I wish I could live in Alaska. Then I _____ go sledding all day!

G: No _____! Alaska is a very _____ _____ .

B: I think it would be fun. I want to _____ a snow house and _____ there on _____ .

G: _____ in a snow house _____ fun!

Listen and Speak 1 C

A: Look at _____ houses. They look very _____ .

B: Wow, I wish I could _____ _____ here.

A: _____ house would you _____ like to _____ _____ ?

B: I wish I could live in the stone house. It looks very _____ .

Listen and Speak 2 A-1

B: This is my dream house, Alice. _____ do you think?

G: Oh, the house has wheels! Is it a _____ of car?

B: Yes, it can _____ _____ a car.

G: So _____ would you do if you _____ in that house?

B: I would _____ to many places _____ my family.

G: That sounds _____ .

해석

G Julia한테서 소식 들었니? 그 애는 터키에서 여행 중이잖아, 맞지?

B 응, Julia가 나한테 사진 몇 장을 보내 왔어. 사진 보고 싶니?

G 응, 보고 싶어.

B 알겠어, 봐.

G 오, 저 동굴 집 좀 봐! 정말 특이하다, 그렇지 않니? 난 그곳에서 살아 봤으면 좋겠어.

B 난 저 열기구가 마음에 들어. 매우 아름다워 보여!

G 내 생각엔 터키가 방문하기에 정말 멋진 곳 같아. 언제 한 번 방문해 보고 싶다.

B 나도 그래!

B: 오늘 눈이 오는 거니?

G: 나도 모르겠어. 태호야. 왜 눈을 기다리는 거니?

B: 내 생일 선물로 새 썰매를 받았거든. 그거 빨리 시험해 보고 싶어.

G: 날씨 좀 확인해 볼게. 음, 당분간은 눈 소식이 없을 거래.

B: 알래스카에 살면 좋을 텐데. 그럼 온종일 썰매를 타러 갈 수 있을 텐데!

G: 말도 안 돼! 알래스카는 정말 추운 곳이야.

B: 내 생각엔 정말 즐거울 것 같아. 눈으로 집을 짓고 방학 때 그곳에서 지내고 싶어.

G: 눈으로 만든 집에 사는 건 재미있을 것 같아!

A: 이 집들 좀 봐. 매우 자연 그대로인 것 같아.

B: 우와, 이곳에 살아 봤으면 좋겠어.

A: 어느 집에서 가장 살아보고 싶니?

B: 돌로 만든 집에서 살아 보면 좋을 텐데. 매우 튼튼해 보여.

B: 이게 내 꿈의 집이야, Alice. 어떻게 생각하니?

G: 와, 바퀴가 달린 집이라니! 자동차의 일종이니?

B: 응, 자동차처럼 움직일 수 있어.

G: 그래서 그 집에서 살게 되면 뭘 할 거니?

B: 나는 가족들이랑 많은 곳을 여행할 거야.

G: 정말 신나게 들린다.

Listen and Speak 2 A-2

G: What would you do if you _____ a _____, Juwon?

B: I would _____ my own house.

G: What _____ of house would you _____?

B: I would build a house that is completely _____ _____ mirrors.

G: Why?

B: The _____ would make the house _____ _____. Wouldn't that be cool?

G: That _____ be cool!

Listen and Speak 2 A-3

G: Look. The house in this picture is _____ _____.

B: That's _____. Does anybody live there?

G: No, it would not be _____ to live there _____ the inside is also _____ _____.

B: Really? But I want to _____ _____ there.

G: _____ would you do if you _____ in that house?

B: I would walk upside down _____ Spider-Man. I could also see things _____.

Listen and Speak 2 B

G: Dohun, we _____ to start our project on our dream country to _____.

B: That's right. _____ _____ do you want to visit, Emma?

G: In my _____, I want to visit Spain.

B: What _____ you do if you _____ Spain?

G: I'm _____ in buildings. So I would go see La Sagrada Familia.

B: Isn't _____ the _____ Antoni Gaudi _____?

G: Yes, it is. It would be interesting to see _____ his design was _____ _____ _____.

B: Hmm... . _____ about *Gaudí and Spain* _____ the title for our project?

G: I love it!

Listen and Speak 2 C

A: _____ would you do if you could have a _____ _____?

B: I would _____ _____ a bird. Then I would be _____ _____ _____ _____ in the sky.

A: That's cool.

G: 주원아, 백만장자가 되면 뭘 할 거니?
B: 나는 나만의 집을 지을 거야.
G: 어떤 집을 짓고 싶은데?
B: 나는 거울로 완전히 덮인 집을 지을 거야.
G: 왜?
B: 그 거울들이 집을 거의 안 보이게 만들어줄 거야. 멋지지 않니?
G: 그건 멋질 거야!

G: 봐, 이 사진에 있는 집은 거꾸로 되어 있어.
B: 흥미로운데. 그 집에 누가 사는 건가?
G: 아니, 내부도 거꾸로 되어 있으니까 그곳에서 살기는 쉽지 않을 거야.
B: 정말? 하지만 나는 그곳에서 살아 보고 싶어.
G: 저 집에 살게 된다면 너는 뭘 할 거니?
B: 나는 스파이더맨처럼 거꾸로 걸어다닐 거야. 난 또한 사물을 다르게 볼 수 있을 거야.

G: 도훈아, 우리가 방문하고 싶은 꿈꾸는 나라에 대한 프로젝트를 시작해야 돼.
B: 맞아. Emma, 너는 어느 나라를 방문하고 싶니?
G: 내 경우에는 스페인에 가 보고 싶어.
B: 스페인에 가게 되면 뭘 할 건데?
G: 나는 건물들에 관심이 있어. 그래서 나는 La Sagrada Familia에 가 볼 거야.
B: 그 성당은 Antoni Gaudi가 디자인한 교회 아니니?
G: 응, 맞아. 그의 디자인이 어떻게 자연에서 영감을 얻었는지 보면 흥미로울 거야.
B: 흠… '가우디와 스페인'을 우리 프로젝트 제목으로 하는 건 어떠니?
G: 아주 좋아!

A: 마법의 힘을 갖게 된다면 너는 무엇을 할 거니?
B: 난 새로 변할 거야. 그러면 하늘을 자유롭게 날 수 있겠지.
A: 그거 멋있다.

Real Life Communication A

Jinho: I think _____ in a jungle would be really _____. Don't you think _____?

Claire: But there are _____ _____ animals in the jungle, Jinho.

Jinho: I know. But the jungle is _____ of adventure. I wish I _____ _____ there.

Claire: What _____ you do if you _____ in the jungle?

Jinho: I would _____ it. Maybe I could make some animal friends.

Claire: Then _____ would you sleep? In a _____?

Jinho: No, I would _____ _____ a tree house. _____ I would be safe from _____ _____.

Claire: That _____ _____.

Jinho: 내 생각엔 정글에서 사는 건 정말 신날 거야. 그렇게 생각하지 않니?

Claire: 근데 진호야. 정글에는 몇몇 위험한 동물들이 있어.

Jinho: 나도 알아. 하지만 정글은 모험으로 가득하잖아. 내가 거기서 살 수 있다면 좋을 텐데.

Claire: 정글에서 살 수 있다면 뭘 할 건데?

Jinho: 난 정글을 탐험할 거야. 아마도 동물 친구들도 좀 만들 수 있겠지.

Claire: 그러면 어디서 잠을 잘 건데? 동굴에서?

Jinho: 아니, 나무로 만든 집에서 지낼 거야. 그러면 위험한 동물들한테서 안전해지겠지.

Claire: 그건 말이 되네.

Real Life Communication B

A: I wish I could _____ in a house on the water _____ my vacation.

B: What _____ you do if you _____ there?

A: I would _____ _____ _____ _____. I would also _____ _____.

B: That _____ fun.

A: 방학 동안에 물 위에 있는 집에서 지내게 되면 좋을 텐데.

B: 그곳에 있다면 뭘 할 건데?

A: 난 매일 수영하러 갈 거야. 그리고 낚시도 하러 갈 거야.

B: 그거 재미있었겠는데.

Let's Check 1

B: _____ is my dream house. _____ do you _____, Alice?

G: Oh, it's in the _____ _____. It looks so _____. So, what _____ you do if you _____ in that house?

B: I have an _____ in _____ _____ animals. _____ I would _____ the deep sea and find some _____ sea animals.

G: _____ sounds cool!

B: 이건 내 꿈의 집이야. Alice, 어떻게 생각하니?

G: 와, 깊은 바다에 있네. 정말 독특해 보인다. 그래서 그 집에 살게 되면 무엇을 할 거니?

B: 난 심해 동물에 관심이 있어. 그래서 심해를 탐험하고 몇몇 특이한 해양 동물을 찾을 거야.

G: 그거 정말 멋진데!

Let's Check 2

A: What's the _____?

B: My computer is so slow. I _____ I _____ _____ a new computer.

A: 무슨 일이니?

B: 내 컴퓨터가 아주 느려. 새 컴퓨터를 갖게 되면 좋을 텐데.

※ 다음 우리말에 맞도록 대화를 영어로 쓰시오.

해석

Listen and Speak 1 A

G: _____

B: _____

G: _____

B: _____

G: _____

B: _____

G: _____

B: _____

G Julia한테서 소식 들었니? 그 애는 터키에서 여행 중이잖아, 맞지?
B 응, Julia가 나한테 사진 몇 장을 보내왔어. 사진 보고 싶니?
G 응, 보고 싶어.
B 알겠어, 봐.
G 오, 저 동굴 집 좀 봐. 정말 특이하다, 그렇지 않니? 난 그곳에서 살아 봤으면 좋겠어.
B 난 저 열기구가 마음에 들어. 매우 아름다워 보여!
G 내 생각엔 터키가 방문하기에 정말 멋진 곳 같아. 언제 한 번 방문해 보고 싶다.
B 나도 그래!

Listen and Speak 1 B

B: _____

G: _____

B: _____

G: _____

B: _____

G: _____

B: _____

G: _____

B: 오늘 눈이 오는 거니?
G: 나도 모르겠어. 태호야, 왜 눈을 기다리는 거니?
B: 내 생일 선물로 새 썰매를 받았거든. 그거 빨리 시험해 보고 싶어.
G: 날씨 좀 확인해 볼게. 음, 당분간은 눈 소식이 없을 거래.
B: 알래스카에 살면 좋을 텐데. 그럼 온종일 썰매를 타러 갈 수 있을 텐데.
G: 말도 안 돼! 알래스카는 정말 추운 곳이야.
B: 내 생각엔 정말 즐거울 것 같아. 눈으로 집을 짓고 방학 때 그곳에서 지내고 싶어.
G: 눈으로 만든 집에 사는 건 재미있을 것 같아!

Listen and Speak 1 C

A: _____

B: _____

A: _____

B: _____

A: 이 집들 좀 봐. 매우 자연 그대로인 것 같아.
B: 우와, 이곳에 살아 봤으면 좋겠어.
A: 어느 집에서 가장 살아보고 싶니?
B: 돌로 만든 집에서 살아 보면 좋을 텐데. 매우 튼튼해 보여.

Listen and Speak 2 A-1

B: _____

G: _____

B: _____

G: _____

B: _____

G: _____

B: 이게 내 꿈의 집이야, Alice. 어떻게 생각하니?
G: 와, 바퀴가 달린 집이라니! 자동차의 일종이니?
B: 응, 자동차처럼 움직일 수 있어.
G: 그래서 그 집에서 살게 되면 뭘 할 거니?
B: 나는 가족들이랑 많은 곳을 여행할 거야.
G: 정말 신나게 들린다!

Listen and Speak 2 A-2

G: _____

B: _____

G: _____

B: _____

G: _____

B: _____

G: _____

G: 주원아, 백만장자가 되면 뭘 할 거니?
B: 나는 나만의 집을 지을 거야.
G: 어떤 집을 짓고 싶은데?
B: 나는 거울로 완전히 덮인 집을 지을 거야.
G: 왜?
B: 그 거울들이 집을 거의 안 보이게 만들어줄 거야. 멋지지 않니?
G: 그건 멋질 거야!

Listen and Speak 2 A-3

G: _____

B: _____

G: _____

B: _____

G: _____

B: _____

G: 봐, 이 사진에 있는 집은 거꾸로 되어 있어.
B: 흥미로운데. 그 집에 누가 사는 건가?
G: 아니, 내부도 거꾸로 되어 있으니까 그곳에서 살기는 쉽지 않을 거야.
B: 정말? 하지만 나는 그곳에서 살아 보고 싶어.
G: 저 집에 살게 된다면 너는 뭘 거니?
B: 나는 스파이더맨처럼 거꾸로 걸어다닐 거야. 난 또한 사물을 다르게 볼 수 있을 거야.

Listen and Speak 2 B

G: _____

B: _____

G: _____

B: _____

G: _____

B: _____

G: _____

B: _____

G: _____

G: 도훈아, 우리가 방문하고 싶은 꿈꾸는 나라에 대한 프로젝트를 시작해야 돼.
B: 맞아. Emma, 너는 어느 나라를 방문하고 싶니?
G: 내 경우에는 스페인에 가 보고 싶어.
B: 스페인에 가게 되면 뭘 할 건데?
G: 나는 건물들에 관심이 있어. 그래서 나는 La Sagrada Familia에 가 볼 거야.
B: 그 성당은 Antoni Gaudi가 디자인한 교회 아니니?
G: 응, 맞아. 그의 디자인이 어떻게 자연에서 영감을 얻었는지 보면 흥미로울 거야.
B: 흠… '가우디와 스페인'을 우리 프로젝트 제목으로 하는 건 어떠니?
G: 아주 좋아!

Listen and Speak 2 C

A: _____

B: _____

A: _____

A: 마법의 힘을 갖게 된다면 너는 무엇을 할 거니?
B: 난 새로 변할 거야. 그러면 하늘을 자유롭게 날 수 있겠지.
A: 그거 멋있다.

Real Life Communication A

Jinho: _____

Claire: _____

Jinho: _____

Claire: _____

Jinho: _____

Claire: _____

Jinho: _____

_____

Claire: _____

Real Life Communication B

A: _____

B: _____

A: _____

B: _____

Let's Check 1

B: _____

G: _____

_____

B: _____

_____

G: _____

Let's Check 2

A: _____

B: _____

Jinho: 내 생각엔 정글에서 사는 건 정말 신날 거야. 그렇게 생각하지 않니?

Claire: 근데 진호야, 정글에는 몇몇 위험한 동물들이 있어.

Jinho: 나도 알아. 하지만 정글은 모험으로 가득하잖아. 내가 거기서 살 수 있다면 좋을 텐데.

Claire: 정글에서 살 수 있다면 뭘 할 건데?

Jinho: 난 정글을 탐험할 거야. 아마도 동물 친구들도 좀 만들 수 있겠지.

Claire: 그러면 어디서 잠을 잘 건데? 동굴에서?

Jinho: 아니, 나무로 만든 집에서 지낼 거야. 그러면 위험한 동물들한테서 안전해지겠지.

Claire: 그건 말이 되네.

A: 방학 동안에 물 위에 있는 집에서 지내게 되면 좋을 텐데.

B: 그곳에 있다면 뭘 할 건데?

A: 난 매일 수영하러 갈 거야. 그리고 낚시도 하러 갈 거야.

B: 그거 재미있겠는데.

B: 이건 내 꿈의 집이야. Alice, 어떻게 생각하니?

G: 와, 깊은 바다에 있네. 정말 독특해 보인다. 그래서 그 집에 살게 되면 무엇을 할 거니?

B: 난 심해 동물에 관심이 있어. 그래서 심해를 탐험하고 몇몇 특이한 해양 동물을 찾을 거야.

G: 그거 정말 멋진데!

A: 무슨 일이니?

B: 내 컴퓨터가 아주 느려. 새 컴퓨터를 갖게 된다면 좋을 텐데.

Step1

※ 다음 우리말과 일치하도록 빈칸에 알맞은 것을 골라 쓰시오.

1 _____ people _____ _____ different _____ .
A. in　　　　B. different　　　　C. houses　　　　D. live

2 _____ use _____ to _____ their houses. _____ live in houses on the water.
A. enter　　　　B. some　　　　C. ladders　　　　D. others

3 And _____ _____ their _____ _____ many people.
A. with　　　　B. others　　　　C. houses　　　　D. share

4 _____ you live in _____ of these houses. How would that _____ your _____ ?
A. one　　　　B. life　　　　C. imagine　　　　D. change

Pueblos in New Mexico, USA

5 If I _____ in a *pueblo*, I _____ _____ up a ladder to _____ my house.
A. climb　　　　B. lived　　　　C. enter　　　　D. would

6 _____ a _____ _____ on _____ of the house.
A. top　　　　B. hidden　　　　C. there's　　　　D. opening

7 If _____ visitors _____ , I would pull the ladder up to _____ them _____ entering.
A. stop　　　　B. unwelcome　　　　C. from　　　　D. appeared

8 The _____ walls are _____ _____ earth, _____ , and water.
A. made　　　　B. thick　　　　C. straw　　　　D. of

9 They would _____ _____ _____ in summer and _____ in winter.
A. cool　　　　B. keep　　　　C. warm　　　　D. me

10 The house has a _____ _____ . I would sometimes sleep _____ on the roof _____ the moon and stars.
A. under　　　　B. flat　　　　C. up　　　　D. roof

Houses on Water in Venice, Italy

11 _____ I _____ in Venice, I _____ _____ a gondola to school every morning.
A. take　　　　B. lived　　　　C. would　　　　D. if

12 Venice has 118 small islands. _____ weekends, I would travel _____ island _____ island _____ a *vaporetto*, a water bus.
A. to　　　　B. from　　　　C. by　　　　D. on

13 At high _____ , the water from the Adriatic Sea often _____ and leaves the streets _____ _____ water.
A. rises　　　　B. of　　　　C. tide　　　　D. full

14 _____ , I would be able to walk _____ the town _____ the _____ walkways.
A. around　　　　B. however　　　　C. raised　　　　D. through

15 Venice _____ _____ the " _____ city."
A. known　　　　B. is　　　　C. floating　　　　D. is

1 다양한 사람들이 다양한 집에서 살고 있습니다.

2 어떤 사람들은 집에 들어가기 위해 사다리를 이용합니다. 다른 사람들은 물 위에 있는 집에서 살고 있습니다.

3 그리고 또 다른 사람들은 많은 사람들과 함께 집을 공유합니다.

4 여러분이 이 집들 중 하나에 산다고 상상해 보세요. 여러분의 삶은 어떻게 바뀔까요?

푸에블로 – 미국 뉴멕시코

5 내가 만약 푸에블로에 산다면, 나는 집에 들어가기 위해 사다리를 오를 것이다.

6 집 꼭대기에는 숨겨진 구멍이 있다.

7 반갑지 않은 방문객이 나타난다면 나는 사다리를 끌어올려 그들이 들어오지 못하게 할 것이다.

8 두꺼운 벽은 흙, 지푸라기, 물로 만들어져 있다.

9 그것들은 여름에는 시원하게, 겨울에는 따뜻하게 유지시켜 준다.

10 집에는 평평한 지붕이 있다. 때때로 나는 달과 별들 아래의 지붕 위에서 잠을 잘 것이다.

물 위에 있는 집 – 이탈리아 베니스

11 내가 만약 베니스에 산다면, 나는 매일 아침 곤돌라를 타고 학교에 갈 것이다.

12 베니스는 118개의 작은 섬이 있다. 주말마다 나는 수상 버스인 바포레토를 타고 이 섬 저 섬을 여행할 것이다.

13 조수가 높을 때에는 아드리아 해의 물이 자주 범람하고 거리는 물로 가득 찬다.

14 그러나 나는 돌출되어 있는 통로로 도심 주변을 걸어다닐 수 있을 것이다.

15 베니스는 '떠다니는 도시'로 알려져 있다.

16 In Venice, _____ _____ many _____ _____ on the water.

    A. houses   B. are   C. there   D. colorful

17 You may _____ _____ and _____ they _____ the houses on the water.

    A. how   B. built   C. why   D. wonder

18 The old Venetians _____ to live there to _____ themselves _____ from _____ .

    A. safe   B. decided   C. invaders   D. keep

19 But it was not _____ for them to _____ their homes on this _____ _____ .

    A. swampy   B. easy   C. surface   D. build

20 _____ they _____ more than 10 million _____ _____ in the ground.

    A. wooden   B. installed   C. so   D. poles

21 It is these _____ _____ that _____ Venice _____ this day.

    A. poles   B. to   C. support   D. wooden

Tulou in Fujian, China

22 If I _____ in a *tulou*, a _____ _____ house in Fujian, China, I would always have friends at home to play _____ .

    A. with   B. round   C. lived   D. huge

23 I would sometimes hear my _____ _____ me to _____ _____ for tea or dinner.

    A. calling   B. over   C. neighbor   D. come

24 In a *tulou*, there are usually _____ _____ _____ _____ _____ .

    A. to   B. floors   C. five   D. three

25 The first _____ _____ _____ _____ cooking and eating.

    A. used   B. floor   C. for   D. is

26 And people _____ _____ and _____ on the second _____ .

    A. tools   B. store   C. floor   D. food

27 Do you _____ where I would sleep? My bedroom would be _____ the _____ or fourth _____ .

    A. third   B. wonder   C. floor   D. on

28 A *tulou* is _____ a village. The people _____ in a *tulou* _____ have the _____ family name.

    A. living   B. same   C. like   D. mostly

29 Some large *tulou* can house _____ _____ 50 families. They _____ _____ and share many things.

    A. to   B. together   C. up   D. work

30 _____ _____ in one building _____ them _____ .

    A. keeps   B. living   C. safe   D. together

31 Homes are _____ . But they are _____ all over the world. _____ is your home _____ ?

    A. different   B. like   C. what   D. everywhere

16 베니스에는 물 위에 있는 색색의 건물들이 많다.

17 여러분은 어떻게, 그리고 왜 그들이 물 위에 집을 지었는지 궁금할 것이다.

18 옛 베니스 사람들은 침략자들로부터 자신들을 안전하게 지키기 위해 그곳에 살기로 결정했다.

19 하지만 그들이 이 습지 위에 집을 짓는 것은 쉽지가 않았다.

20 그래서 그들은 땅에 천만 개 이상의 나무 기둥을 설치했다.

21 이 나무 기둥들이 바로 지금까지 베니스를 지탱해 주고 있는 것이다.

토루 – 중국 푸젠

22 내가 만약 거대하고 둥그런 집인 중국 푸젠의 토루(tulou)에 산다면, 나는 항상 집에 함께 놀 친구들이 있을 것이다.

23 때때로 나의 이웃이 차를 마시거나 저녁 식사를 하러 집에 들르라고 나를 부르는 소리를 듣게 될 것이다.

24 토루는 대개 3층에서 5층으로 되어 있다.

25 1층은 요리하고 식사하는 데에 사용된다.

26 그리고 사람들은 2층에 식량과 도구를 보관한다.

27 내가 어디에서 잠을 잘지 궁금한가? 내 침실은 3층이나 4층에 있을 것이다.

28 토루는 마을과 같다. 토루에 사는 사람들은 대부분 같은 성(姓)을 가지고 있다.

29 몇몇 큰 토루는 50가구까지 수용할 수 있다. 그들은 함께 일하고 많은 것을 공유한다.

30 한 건물에 함께 사는 것은 그들을 안전하게 지켜 준다.

31 집은 어디에나 있습니다. 그러나 전 세계의 집은 모두 다릅니다. 여러분의 집은 어떤가요?

※ 다음 우리말과 일치하도록 빈칸에 알맞은 것을 골라 쓰시오.

1 _____ people _____ _____ different houses.

2 Some _____ _____ _____ _____ _____ _____ _____ _____ _____ _____ _____. _____ _____ _____ _____ houses _____ the water.

3 And _____ _____ their houses _____ many people.

4 _____ you _____ _____ _____ _____ _____ these houses. How would _____ _____ your life?

Pueblos in New Mexico, USA

5 If I _____ _____ a *pueblo*, I _____ _____ up a ladder _____ _____ _____ house.

6 There's a _____ _____ _____ _____ of the house.

7 _____ unwelcome visitors _____, I _____ _____ the ladder _____ _____ _____ them _____ entering.

8 The thick walls _____ _____ _____ earth, straw, and water.

9 They would _____ _____ in summer and _____ in winter.

10 The house has _____ _____ _____. I would sometimes _____ _____ _____ _____ _____ under the moon and stars.

Houses on Water in Venice, Italy

11 If I _____ _____ Venice, I _____ _____ _____ to school every morning.

12 Venice _____ 118 small _____. _____ _____, I would travel _____ _____ _____ _____ _____ by a *vaporetto*, a water bus.

13 At _____ _____, the water _____ the Adriatic Sea often _____ and _____ the streets _____ _____.

14 _____, I would _____ _____ _____ _____ _____ the town through the _____ _____.

15 Venice _____ _____ _____ the "_____ city."

1 다양한 사람들이 다양한 집에서 살고 있습니다.

2 어떤 사람들은 집에 들어가기 위해 사다리를 이용합니다. 다른 사람들은 물 위에 있는 집에서 살고 있습니다.

3 그리고 또 다른 사람들은 많은 사람들과 함께 집을 공유합니다.

4 여러분이 이 집들 중 하나에 산다고 상상해 보세요. 여러분의 삶은 어떻게 바뀔까요?

푸에블로 - 미국 뉴멕시코

5 내가 만약 푸에블로에 산다면, 나는 집에 들어가기 위해 사다리를 오를 것이다.

6 집 꼭대기에는 숨겨진 구멍이 있다.

7 반갑지 않은 방문객이 나타난다면 나는 사다리를 끌어올려 그들이 들어오지 못하게 할 것이다.

8 두꺼운 벽은 흙, 지푸라기, 물로 만들어져 있다.

9 그것들은 여름에는 시원하게, 겨울에는 따뜻하게 유지시켜 준다.

10 집에는 평평한 지붕이 있다. 때때로 나는 달과 별들 아래의 지붕 위에서 잠을 잘 것이다.

물 위에 있는 집 - 이탈리아 베니스

11 내가 만약 베니스에 산다면, 나는 매일 아침 곤돌라를 타고 학교에 갈 것이다.

12 베니스는 118개의 작은 섬이 있다. 주말마다 나는 수상 버스인 바포레토를 타고 이 섬 저 섬을 여행할 것이다.

13 조수가 높을 때에는 아드리아해의 물이 자주 범람하고 거리는 물로 가득 찬다.

14 그러나 나는 돌출되어 있는 통로로 도심 주변을 걸어다닐 수 있을 것이다.

15 베니스는 '떠다니는 도시'로 알려져 있다.

16 In Venice, _____ _____ many _____ _____ on the water.

17 You may _____ _____ and _____ _____ _____ _____ _____ _____ the water.

18 The old Venetians _____ _____ _____ _____ _____ _____ to keep _____ _____ _____ _____ _____.

19 But it was not easy _____ _____ _____ _____ _____ their homes on this _____ _____.

20 So they _____ more than 10 million _____ _____ in the ground.

21 It is these _____ _____ that _____ Venice _____ this day.

Tulou in Fujian, China

22 If I _____ in a *tulou*, a _____ _____ house in Fujian, China, I _____ always _____ _____ at home _____ _____ _____.

23 I would sometimes _____ my neighbor _____ _____ _____ _____ _____ for tea or dinner.

24 In a *tulou*, there _____ usually _____ _____ _____ _____.

25 The first floor _____ _____ _____ cooking and eating.

26 And people _____ _____ and _____ _____ the _____ _____.

27 Do you wonder _____ _____ _____ _____? My bedroom _____ _____ _____ _____ the third or fourth floor.

28 A *tulou* is _____ a village. The people _____ _____ a *tulou* mostly _____ the same _____ _____.

29 Some large *tulou* _____ _____ _____ _____ 50 families. They _____ _____ and _____ many things.

30 _____ together in one building _____ _____ _____.

31 Homes are everywhere. But they are _____ _____ _____ _____. _____ is your home _____?

16 베니스에는 물 위에 있는 색색의 건물들이 많다.

17 여러분은 어떻게, 그리고 왜 그들이 물 위에 집을 지었는지 궁금할 것이다.

18 옛 베니스 사람들은 침략자들로부터 자신들을 안전하게 지키기 위해 그곳에 살기로 결정했다.

19 하지만 그들이 이 습지 위에 집을 짓는 것은 쉽지가 않았다.

20 그래서 그들은 땅에 천만 개 이상의 나무 기둥을 설치했다.

21 이 나무 기둥들이 바로 지금까지 베니스를 지탱해 주고 있는 것이다.

토루 – 중국 푸젠

22 내가 만약 거대하고 둥그런 집인 중국 푸젠의 토루(tulou)에 산다면, 나는 항상 집에 함께 놀 친구들이 있을 것이다.

23 때때로 나의 이웃이 차를 마시거나 저녁 식사를 하러 집에 들르라고 나를 부르는 소리를 듣게 될 것이다.

24 토루는 대개 3층에서 5층으로 되어 있다.

25 1층은 요리하고 식사하는 데에 사용된다.

26 그리고 사람들은 2층에 식량과 도구를 보관한다.

27 내가 어디에서 잠을 잘지 궁금한가? 내 침실은 3층이나 4층에 있을 것이다.

28 토루는 마을과 같다. 토루에 사는 사람들은 대부분 같은 성(姓)을 가지고 있다.

29 몇몇 큰 토루는 50가구까지 수용할 수 있다. 그들은 함께 일하고 많은 것을 공유한다.

30 한 건물에 함께 사는 것은 그들을 안전하게 지켜 준다.

31 집은 어디에나 있습니다. 그러나 전 세계의 집은 모두 다릅니다. 여러분의 집은 어떤가요?

※ 다음 문장을 우리말로 쓰시오.

1 Different people live in different houses.

➡ _____

2 Some use ladders to enter their houses. Others live in houses on the water.

➡ _____

3 And others share their houses with many people.

➡ _____

4 Imagine you live in one of these houses. How would that change your life?

➡ _____

Pueblos in New Mexico, USA

5 If I lived in a *pueblo*, I would climb up a ladder to enter my house.

➡ _____

6 There's a hidden opening on top of the house.

➡ _____

7 If unwelcome visitors appeared, I would pull the ladder up to stop them from entering.

➡ _____

8 The thick walls are made of earth, straw, and water.

➡ _____

9 They would keep me cool in summer and warm in winter.

➡ _____

10 The house has a flat roof. I would sometimes sleep up on the roof under the moon and stars.

➡ _____

Houses on Water in Venice, Italy

11 If I lived in Venice, I would take a gondola to school every morning.

➡ _____

12 Venice has 118 small islands. On weekends, I would travel from island to island by a *vaporetto*, a water bus.

➡ _____

13 At high tide, the water from the Adriatic Sea often rises and leaves the streets full of water.

➡ _____

14 However, I would be able to walk around the town through the raised walkways.

➡ _____

15 Venice is known as the "floating city."

➡ _____

16 ▸ In Venice, there are many colorful houses on the water.

➡ _____

17 ▸ You may wonder how and why they built the houses on the water.

➡ _____

18 ▸ The old Venetians decided to live there to keep themselves safe from invaders.

➡ _____

19 ▸ But it was not easy for them to build their homes on this swampy surface.

➡ _____

20 ▸ So they installed more than 10 million wooden poles in the ground.

➡ _____

21 ▸ It is these wooden poles that support Venice to this day.

➡ _____

Tulou in Fujian, China

22 ▸ If I lived in a *tulou*, a huge round house in Fujian, China, I would always have friends at home to play with.

➡ _____

23 ▸ I would sometimes hear my neighbor calling me to come over for tea or dinner.

➡ _____

24 ▸ In a *tulou*, there are usually three to five floors.

➡ _____

25 ▸ The first floor is used for cooking and eating.

➡ _____

26 ▸ And people store food and tools on the second floor.

➡ _____

27 ▸ Do you wonder where I would sleep? My bedroom would be on the third or fourth floor.

➡ _____

28 ▸ A *tulou* is like a village. The people living in a *tulou* mostly have the same family name.

➡ _____

29 ▸ Some large *tulou* can house up to 50 families. They work together and share many things.

➡ _____

30 ▸ Living together in one building keeps them safe.

➡ _____

31 ▸ Homes are everywhere. But they are different all over the world. What is your home like?

➡ _____

※ 다음 괄호 안의 단어들을 우리말에 맞도록 바르게 배열하시오.

1 (people / different / in / live / houses. / different)
➡ _____

2 (use / some / to / ladders / their / enter / houses. // live / others / houses / in / the / on / water.)
➡ _____

3 (others / and / their / share / with / houses / people. / many)
➡ _____

4 (you / imagine / live / one / in / these / of / houses. // would / how / change / that / life? / your)
➡ _____

Pueblos in New Mexico, USA

5 (I / if / in / lived / *pueblo*, / a / would / I / up / climb / ladder / a / enter / to / house. / my)
➡ _____

6 (a / there's / hidden / on / opening / top / the / of / house.)
➡ _____

7 (unwelcome / if / appeared, / visitors / would / I / the / pull / up / ladder / stop / to / from / them / entering.)
➡ _____

8 (thick / the / are / walls / of / made / earth, / and / straw, / water.)
➡ _____

9 (would / they / me / keep / in / cool / summer / and / in / warm / winter.)
➡ _____

10 (house / the / a / has / roof. / flat / would / I / sleep / sometimes / up / the / on / under / roof / moon / the / stars. / and)
➡ _____

Houses on Water in Venice, Italy

11 (I / if / in / lived / Venice, / would / I / a / take / gondola / school / to / morning. / every)
➡ _____

12 (has / Venice / small / 118 / islands. // weekends, / on / would / I / from / travel / island / to / by / island / *vaporetto*, / a / water / a / bus.)
➡ _____

13 (high / at / tide, / water / the / the / from / Sea / Adriatic / rises / often / and / the / leaves / full / streets / water. / of)
➡ _____

14 (I / however, / would / be / to / able / around / walk / town / the / the / through / walkways. / raised)
➡ _____

15 (is / Venice / as / known / the / city." / "floating)
➡ _____

1 다양한 사람들이 다양한 집에서 살고 있습니다.

2 어떤 사람들은 집에 들어가기 위해 사다리를 이용합니다. 다른 사람들은 물 위에 있는 집에서 살고 있습니다.

3 그리고 또 다른 사람들은 많은 사람들과 함께 집을 공유합니다.

4 여러분이 이 집들 중 하나에 산다고 상상해 보세요. 여러분의 삶은 어떻게 바뀔까요?

푸에블로 – 미국 뉴멕시코

5 내가 만약 푸에블로에 산다면, 나는 집에 들어가기 위해 사다리를 오를 것이다.

6 집 꼭대기에는 숨겨진 구멍이 있다.

7 반갑지 않은 방문객이 나타난다면 나는 사다리를 끌어올려 그들이 들어오지 못하게 할 것이다.

8 두꺼운 벽은 흙, 지푸라기, 물로 만들어져 있다.

9 그것들은 여름에는 시원하게, 겨울에는 따뜻하게 유지시켜 준다.

10 집에는 평평한 지붕이 있다. 때때로 나는 달과 별들 아래의 지붕 위에서 잠을 잘 것이다.

물 위에 있는 집 – 이탈리아 베니스

11 내가 만약 베니스에 산다면, 나는 매일 아침 곤돌라를 타고 학교에 갈 것이다.

12 베니스는 **118**개의 작은 섬이 있다. 주말마다 나는 수상 버스인 바포레토를 타고 이 섬 저 섬을 여행할 것이다.

13 조수가 높을 때에는 아드리아 해의 물이 자주 범람하고 거리는 물로 가득 찬다.

14 그러나 나는 돌출되어 있는 통로로 도심 주변을 걸어다닐 수 있을 것이다.

15 베니스는 '떠다니는 도시'로 알려져 있다.

16 (Venice, / in / are / there / colorful / many / houses / the / on / water.)
➡ _____

17 (may / you / wonder / and / how / why / built / they / houses / the / on / water. / the)
➡ _____

18 (old / the / Venetians / to / decided / there / live / keep / to / safe / themselves / invaders. / from)
➡ _____
_____

19 (it / but / not / was / for / easy / to / them / build / homes / their / on / swampy / this / surface.)
➡ _____
_____

20 (they / so / more / installed / than / million / 10 / poles / wooden / the / in / ground.)
➡ _____
_____

21 (is / it / wooden / these / poles / support / that / to / Venice / this / day.)
➡ _____

Tulou in Fujian, China

22 (I / if / in / a / lived / *tulou*, / a / round / huge / in / house / China, / Fujian, / would / I / have / always / friends / home / at / play / to / with.)
➡ _____
_____

23 (would / I / hear / sometimes / neighbor / my / me / calling / to / over / come / tea / for / dinner. / or)
➡ _____
_____

24 (a / in / *tulou*, / are / there / three / usually / five / to / floors.)
➡ _____

25 (first / the / is / floor / for / used / cooking / eating. / and)
➡ _____

26 (people / and / food / store / and / on / tools / the / floor. / second)
➡ _____

27 (you / do / where / wonder / would / I / sleep? // bedroom / my / be / would / the / on / or / third / floor. / fourth)
➡ _____
_____

28 (*tulou* / a / like / is / village. / a // people / the / in / living / a / mostly / *tulou* / the / have / family / same / name.)
➡ _____
_____

29 (large / some / can / *tulou* / up / house / 50 / to / families. // work / they / and / together / many / share / things.)
➡ _____
_____

30 (together / living / one / in / keeps / building / safe. / them)
➡ _____

31 (are / everywhere. / homes // they / but / different / are / over / all / world. / the // is / what / home / your / like?)
➡ _____
_____

---

16 베니스에는 물 위에 있는 색색의 건물들이 많다.

17 여러분은 어떻게, 그리고 왜 그들이 물 위에 집을 지었는지 궁금할 것이다.

18 옛 베니스 사람들은 침략자들로부터 자신들을 안전하게 지키기 위해 그곳에 살기로 결정했다.

19 하지만 그들이 이 습지 위에 집을 짓는 것은 쉽지가 않았다.

20 그래서 그들은 땅에 천만 개 이상의 나무 기둥을 설치했다.

21 이 나무 기둥들이 바로 지금까지 베니스를 지탱해 주고 있는 것이다.

토루 – 중국 푸젠

22 내가 만약 거대하고 둥그런 집인 중국 푸젠의 토루(tulou)에 산다면, 나는 항상 집에 함께 놀 친구들이 있을 것이다.

23 때때로 나의 이웃이 차를 마시거나 저녁 식사를 하러 집에 들르라고 나를 부르는 소리를 듣게 될 것이다.

24 토루는 대개 3층에서 5층으로 되어 있다.

25 1층은 요리하고 식사하는 데에 사용된다.

26 그리고 사람들은 2층에 식량과 도구를 보관한다.

27 내가 어디에서 잠을 잘지 궁금한가? 내 침실은 3층이나 4층에 있을 것이다.

28 토루는 마을과 같다. 토루에 사는 사람들은 대부분 같은 성(姓)을 가지고 있다.

29 몇몇 큰 토루는 50가구까지 수용할 수 있다. 그들은 함께 일하고 많은 것을 공유한다.

30 한 건물에 함께 사는 것은 그들을 안전하게 지켜 준다.

31 집은 어디에나 있습니다. 그러나 전 세계의 집은 모두 다릅니다. 여러분의 집은 어떤가요?

※ 다음 우리말을 영어로 쓰시오.

1 다양한 사람들이 다양한 집에서 살고 있습니다.

➡ _____

2 어떤 사람들은 집에 들어가기 위해 사다리를 이용합니다. 다른 사람들은 물 위에 있는 집에서 살고 있습니다.

➡ _____

3 그리고 또 다른 사람들은 많은 사람들과 함께 집을 공유합니다.

➡ _____

4 여러분이 이 집들 중 하나에 산다고 상상해 보세요. 여러분의 삶은 어떻게 바뀔까요?

➡ _____

Pueblos in New Mexico, USA

5 내가 만약 푸에블로에 산다면, 나는 집에 들어가기 위해 사다리를 오를 것이다.

➡ _____

6 집 꼭대기에는 숨겨진 구멍이 있다.

➡ _____

7 반갑지 않은 방문객이 나타난다면 나는 사다리를 끌어올려 그들이 들어오지 못하게 할 것이다.

➡ _____

8 두꺼운 벽은 흙, 지푸라기, 물로 만들어져 있다.

➡ _____

9 그것들은 여름에는 시원하게, 겨울에는 따뜻하게 유지시켜 준다.

➡ _____

10 집에는 평평한 지붕이 있다. 때때로 나는 달과 별들 아래의 지붕 위에서 잠을 잘 것이다.

➡ _____

Houses on Water in Venice, Italy

11 내가 만약 베니스에 산다면, 나는 매일 아침 곤돌라를 타고 학교에 갈 것이다.

➡ _____

12 베니스는 118개의 작은 섬이 있다. 주말마다 나는 수상 버스인 바포레토를 타고 이 섬 저 섬을 여행할 것이다.

➡ _____

13 조수가 높을 때에는 아드리아 해의 물이 자주 범람하고 거리는 물로 가득 찬다.

➡ _____

14 그러나 나는 돌출되어 있는 통로로 도심 주변을 걸어다닐 수 있을 것이다.

➡ _____

15 베니스는 '떠다니는 도시'로 알려져 있다.

➡ _____

16 베니스에는 물 위에 있는 색색의 건물들이 많다.

➡ _____

17 여러분은 어떻게, 그리고 왜 그들이 물 위에 집을 지었는지 궁금할 것이다.

➡ _____

18 옛 베니스 사람들은 침략자들로부터 자신들을 안전하게 지키기 위해 그곳에 살기로 결정했다.

➡ _____

19 하지만 그들이 이 습지 위에 집을 짓는 것은 쉽지가 않았다.

➡ _____

20 그래서 그들은 땅에 천만 개 이상의 나무 기둥을 설치했다.

➡ _____

21 이 나무 기둥들이 바로 지금까지 베니스를 지탱해 주고 있는 것이다.

➡ _____

Tulou in Fujian, China

22 내가 만약 거대하고 둥그런 집인 중국 푸젠의 토루(*tulou*)에 산다면, 나는 항상 집에 함께 놀 친구들이 있을 것이다.

➡ _____

_____

23 때때로 나의 이웃이 차를 마시거나 저녁 식사를 하러 집에 들르라고 나를 부르는 소리를 듣게 될 것이다.

➡ _____

24 토루는 대개 3층에서 5층으로 되어 있다.

➡ _____

25 1층은 요리하고 식사하는 데에 사용된다.

➡ _____

26 그리고 사람들은 2층에 식량과 도구를 보관한다.

➡ _____

27 내가 어디에서 잠을 잘지 궁금한가? 내 침실은 3층이나 4층에 있을 것이다.

➡ _____

28 토루는 마을과 같다. 토루에 사는 사람들은 대부분 같은 성(姓)을 가지고 있다.

➡ _____

29 몇몇 큰 토루는 50가구까지 수용할 수 있다. 그들은 함께 일하고 많은 것을 공유한다.

➡ _____

30 한 건물에 함께 사는 것은 그들을 안전하게 지켜 준다.

➡ _____

31 집은 어디에나 있습니다. 그러나 전 세계의 집은 모두 다릅니다. 여러분의 집은 어떤가요?

➡ _____

※ 다음 우리말과 일치하도록 빈칸에 알맞은 말을 쓰시오.

Let's Write

1. When you visit Korea, you _____ _____ _____ _____ _____ _____.

2. _____ _____ _____ _____ _____ in a *hanok*?

3. A *hanok* is _____ _____ _____ _____ _____ _____.

4. If you _____ in a *hanok*, you _____ _____ on the floor _____ _____.

5. *Hanok* houses _____ _____ _____ _____ _____ natural materials _____ _____ _____, stone, _____, paper, _____ _____.

6. These materials _____ _____ _____ _____ _____.

7. In the cold winter, the _____ _____ _____ _____ _____.

8. The doors in *hanok* _____ _____ _____ _____.

9. They _____ _____ _____ _____ in summer.

1. 여러분이 한국을 방문할 때, 어디에서 머물지 궁금할 것입니다.
2. 한옥에서 머물러 보면 어떨까요?
3. 한옥은 한국의 전통 가옥입니다.
4. 만약 여러분이 한옥에서 지낸다면, 여러분은 침대가 없기 때문에 바닥에서 잠을 자게 될 것입니다.
5. 한옥 집은 대개 나무, 돌, 지푸라기, 종이, 흙과 같은 천연 재료로 지어져 있습니다.
6. 이 재료들은 여러분의 피부를 건강하게 유지하도록 도와줍니다.
7. 추운 겨울에는 따뜻한 온돌 바닥이 여러분의 몸을 데워줍니다.
8. 한옥 문들은 얇은 종이로 덮여 있습니다.
9. 그 문들은 여름에 여러분이 시원하게 지내도록 도와줍니다.

Culture & Life

1. If you _____ _____ a street in the village of the Ndebele in South Africa, you _____ _____ _____ _____ _____ _____ _____ _____ and styles.

2. _____ _____ _____ _____ a different story.

3. Some stories _____ _____ _____ _____ _____ _____.

4. _____ express _____ _____.

5. _____ _____ _____ _____ _____, the Ndebele _____ _____ _____ the Boers.

6. When the Boers _____ _____ _____, the Ndebele painted their houses _____ _____ _____ _____.

7. So, their enemies couldn't understand _____ they were _____ _____ _____.

8. The symbols _____ _____ _____ _____ _____.

9. Those symbols _____ _____ _____ mothers _____ daughters.

10. And they have _____ _____ _____ _____ _____.

1. 남아프리카 은데벨레족 마을의 거리를 걸어가다 보면, 많은 독특한 모양과 양식의 집들을 보게 될 것이다.
2. 각각의 집들은 서로 다른 이야기를 한다.
3. 어떤 이야기들은 이웃 아이들에 관한 것일지 모른다.
4. 또 다른 이야기들은 개인적인 의견을 표현한다.
5. 오래전, 은데벨레족은 보어인과 전쟁을 치렀다.
6. 보어인들이 그들의 땅을 침략했을 때, 은데벨레족은 여러 색의 상징으로 집을 칠했다.
7. 그래서 적들은 그들이 비밀리에 주고받는 의사소통을 이해하지 못했다.
8. 이러한 상징들은 슬픔과 같은 감정들을 표현했다.
9. 그 상징들은 엄마들에게서 딸들에게로 전해져 왔다.
10. 그리고 그들은 자신들의 전통이 계속 살아 있도록 유지해 왔다.

※ 다음 우리말을 영어로 쓰시오.

Let's Write

1. 여러분이 한국을 방문할 때, 어디에서 머물지 궁금할 것입니다.
   ➡ _____

2. 한옥에서 머물러 보면 어떨까요?
   ➡ _____

3. 한옥은 한국의 전통 가옥입니다.
   ➡ _____

4. 만약 여러분이 한옥에서 지낸다면, 여러분은 침대가 없기 때문에 바닥에서 잠을 자게 될 것입니다.
   ➡ _____

5. 한옥 집은 대개 나무, 돌, 지푸라기, 종이, 흙과 같은 천연 재료로 지어져 있습니다.
   ➡ _____

6. 이 재료들은 여러분의 피부를 건강하게 유지하도록 도와줍니다.
   ➡ _____

7. 추운 겨울에는 따뜻한 온돌 바닥이 여러분의 몸을 데워줍니다.
   ➡ _____

8. 한옥 문들은 얇은 종이로 덮여 있습니다.
   ➡ _____

9. 그 문들은 여름에 여러분이 시원하게 지내도록 도와줍니다.
   ➡ _____

Culture & Life

1. 남아프리카 은데벨레족 마을의 거리를 걸어가다 보면, 많은 독특한 모양과 양식의 집들을 보게 될 것이다.
   ➡ _____

2. 각각의 집들은 서로 다른 이야기를 한다.
   ➡ _____

3. 어떤 이야기들은 이웃 아이들에 관한 것일지 모른다.
   ➡ _____

4. 또 다른 이야기들은 개인적인 의견을 표현한다.
   ➡ _____

5. 오래전, 은데벨레족은 보어인과 전쟁을 치렀다.
   ➡ _____

6. 보어인들이 그들의 땅을 침략했을 때, 은데벨레족은 여러 색의 상징으로 집을 칠했다.
   ➡ _____

7. 그래서 적들은 그들이 비밀리에 주고받는 의사소통을 이해하지 못했다.
   ➡ _____

8. 이러한 상징들은 슬픔과 같은 감정들을 표현했다.
   ➡ _____

9. 그 상징들은 엄마들에게서 딸들에게로 전해져 왔다.
   ➡ _____

10. 그리고 그들은 자신들의 전통이 계속 살아 있도록 유지해 왔다.
   ➡ _____

※ 다음 영어를 우리말로 쓰시오.

01	article		22	facial	
02	break		23	poisonous	
03	reason		24	struggle	
04	vote		25	realize	
05	wave		26	helpful	
06	adventure		27	celebrate	
07	courageous		28	solution	
08	repeat		29	claim	
09	muscle		30	greedy	
10	equal		31	result	
11	survey		32	match	
12	anyway		33	lastly	
13	represent		34	science-fiction	
14	matter		35	get back	
15	election		36	be related to	
16	soldier		37	one by one	
17	chase		38	run for	
18	sum		39	pick up	
19	importance		40	in other words	
20	suddenly		41	be about to	
21	midnight		42	be proud of	
			43	be regarded as	

※ 다음 우리말을 영어로 쓰시오.

01 군인, 병사	_____	22 투쟁하다, 분투하다
02 타자기	_____	23 탐욕스러운, 욕심 많은
03 설문조사하다	_____	24 갑자기
04 세금	_____	25 도움이 되는
05 일치하다	_____	26 근육
06 계산, 총계	_____	27 중요성
07 주장하다	_____	28 독이 있는
08 투표하다	_____	29 결과
09 해결책	_____	30 짭짤한
10 얼굴의	_____	31 공상 과학의
11 모험	_____	32 깨닫다
12 이유	_____	33 화살
13 용감한	_____	34 손을 흔들다
14 선거	_____	35 잠복하다
15 기념하다	_____	36 ~을 자랑스러워하다
16 글, 기사	_____	37 올려보다
17 게다가, 어쨌든	_____	38 막 ~하려고 하다
18 같다	_____	39 다시 말하면
19 자정	_____	40 ~와 연관되어 있다
20 나타내다	_____	41 하나씩
21 뒤쫓다	_____	42 ~로 여겨지다
		43 더 이상 ~ 않다

※ 다음 영영풀이에 알맞은 단어를 <보기>에서 골라 쓴 후, 우리말 뜻을 쓰시오.

1 _____ : to be important: _____

2 _____ : a member of an army: _____

3 _____ : 12 o'clock at night: _____

4 _____ : to understand clearly: _____

5 _____ : full of containing poison: _____

6 _____ : to say something in a loud voice: _____

7 _____ : a piece of writing appearing in a newspaper: _____

8 _____ : to express by some symbol or character: _____

9 _____ : to signal in greeting, by raising the hand and moving the fingers:

    _____

10 _____ : wanting a lot more food, money, etc. than you need: _____

11 _____ : at the end; after all the other things that you have mentioned: _____

12 _____ : a long written story about characters and events that have been invented

    by the writer: _____

13 _____ : the total of two or more numbers or quantities, determined by mathematical

    process: _____

14 _____ : an amount of money that you have to pay to the government so that it

    can pay for public services: _____

15 _____ : to say that something is true although it has not been proved and other

    people may not believe it: _____

16 _____ : to take part in special enjoyable activities in order to show that a particular

    occasion is important: _____

lastly	wave	realize	soldier
greedy	celebrate	claim	midnight
tax	novel	matter	sum
represent	poisonous	shout	article

대화문 Test

※ 다음 우리말과 일치하도록 빈칸에 알맞은 말을 쓰시오.

 해석

Listen & Speak 1 A

B: Minju, what is this _____ _____?

G: I did a _____ on the_____ of pets my classmates have.

B: What were the _____?

G: Eighty _____ of the students have pets. _____ five _____ _____ twenty-five students don't have pets.

B: _____ _____ _____ pets do they have?

G: Well, ten students have dogs and three students _____ _____.

B: What about _____ _____?

G: Seven students have _____.

Listen & Speak 1 B

M: Mason, how was the _____?

B: It was _____. I didn't _____.

M: _____ _____?

B: Yura won. _____ sixty percent of the students _____ her.

M: Well, you tried _____ _____ and that's _____ _____.

B: I _____ so. I have learned many things _____ _____ class _____.

M: I'm really _____ _____ you.

B: Thanks, Dad.

Listen & Speak 2 A

B: Emma, can you _____ me _____ this math problem?

G: Sure, what is it?

B: You _____ _____ move one stick _____ _____ this _____ right. _____ could four _____ five _____ six?

G: Oh, it's simple. You _____ _____ move one of the _____ in number four _____ _____ it eleven. Do you see _____ _____ _____?

B: Yes, now I see _____ you mean. Eleven _____ five _____ six. _____ clever!

G: _____ _____ _____ _____ can be _____ sometimes.

B: 민주야, 이 그래프는 무엇에 관한 거야?
G: 나는 우리 반 친구들이 가지고 있는 애완동물의 종류에 대해 설문 조사했어.
B: 결과가 어땠어?
G: 학생들의 80%가 애완동물을 가지고 있었어. 25명의 학생들 중 5명만이 애완동물이 없었어.
B: 그들은 어떤 종류의 애완동물을 가지고 있니?
G: 음, 10명은 개, 3명은 고양이를 가지고 있어.
B: 나머지는?
G: 7명은 물고기를 가지고 있어.

M: Mason, 선거는 어땠니?
B: 안 좋았어요. 저는 이기지 못했어요.
M: 어째서?
B: 유라가 이겼어요. 학생들의 60% 이상이 그녀에게 투표했어요.
M: 음, 너는 최선을 다했고, 그게 중요한 거란다.
B: 저도 그렇게 생각해요. 반장 선거에 출마한 동안 많은 것을 배웠어요.
M: 나는 네가 정말 자랑스럽구나.
B: 고마워요, 아빠.

B: Emma, 이 수학 문제 좀 도와줄래?
G: 물론이지, 뭔데?
B: 이 계산이 맞도록 너는 한 개의 막대기를 옮겨야 해. 어떻게 4빼기 5가 6이 되지?
G: 오, 이건 간단해. 너는 숫자 4를 11로 만들기 위해 막대기 하나를 옮기면 돼. 무슨 말인지 알겠니?
B: 응, 이제 네 말이 무슨 뜻인지 알겠어. 11 빼기 5는 6이지. 너 정말 똑똑하구나!
G: 틀 밖에서 생각하는 것은 때때로 도움이 될 수 있지.

Listen & Speak 2 B

B: Jian, what's _____ _____? You _____ _____.

G: My brother _____ my computer. I'm so _____.

B: _____ _____ _____ _____ that, but your _____ muscles must _____ _____.

G: _____ _____ _____ _____ _____?

B: Well, it _____ a lot of _____ _____ _____ angry, but only _____ _____ to smile. Do you see _____ I mean?

G: Oh, I _____ it. I guess it's not good _____ _____ angry _____ _____ _____ _____ _____.

B: That's right. Remember, _____ always _____ _____ _____!

Real Life Communication

Mina: Henry, what are you _____?

Henry: I'm writing an _____ about students' _____ _____. I'_____ _____ _____ their health.

Mina: Why?

Henry: Well, I _____ 100 students and the _____ show that _____ _____ of the students liked pizza and fried chicken for snacks. _____ _____ _____ what I _____?

Mina: Oh, _____ _____ _____. Students really like fast food. _____ _____ did they like?

Henry: _____ _____ of the students _____ chocolate cake _____ their _____.

Mina: Wow, students should really _____ _____ eat _____ snacks!

Let's Check

B: _____ _____, you don't need _____ _____ to watch a movie or go to a concert. You just need to _____ your ticket _____ your cell phone. Then _____ the ticket on your phone's _____ before you _____ _____. You _____ _____ _____ _____ the _____ _____ _____ out tickets. Do you see _____ _____?

B: 지안아, 무슨 문제 있니? 너 속상해 보여.

G: 내 남동생이 내 컴퓨터를 고장 냈어. 정말 화나.

B: 그렇다니 유감이지만, 너의 얼굴 근육은 피곤할 거야.

G: 무슨 뜻이니?

B: 음, 화난 표정을 지을 때는 많은 근육이 필요하지만, 웃을 때는 몇 개의 근육만 필요하거든. 무슨 말인지 알겠어?

G: 오, 이해했어. 오랫동안 화난 상태로 있으면 좋지 않겠구나.

B: 맞아. 기억해, 웃는 게 항상 더 낫다는 것을 말이야!

미나: Henry, 너 뭐 하고 있니?

Henry: 난 학생들이 가장 좋아하는 간식에 관한 기사를 쓰고 있어. 나는 그들의 건강이 걱정 돼.

미나: 왜?

Henry: 음, 난 100명의 학생들에게 설문 조사를 했고, 학생들의 80%가 간식으로 피자나 프라이드치킨을 좋아한다는 결과가 나왔어. 무슨 뜻인지 알겠니?

미나: 아, 알겠어. 학생들은 패스트푸드를 정말 좋아하지. 그들은 또 어떤 것을 좋아했니?

Henry: 학생들의 12%가 가장 좋아하는 것으로 초콜릿 케이크를 골랐어.

미나: 와우, 학생들은 더 건강한 간식을 먹도록 정말로 노력해야겠다!

B: 요즘에, 당신은 영화를 보거나 공연장에 가기 위해 종이 티켓이 필요하지 않습니다. 당신은 단지 당신의 휴대전화에 티켓을 저장하면 됩니다. 그러고 나서 입장하기 전에 휴대전화 화면 위의 티켓을 보여줍니다. 당신은 번거롭게 티켓을 출력할 필요가 없습니다. 무슨 뜻인지 아시겠어요?

※ 다음 우리말에 맞도록 대화를 영어로 쓰시오.

Listen & Speak 1 A

B: _____

G: _____

B: _____

G: _____

_____

B: _____

G: _____

B: _____

G: _____

B: 민주야, 이 그래프는 무엇에 관한 거야?
G: 나는 우리 반 친구들이 가지고 있는 애완동물의 종류에 대해 설문 조사했어.
B: 결과가 어땠어?
G: 학생들의 80%가 애완동물을 가지고 있었어. 25명의 학생들 중 5명만 이 애완동물이 없었어.
B: 그들은 어떤 종류의 애완동물을 가지고 있니?
G: 음. 10명은 개, 3명은 고양이를 가지고 있어.
B: 나머지는?
G: 7명은 물고기를 가지고 있어.

Listen & Speak 1 B

M: _____

B: _____

M: _____

B: _____

M: _____

B: _____

M: _____

B: _____

M: Mason, 선거는 어땠니?
B: 안 좋았어요. 저는 이기지 못했어요.
M: 어째서?
B: 유라가 이겼어요. 학생들의 60% 이상이 그녀에게 투표했어요.
M: 음, 너는 최선을 다했고, 그게 중요한 거란다.
B: 저도 그렇게 생각해요. 반장 선거에 출마한 동안 많은 것을 배웠어요.
M: 나는 네가 정말 자랑스럽구나.
B: 고마워요, 아빠.

Listen & Speak 2 A

B: _____

G: _____

B: _____

_____

G: _____

_____

B: _____

G: _____

B: Emma, 이 수학 문제 좀 도와줄래?
G: 물론이지, 뭔데?
B: 이 계산이 맞도록 너는 한 개의 막대기를 옮겨야 해. 어떻게 4빼기 5가 6이 되지?
G: 오, 이건 간단해. 너는 숫자 4를 11로 만들기 위해 막대기 하나를 옮기면 돼. 무슨 말인지 알겠니?
B: 응, 이제 네 말이 무슨 뜻인지 알겠어. 11 빼기 5는 6이지. 너 정말 똑똑하구나!
G: 틀 밖에서 생각하는 것은 때때로 도움이 될 수 있지.

Listen & Speak 2 B

B: _____

G: _____

B: _____

G: _____

B: _____

G: _____

B: _____

B: 지안아, 무슨 문제 있니? 너 속상해 보여.

G: 내 남동생이 내 컴퓨터를 고장 냈어. 정말 화나.

B: 그렇다니 유감이지만, 너의 얼굴 근육은 피곤할 거야.

G: 무슨 뜻이니?

B: 음, 화난 표정을 지을 때는 많은 근육이 필요하지만, 웃을 때는 몇 개의 근육만 필요하거든. 무슨 말인지 알겠어?

G: 오, 이해했어. 오랫동안 화난 상태로 있으면 좋지 않겠구나.

B: 맞아. 기억해, 웃는 게 항상 더 낫다는 것을 말이야!

Real Life Communication

Mina: _____

Henry: _____

_____

Mina: _____

Henry: _____

_____

Mina: _____

Henry: _____

Mina: _____

미나: Henry, 너 뭐 하고 있니?

Henry: 난 학생들이 가장 좋아하는 간식에 관한 기사를 쓰고 있어. 나는 그들의 건강이 걱정 돼.

미나: 왜?

Henry: 음, 난 100명의 학생들에게 설문 조사를 했고, 학생들의 80%가 간식으로 피자나 프라이드치킨을 좋아한다는 결과가 나왔어. 무슨 뜻인지 알겠니?

미나: 아, 알겠어. 학생들은 패스트푸드를 정말 좋아하지. 그들은 또 어떤 것을 좋아했니?

Henry: 학생들의 12%가 가장 좋아하는 것으로 초콜릿 케이크를 골랐어.

미나: 와우, 학생들은 더 건강한 간식을 먹도록 정말로 노력해야겠다!

Let's Check

B: _____

_____

_____

_____

B: 요즘에, 당신은 영화를 보거나 공연장에 가기 위해 종이 티켓이 필요하지 않습니다. 당신은 단지 당신의 휴대전화에 티켓을 저장하면 됩니다. 그러고 나서 입장하기 전에 휴대전화 화면위의 티켓을 보여줍니다. 당신은 번거롭게 티켓을 출력할 필요가 없습니다. 무슨 뜻인지 아시겠어요?

※ 다음 우리말과 일치하도록 빈칸에 알맞은 것을 골라 쓰시오.

1 Pascal was _____ his _____ homework in his room. He was _____ _____ graphs.

    A. math   B. with   C. doing   D. struggling

2 "It's _____ hard to read and _____ graphs. Why do I need these _____ ? No one needs graphs in _____ life."

    A. anyway   B. too   C. draw   D. real

3 He _____ _____ his pen and _____ _____ his favorite book, *Robin Hood*.

    A. down   B. up   C. put   D. picked

4 He _____ to read _____ to sleep. When he was _____ to open the book, he _____ a voice.

    A. himself   B. heard   C. decided   D. about

5 He _____ _____ _____ the book to see who was _____ .

    A. up   B. talking   C. from   D. looked

6 He _____ _____ his eyes. It was his dog, Manny, _____ _____ talking!

    A. who   B. couldn't   C. was   D. believe

7 "_____ your _____ and _____ _____ me. *Cogito ergo sum*," said Manny.

    A. repeat   B. close   C. after   D. eyes

8 "You _____ _____ ?" "_____ _____ ! *Cogito ergo sum*."

    A. talk   B. repeat   C. can   D. just

9 Pascal closed his eyes and _____ the _____ . Suddenly, he _____ men _____ .

    A. heard   B. words   C. repeated   D. shouting

10 _____ he _____ his eyes, he saw _____ _____ horses.

    A. on   B. opened   C. when   D. soldiers

11 They were _____ a man _____ _____ in his hand. The man saw Pascal and _____ .

    A. arrows   B. chasing   C. shouted   D. with

12 "It's too _____ _____ _____ to _____ there. Come on."

    A. for   B. dangerous   C. stand   D. you

---

1 파스칼은 그의 방에서 수학 숙제를 하고 있었습니다. 그는 그래프 문제에 고군분투하고 있었습니다.

2 "그래프를 읽고 그리는 것은 너무 어려워. 게다가 내가 왜 그래프가 필요하겠어? 아무도 실제 생활에서는 그래프가 필요하지 않아."

3 그는 그의 펜을 내려놓고, 그가 가장 좋아하는 책, '로빈 후드'를 집어 들었습니다.

4 그는 책을 읽으며 잠들기로 했습니다. 그가 책을 펴려고 할 때, 그는 목소리를 들었습니다.

5 누가 말하고 있는지 보기 위해 그는 책에서 눈을 들어 올려다보았습니다.

6 그는 그의 눈을 믿을 수 없었습니다. 말하는 것은 바로 자신의 개, Manny였습니다!

7 "눈을 감고 내 말을 따라 말하세요. 코기토 에르고 숨." Manny가 말했습니다.

8 "너는 말할 수 있니?" "그냥 따라 하세요! 코기토 에르고 숨."

9 파스칼은 그의 눈을 감고 그 단어들을 따라 말했습니다. 갑자기 그는 남자들이 소리치는 것을 들었습니다.

10 그가 눈을 떴을 때, 그는 말을 탄 병사들을 보았습니다.

11 그들은 손에 화살을 든 남자를 뒤쫓고 있었습니다. 그 남자는 파스칼을 보고 소리쳤습니다.

12 "네가 거기 서 있는 것은 너무 위험해. 이리 와."

13 The man _____ Pascal _____ his horse and _____ into the _____.

    A. onto   B. pulled   C. woods   D. rode

14 When they _____ at a house, the man _____ and _____ his horse.

    A. stopped   B. off   C. arrived   D. got

15 "Hello, _____ _____ _____ Robin Hood."

    A. is   B. name   C. my

16 "Wow! _____ you the Robin Hood _____ the _____?"

    A. from   B. are   C. book

17 "No, I'm the Robin Hood of Sherwood Forest. _____ are you and _____ are you _____?"

    A. why   B. who   C. here

18 "My name is Pascal. I don't know why I'm here, but there _____ be a _____. You saved me from the _____. Thank you so much. Is there _____ I can do for you?"

    A. reason   B. anything   C. soldiers   D. must

19 "Well, can you help us _____ _____ the money that the king _____ from the people? He _____ them too much.

    A. took   B. get   C. taxed   D. back

20 He is too _____ to _____ with the people, so they don't have _____ money to _____ food.

    A. buy   B. greedy   C. enough   D. share

21 I want to help them _____ their money _____. However, there are many soldiers in the tower, _____ no one can get _____."

    A. so   B. get   C. inside   D. back

22 "Hmm… I think I have a _____. But first, can you _____ me to the tower? I need to _____ the _____ of soldiers."

    A. take   B. number   C. solution   D. count

23 Robin and Pascal _____ _____ in a tree and _____ the soldiers one _____ one.

    A. by   B. hid   C. counted   D. up

24 "_____ _____ five soldiers _____ midnight _____ six in the morning.

    A. from   B. are   C. to   D. there

13 그 남자는 파스칼을 그의 말에 올려 태우고 숲으로 말을 몰았습니다.

14 그들이 한 집 앞에 이르렀을 때, 그 남자는 멈추고 말에서 내렸습니다.

15 "안녕, 내 이름은 로빈 후드야."

16 "와우! 당신이 책 속의 로빈 후드인가요?"

17 "아니. 나는 셔우드 숲의 로빈 후드야. 너는 누구이고 왜 여기에 있니?"

18 "제 이름은 파스칼이에요. 저는 제가 왜 여기 있는지 모르지만 이유가 분명 있을 거예요. 당신은 저를 병사들로부터 구해줬어요. 정말 감사드려요. 제가 당신을 위해 할 수 있는 것이 있을까요?"

19 "음. 우리가 왕이 사람들에게서 가져간 돈을 되찾는 것을 도와줄 수 있니? 그는 그들에게 세금을 너무 많이 부과했어.

20 그는 너무 탐욕스러워서 사람들과 나누지 않아. 그래서 그들은 음식을 살 충분한 돈이 없어.

21 나는 그들의 돈을 다시 찾을 수 있도록 돕고 싶어. 하지만 탑 안에 병사들이 많아서 아무도 들어갈 수 없어."

22 "흠… 제게 해결책이 있는 것 같아요. 그러나 우선 저를 탑에 데려가 주실 수 있나요? 저는 병사들의 수를 세야 해요."

23 로빈과 파스칼은 나무에 숨어서 병사들의 수를 한 명씩 세었습니다.

24 "자정부터 새벽 여섯 시까지는 다섯 명의 병사들이 있어요.

25 Next, there are _____ _____ _____ _____, and then there are eight soldiers until six in the evening.

    A. until   B. three   C. noon   D. soldiers

26 _____, there are twelve soldiers _____ midnight. So, you should go inside _____ six in the morning _____ noon."

    A. until   B. and   C. lastly   D. between

27 "What? I _____ _____ _____."

    A. get   B. don't   C. it

28 Pascal thought for a _____. 'Hmm… A graph _____ _____ this _____ to understand.'

    A. make   B. moment   C. easier   D. might

29 Pascal _____ a _____ and _____ it _____ Robin.

    A. to   B. graph   C. showed   D. drew

30 "Look, _____ _____ _____ time is between six in the evening and _____.

    A. dangerous   B. most   C. midnight   D. the

31 Four times more soldiers _____ at that time _____ from six in the morning until noon. Do you see _____ I _____?"

    A. than   B. what   C. work   D. mean

32 "Aha! I _____ _____ now. Thank you _____ _____, Pascal!"

    A. so   B. get   C. much   D. it

33 "You're welcome. Now I _____ the _____ of graphs. No one can say _____ we don't need them _____."

    A. that   B. realize   C. anymore   D. importance

34 Pascal _____ _____ of the woods. When he looked _____, he saw Robin Hood _____ at him.

    A. waving   B. out   C. back   D. walked

35 Pascal _____ _____ and said to _____, "It was a great _____. How do I go back? Oh, I know. I should say the words *Cogito ergo sum*!"

    A. back   B. himself   C. waved   D. adventure

25 그다음, 정오까지는 세 명의 병사들이 있고, 오후 여섯 시까지는 여덟 명의 병사들이 있어요.

26 마지막으로, 자정까지는 열두 명의 병사들이 있어요. 그래서 당신은 새벽 여섯 시에서 정오 사이에 들어가야 해요."

27 "뭐라고? 나는 이해하지 못했어."

28 파스칼은 잠시 생각에 잠겼습니다. '흠…그래프가 이것을 이해하는 것을 쉽게 해 줄지도 몰라.'

29 파스칼은 그래프를 그려서 그것을 로빈에게 보여주었습니다.

30 "보세요, 가장 위험한 시간은 저녁 여섯 시에서 자정까지예요.

31 오전 여섯 시부터 정오까지보다 그 시간에 네 배나 더 많은 병사들이 일해요. 제 말이 무슨 뜻인지 아시겠어요?"

32 "아하! 이제 이해했어. 너무 고마워, 파스칼!"

33 "천만에요. 이제 저는 그래프의 중요성을 깨달았어요. 아무도 그래프가 더 이상 필요 없다고 말할 수 없을 거예요."

34 파스칼은 숲에서 걸어 나왔습니다. 그가 뒤돌아봤을 때, 그는 로빈 후드가 그에게 손을 흔들고 있는 것을 보았습니다.

35 파스칼은 손을 흔들어 답하고 혼잣말을 했습니다. "정말 멋진 모험이었어. 나는 어떻게 돌아가지? 오, 알겠어. 나는 코기토 에르고 숨이라는 말을 해야 해!"

※ 다음 우리말과 일치하도록 빈칸에 알맞은 것을 골라 쓰시오.

1 Pascal _____ _____ _____ _____ _____ in his room. He was _____ _____ graphs.

2 "It's _____ _____ _____ _____ _____ and _____ graphs. Why do I need _____ anyway? No one _____ _____ in _____ _____."

3 He _____ _____ his pen and _____ _____ his favorite book, *Robin Hood*.

4 He _____ _____ _____ _____ _____ to sleep. When he _____ _____ _____ _____ _____ the book, he _____ a voice.

5 He _____ _____ _____ the book _____ _____ _____ _____ _____.

6 He couldn't believe his eyes. It was his dog, Manny, _____ _____ talking!

7 "_____ your eyes and _____ _____ me. *Cogito ergo sum*," said Manny.

8 "_____ _____ _____?" "Just _____! *Cogito ergo sum*."

9 Pascal closed his eyes and _____ _____ _____ _____. _____, he _____ men _____.

10 _____ he opened his eyes, he saw soldiers _____ _____.

11 They were _____ a man _____ _____ in his hand. The man saw Pascal and _____.

12 "_____ too dangerous _____ there. Come on."

13 The man _____ Pascal _____ his horse and _____ into the woods.

14 When they _____ _____ a house, the man _____ and _____ _____ his horse.

15 "Hello, _____ _____ Robin Hood."

16 "Wow! Are you _____ _____ _____ _____ the book?"

17 "No, I'm the Robin Hood of Sherwood Forest. _____ _____ _____ and why _____ _____ here?"

18 "My name is Pascal. I don't know _____ _____ _____ _____, but there _____ _____ a reason. You _____ me _____ the soldiers. Thank you so much. _____ _____ _____ _____ I can do _____ you?"

1 파스칼은 그의 방에서 수학 숙제를 하고 있었습니다. 그는 그 래프 문제에 고군분투하고 있었 습니다.

2 "그래프를 읽고 그리는 것은 너 무 어려워. 게다가 내가 왜 그래 프가 필요하겠어? 아무도 실제 생활에서는 그래프가 필요하지 않아."

3 그는 그의 펜을 내려놓고, 그가 가장 좋아하는 책, '로빈 후드'를 집어 들었습니다.

4 그는 책을 읽으며 잠들기로 했습 니다. 그가 책을 펴려고 할 때, 그는 목소리를 들었습니다.

5 누가 말하고 있는지 보기 위해 그는 책에서 눈을 들어 올려다 보았습니다.

6 그는 그의 눈을 믿을 수 없었습 니다. 말하는 것은 바로 자신의 개, Manny였습니다!

7 "눈을 감고 내 말을 따라 말 하세요. 코기토 에르고 숨." Manny가 말했습니다.

8 "너는 말할 수 있니?" "그냥 따 라 하세요! 코기토 에르고 숨."

9 파스칼은 그의 눈을 감고 그 단 어들을 따라 말했습니다. 갑자 기 그는 남자들이 소리치는 것 을 들었습니다.

10 그가 눈을 떴을 때, 그는 말을 탄 병사들을 보았습니다.

11 그들은 손에 화살을 든 남자를 뒤쫓고 있었습니다. 그 남자는 파스칼을 보고 소리쳤습니다.

12 "네가 거기 서 있는 것은 너무 위험해. 이리 와."

13 그 남자는 파스칼을 그의 말에 올려 태우고 숲으로 말을 몰았 습니다.

14 그들이 한 집 앞에 이르렀을 때, 그 남자는 멈추고 말에서 내렸 습니다.

15 "안녕, 내 이름은 로빈 후드야."

16 "와우! 당신이 책 속의 로빈 후 드인가요?"

17 "아니, 나는 셔우드 숲의 로빈 후드야. 너는 누구이고 왜 여기 에 있니?"

18 "제 이름은 파스칼이에요. 저는 제가 왜 여기 있는지 모르지만 이 유가 분명 있을 거예요. 당신은 저를 병사들로부터 구해줬어요. 정말 감사드려요. 제가 당신을 위 해 할 수 있는 것이 있을까요?"

19 "Well, can you help us _____ _____ the money _____ the king _____ from the people? He _____ _____ too much.

20 He is _____ _____ _____ _____ with the people, so they don't have _____ _____ _____ _____ food.

21 I want to _____ _____ _____ their money _____. _____, there are many soldiers in the tower, so _____ _____ _____ _____ _____."

22 "Hmm… I think I have a solution. But first, can you _____ _____ _____ _____ _____ _____? I need to _____ _____ _____ _____ soldiers."

23 Robin and Pascal _____ _____ in a tree and _____ the soldiers _____ _____ _____.

24 "_____ _____ five soldiers _____ midnight _____ six in the morning.

25 Next, there are _____ _____ _____ _____ _____, and then there are _____ _____ _____ six in the evening.

26 _____, _____ _____ twelve soldiers _____ midnight. So, you should _____ _____ _____ six in the morning _____ _____."

27 "What? I _____ _____ _____."

28 Pascal thought for a _____. 'Hmm… A graph _____ _____ _____ _____ _____ understand.'

29 Pascal _____ a graph and _____ _____ to Robin.

30 "Look, _____ _____ _____ _____ _____ is _____ six in the evening _____ midnight.

31 _____ _____ _____ _____ _____ work at that time _____ from six in the morning _____ noon. Do you see _____ _____ _____?"

32 "Aha! I _____ _____ now. Thank you _____ _____, Pascal!"

33 "You're welcome. Now I _____ _____ _____ _____ _____. _____ _____ can say _____ we don't need _____ anymore."

34 Pascal _____ _____ _____ the woods. When he _____ _____, he saw Robin Hood _____ at him.

35 Pascal _____ _____ and said to _____, "It was a great _____. How _____ _____ _____ _____ _____? Oh, I know. I _____ the words *Cogito ergo sum*!"

19 "음, 우리가 왕이 사람들에게서 가져간 돈을 되찾는 것을 도와줄 수 있니? 그는 그들에게 세금을 너무 많이 부과했어.

20 그는 너무 탐욕스러워서 사람들과 나누지 않아, 그래서 그들은 음식을 살 충분한 돈이 없어.

21 나는 그들의 돈을 다시 찾을 수 있도록 돕고 싶어. 하지만 탑 안에 병사들이 많아서 아무도 들어갈 수 없어."

22 "흠… 제게 해결책이 있는 것 같아요. 그러나 우선 저를 탑에 데려가 주실 수 있나요? 저는 병사들의 수를 세야 해요."

23 로빈과 파스칼은 나무에 숨어서 병사들의 수를 한 명씩 세었습니다.

24 "자정부터 새벽 여섯 시까지는 다섯 명의 병사들이 있어요.

25 그다음, 정오까지는 세 명의 병사들이 있고, 오후 여섯 시까지는 여덟 명의 병사들이 있어요.

26 마지막으로, 자정까지는 열두 명의 병사들이 있어요. 그래서 당신은 새벽 여섯 시에서 정오 사이에 들어가야 해요."

27 "뭐라고? 나는 이해하지 못했어."

28 파스칼은 잠시 생각에 잠겼습니다. '흠…그래프가 이것을 이해하는 것을 쉽게 해 줄지도 몰라.'

29 파스칼은 그래프를 그려서 그것을 로빈에게 보여주었습니다.

30 "보세요, 가장 위험한 시간은 저녁 여섯 시에서 자정까지예요.

31 오전 여섯 시부터 정오까지보다 그 시간에 네 배나 더 많은 병사들이 일해요. 제 말이 무슨 뜻인지 아시겠어요?"

32 "아하! 이제 이해했어. 너무 고마워, 파스칼!"

33 "천만에요. 이제 저는 그래프의 중요성을 깨달았어요. 아무도 그래프가 더 이상 필요 없다고 말할 수 없을 거예요."

34 파스칼은 숲에서 걸어 나왔습니다. 그가 뒤돌아봤을 때, 그는 로빈 후드가 그에게 손을 흔들고 있는 것을 보았습니다.

35 파스칼은 손을 흔들어 답하고 혼잣말을 했습니다. "정말 멋진 모험이었어. 나는 어떻게 돌아가지? 오, 알겠어. 나는 코기토 에르고 숨이라는 말을 해야 해!"

※ 다음 문장을 우리말로 쓰시오.

1 Pascal was doing his math homework in his room. He was struggling with graphs.
➡ _____

2 "It's too hard to read and draw graphs. Why do I need these anyway? No one needs graphs in real life."
➡ _____
_____

3 He put down his pen and picked up his favorite book, *Robin Hood*.
➡ _____

4 He decided to read himself to sleep. When he was about to open the book, he heard a voice.
➡ _____

5 He looked up from the book to see who was talking.
➡ _____

6 He couldn't believe his eyes. It was his dog, Manny, who was talking!
➡ _____

7 "Close your eyes and repeat after me. *Cogito ergo sum*," said Manny.
➡ _____

8 "You can talk?" "Just repeat! *Cogito ergo sum*."
➡ _____

9 Pascal closed his eyes and repeated the words. Suddenly, he heard men shouting.
➡ _____

10 When he opened his eyes, he saw soldiers on horses.
➡ _____

11 They were chasing a man with arrows in his hand. The man saw Pascal and shouted.
➡ _____

12 "It's too dangerous for you to stand there. Come on."
➡ _____

13 The man pulled Pascal onto his horse and rode into the woods.
➡ _____

14 When they arrived at a house, the man stopped and got off his horse.
➡ _____

15 "Hello, my name is Robin Hood."
➡ _____

16 "Wow! Are you the Robin Hood from the book?"
➡ _____

17 "No, I'm the Robin Hood of Sherwood Forest. Who are you and why are you here?"
➡ _____

18 "My name is Pascal. I don't know why I'm here, but there must be a reason. You saved me from the soldiers. Thank you so much. Is there anything I can do for you?"
➡ _____
_____

19 "Well, can you help us get back the money that the king took from the people? He taxed them too much.

➡ _____

20 He is too greedy to share with the people, so they don't have enough money to buy food.

➡ _____

21 I want to help them get their money back. However, there are many soldiers in the tower, so no one can get inside."

➡ _____

22 "Hmm... I think I have a solution. But first, can you take me to the tower? I need to count the number of soldiers."

➡ _____

23 Robin and Pascal hid up in a tree and counted the soldiers one by one.

➡ _____

24 "There are five soldiers from midnight to six in the morning.

➡ _____

25 Next, there are three soldiers until noon, and then there are eight soldiers until six in the evening.

➡ _____

26 Lastly, there are twelve soldiers until midnight. So, you should go inside between six in the morning and noon."

➡ _____

27 "What? I don't get it."

➡ _____

28 Pascal thought for a moment. 'Hmm... A graph might make this easier to understand.'

➡ _____

29 Pascal drew a graph and showed it to Robin.

➡ _____

30 "Look, the most dangerous time is between six in the evening and midnight.

➡ _____

31 Four times more soldiers work at that time than from six in the morning until noon. Do you see what I mean?"

➡ _____

32 "Aha! I get it now. Thank you so much, Pascal!"

➡ _____

33 "You're welcome. Now I realize the importance of graphs. No one can say that we don't need them anymore."

➡ _____

34 Pascal walked out of the woods. When he looked back, he saw Robin Hood waving at him.

➡ _____

35 Pascal waved back and said to himself, "It was a great adventure. How do I go back? Oh, I know. I should say the words *Cogito ergo sum*!"

➡ _____

_____

※ 다음 괄호 안의 단어들을 우리말에 맞도록 바르게 배열하시오.

1 (was / Pascal / his / doing / homework / math / his / in / room. // was / he / with / struggling / graphs.)

➡ _____

_____

2 (too / "it's / to / hard / and / read / graphs. / draw // do / why / need / I / anyway? / these // one / no / graphs / needs / real / in / life.")

➡ _____

_____

3 (put / he / down / pen / his / and / up / picked / favorite / his / Robin / book, / Hood.)

➡ _____

4 (decided / he / read / to / to / himself / sleep. // he / when / about / was / open / to / book, / the / heard / he / voice. / a)

➡ _____

_____

5 (looked / he / up / the / from / to / book / who / see / talking. / was)

➡ _____

6 (couldn't / he / believe / eyes. / his // was / it / dog, / his / who / Manny, / talking! / was)

➡ _____

7 (your / "close / and / eyes / after / repeat / me. // *ergo* / *Cogito* / *sum*," / Manny / said)

➡ _____

8 (can / "you / talk?" // repeat! / "just / *ergo* / *Cogito* / *sum*.")

➡ _____

9 (closed / Pascal / eyes / his / and / the / repeated / words. // he / suddenly, / heard / shouting. / men)

➡ _____

_____

10 (he / when / his / opened / eyes, / saw / he / on / soldiers / horses.)

➡ _____

11 (were / they / a / chasing / man / arrows / with / his / in / hand. // man / the / Pascal / saw / shouted. / and)

➡ _____

_____

12 (too / "it's / dangerous / you / to / for / stand / there. // on." / come)

➡ _____

_____

1 파스칼은 그의 방에서 수학 숙제를 하고 있었습니다. 그는 그래프 문제에 고군분투하고 있었습니다.

2 "그래프를 읽고 그리는 것은 너무 어려워. 게다가 내가 왜 그래프가 필요하겠어? 아무도 실제 생활에서는 그래프가 필요하지 않아."

3 그는 그의 펜을 내려놓고, 그가 가장 좋아하는 책, '로빈 후드'를 집어 들었습니다.

4 그는 책을 읽으며 잠들기로 했습니다. 그가 책을 펴려고 할 때, 그는 목소리를 들었습니다.

5 누가 말하고 있는지 보기 위해 그는 책에서 눈을 들어 올려다보았습니다.

6 그는 그의 눈을 믿을 수 없었습니다. 말하는 것은 바로 자신의 개, Manny였습니다!

7 "눈을 감고 내 말을 따라 말하세요. 코기토 에르고 숨." Manny가 말했습니다.

8 "너는 말할 수 있니?" "그냥 따라 하세요! 코기토 에르고 숨."

9 파스칼은 그의 눈을 감고 그 단어들을 따라 말했습니다. 갑자기 그는 남자들이 소리치는 것을 들었습니다.

10 그가 눈을 떴을 때, 그는 말을 탄 병사들을 보았습니다.

11 그들은 손에 화살을 든 남자를 뒤쫓고 있었습니다. 그 남자는 파스칼을 보고 소리쳤습니다.

12 "네가 거기 서 있는 것은 너무 위험해. 이리 와."

13 (man / the / Pascal / pulled / his / onto / and / horse / the / into / rode / woods.)

➡ _____

14 (they / when / arrived / a / at / house, / man / the / and / stopped / got / his / off / horse.)

➡ _____

15 ("hello, / name / my / Robin / is / Hood.")

➡ _____

16 ("wow! // you / are / Robin / the / from / Hood / book?" / the)

➡ _____

17 (I'm / "no, / the / Hood / Robin / Sherwood / of / Forest. // are / who / and / you / why / you / here?" / are)

➡ _____

18 (name / "my / Pascal. // is / don't / I / why / know / here, / I'm / there / but / be / must / reason. / a // saved / you / me / the / from / soldiers. // you / thank / much. / so // there / is / I / anything / do / can / you?" / for)

➡ _____

➡ _____

19 (can / "well, / help / you / get / us / the / back / money / the / that / king / from / took / people? / the // taxed / he / too / them / much.)

➡ _____

20 (is / he / greedy / too / share / to / the / with / people, / they / so / have / don't / money / enough / buy / to / food.)

➡ _____

21 (want / I / help / to / get / them / money / their / back. // there / however, / many / are / soldiers / the / in / tower, / no / so / one / get / can / inside.")

➡ _____

22 ("hmm... / think / I / have / solution. / a // first, / but / you / can / me / take / the / to / tower? // need / I / count / to / number / the / soldiers.")

➡ _____

➡ _____

23 (Pascal / and / Robin / up / hid / a / in / tree / and / the / counted / one / soldiers / one. / by)

➡ _____

24 (are / "there / soldiers / five / midnight / from / six / to / the / in / morning.)

➡ _____

13 그 남자는 파스칼을 그의 말에 올려 태우고 숲으로 말을 몰았습니다.

14 그들이 한 집 앞에 이르렀을 때, 그 남자는 멈추고 말에서 내렸습니다.

15 "안녕, 내 이름은 로빈 후드야."

16 "와우! 당신이 책 속의 로빈 후드인가요?"

17 "아니, 나는 셔우드 숲의 로빈 후드야. 너는 누구이고 왜 여기에 있니?"

18 "제 이름은 파스칼이에요. 저는 제가 왜 여기 있는지 모르지만 이 유가 분명 있을 거예요. 당신은 저를 병사들로부터 구해줬어요. 정말 감사드려요. 제가 당신을 위해 할 수 있는 것이 있을까요?"

19 "음, 우리가 왕이 사람들에게서 가져간 돈을 되찾는 것을 도와줄 수 있니? 그는 그들에게 세금을 너무 많이 부과했어.

20 그는 너무 탐욕스러워서 사람들과 나누지 않아. 그래서 그들은 음식을 살 충분한 돈이 없어.

21 나는 그들의 돈을 다시 찾을 수 있도록 돕고 싶어. 하지만 탑 안에 병사들이 많아서 아무도 들어갈 수 없어."

22 "흠… 제게 해결책이 있는 것 같아요. 그러나 우선 저를 탑에 데려가 주실 수 있나요? 저는 병사들의 수를 세야 해요."

23 로빈과 파스칼은 나무에 숨어서 병사들의 수를 한 명씩 세었습니다.

24 "자정부터 새벽 여섯 시까지는 다섯 명의 병사들이 있어요.

25 (there / next, / three / are / until / soldiers / noon, / then / and / are / there / soldiers / eight / six / until / the / evening. / in)

➡ _____

_____

26 (there / lastly, / twelve / are / until / soldiers / midnight. // you / so, / go / should / between / inside / in / six / morning / the / noon." / and)

➡ _____

_____

27 ("what? // don't / I / it." / get)

➡ _____

28 (thought / Pascal / a / for / moment. // 'hmm... // graph / a / make / might / easier / this / understand.')

➡ _____

_____

29 (drew / Pascal / graph / a / and / it / showed / Robin. / to)

➡ _____

30 (the / "look, / most / time / dangerous / between / is / in / six / evening / the / midnight. / and)

➡ _____

_____

31 (times / four / soldiers / more / at / work / time / that / from / than / in / six / morning / the / noon. / until // you / do / what / see / mean?" / I)

➡ _____

_____

32 ("aha! // I / it / get / now. // you / thank / much / Pascal!" / so)

➡ _____

33 (welcome. / "you're // I / now / the / realize / of / importance / graphs. // one / no / say / can / that / don't / we / them / need / anymore.")

➡ _____

_____

34 (walked / Pascal / of / out / woods. / the // he / when / back, / looked / saw / he / Hood / Robin / at / waving / him.)

➡ _____

_____

35 (waved / Pascal / said / and / back / himself, / to / was / "it / great / a / adventure. // do / how / I / back? // I / oh, / know. // should / I / the / say / words / *ergo* / *Cogito* / *sum*!")

➡ _____

_____

_____

---

25 그다음, 정오까지는 세 명의 병사들이 있고, 오후 여섯 시까지는 여덟 명의 병사들이 있어요.

26 마지막으로, 자정까지는 열두 명의 병사들이 있어요. 그래서 당신은 새벽 여섯 시에서 정오 사이에 들어가야 해요."

27 "뭐라고? 나는 이해하지 못했어."

28 파스칼은 잠시 생각에 잠겼습니다. '흠…그래프가 이것을 이해하는 것을 쉽게 해 줄지도 몰라.'

29 파스칼은 그래프를 그려서 그것을 로빈에게 보여주었습니다.

30 "보세요, 가장 위험한 시간은 저녁 여섯 시에서 자정까지예요.

31 오전 여섯 시부터 정오까지보다 그 시간에 네 배나 더 많은 병사들이 일해요. 제 말이 무슨 뜻인지 아시겠어요?"

32 "아하! 이제 이해했어. 너무 고마워, 파스칼!"

33 "천만에요. 이제 저는 그래프의 중요성을 깨달았어요. 아무도 그래프가 더 이상 필요 없다고 말할 수 없을 거예요."

34 파스칼은 숲에서 걸어 나왔습니다. 그가 뒤돌아봤을 때, 그는 로빈 후드가 그에게 손을 흔들고 있는 것을 보았습니다.

35 파스칼은 손을 흔들어 답하고 혼잣말을 했습니다. "정말 멋진 모험이었어. 나는 어떻게 돌아가지? 오, 알겠어. 나는 코기토 에르고 숨이라는 말을 해야 해!"

※ 다음 우리말을 영어로 쓰시오.

1 파스칼은 그의 방에서 수학 숙제를 하고 있었습니다. 그는 그래프 문제에 고군분투하고 있었습니다.
➡ _____

2 "그래프를 읽고 그리는 것은 너무 어려워. 게다가 내가 왜 그래프가 필요하겠어? 아무도 실제 생활에서는 그래프가 필요하지 않아."
➡ _____
_____

3 그는 그의 펜을 내려놓고, 그가 가장 좋아하는 책, '로빈 후드'를 집어 들었습니다.
➡ _____

4 그는 책을 읽으며 잠들기로 했습니다. 그가 책을 펴려고 할 때, 그는 목소리를 들었습니다.
➡ _____

5 누가 말하고 있는지 보기 위해 그는 책에서 눈을 들어 올려다보았습니다.
➡ _____

6 그는 그의 눈을 믿을 수 없었습니다. 말하는 것은 바로 자신의 개, Manny였습니다!
➡ _____

7 "눈을 감고 내 말을 따라 말하세요. *코기토 에르고 숨.*" Manny가 말했습니다.
➡ _____

8 "너는 말할 수 있니?" "그냥 따라 하세요! *코기토 에르고 숨.*"
➡ _____

9 파스칼은 그의 눈을 감고 그 단어들을 따라 말했습니다. 갑자기 그는 남자들이 소리치는 것을 들었습니다.
➡ _____

10 그가 눈을 떴을 때, 그는 말을 탄 병사들을 보았습니다.
➡ _____

11 그들은 손에 화살을 든 남자를 뒤쫓고 있었습니다. 그 남자는 파스칼을 보고 소리쳤습니다.
➡ _____

12 "네가 거기 서 있는 것은 너무 위험해. 이리 와."
➡ _____

13 그 남자는 파스칼을 그의 말에 올려 태우고 숲으로 말을 몰았습니다.
➡ _____

14 그들이 한 집 앞에 이르렀을 때, 그 남자는 멈추고 말에서 내렸습니다.
➡ _____

15 "안녕, 내 이름은 로빈 후드야."
➡ _____

16 "와우! 당신이 책 속의 로빈 후드인가요?"
➡ _____

17 "아니, 나는 셔우드 숲의 로빈 후드야. 너는 누구이고 왜 여기에 있니?"
➡ _____

18 "제 이름은 파스칼이에요. 저는 제가 왜 여기 있는지 모르지만 이유가 분명 있을 거예요. 당신은 저를 병사들로부터 구해줬어요. 정말 감사드려요. 제가 당신을 위해 할 수 있는 것이 있을까요?"
➡ _____
_____

19 "음, 우리가 왕이 사람들에게서 가져간 돈을 되찾는 것을 도와줄 수 있니? 그는 그들에게 세금을 너무 많이 부과했어.
➡ _____

20 그는 너무 탐욕스러워서 사람들과 나누지 않아. 그래서 그들은 음식을 살 충분한 돈이 없어.
➡ _____

21 나는 그들의 돈을 다시 찾을 수 있도록 돕고 싶어. 하지만 탑 안에 병사들이 많아서 아무도 들어갈 수 없어."
➡ _____

22 "흠… 제게 해결책이 있는 것 같아요. 그러나 우선 저를 탑에 데려가 주실 수 있나요? 저는 병사들의 수를 세야 해요."
➡ _____

23 로빈과 파스칼은 나무에 숨어서 병사들의 수를 한 명씩 세었습니다.
➡ _____

24 "자정부터 새벽 여섯 시까지는 다섯 명의 병사들이 있어요.
➡ _____

25 그다음, 정오까지는 세 명의 병사들이 있고, 오후 여섯 시까지는 여덟 명의 병사들이 있어요.
➡ _____

26 마지막으로, 자정까지는 열두 명의 병사들이 있어요. 그래서 당신은 새벽 여섯 시에서 정오 사이에 들어가야 해요."
➡ _____

27 "뭐라고? 나는 이해하지 못했어."
➡ _____

28 파스칼은 잠시 생각에 잠겼습니다. '흠… 그래프가 이것을 이해하는 것을 쉽게 해 줄지도 몰라.'
➡ _____

29 파스칼은 그래프를 그려서 그것을 로빈에게 보여주었습니다.
➡ _____

30 "보세요, 가장 위험한 시간은 저녁 여섯 시에서 자정까지예요.
➡ _____

31 오전 여섯 시부터 정오까지보다 그 시간에 네 배나 더 많은 병사들이 일해요. 제 말이 무슨 뜻인지 아시겠어요?"
➡ _____

32 "아하! 이제 이해했어. 너무 고마워, 파스칼!"
➡ _____

33 "천만에요. 이제 저는 그래프의 중요성을 깨달았어요. 아무도 그래프가 더 이상 필요 없다고 말할 수 없을 거예요."
➡ _____

34 파스칼은 숲에서 걸어 나왔습니다. 그가 뒤돌아봤을 때, 그는 로빈 후드가 그에게 손을 흔들고 있는 것을 보았습니다.
➡ _____

35 파스칼은 손을 흔들어 답하고 혼잣말을 했습니다. "정말 멋진 모험이었어. 나는 어떻게 돌아가지? 오, 알겠어. 나는 코기토 에르고 숨이라는 말을 해야 해!"
➡ _____
_____

※ 다음 우리말과 일치하도록 빈칸에 알맞은 말을 쓰시오.

Communication Task

1. I did a survey on the books _____ _____ _____ _____ _____ _____.

2. _____ _____ says _____ thirteen _____ _____ twenty students _____ _____.

3. That is _____ _____ of the _____.

4. _____ _____ _____ _____ _____ _____ chose _____ _____.

5. _____, only _____ _____ _____ _____ _____ chose history books.

6. From this _____ _____, _____ _____ the school library _____ _____ _____ _____.

7. Do you see _____ I _____?

1. 나는 우리 학교 도서관에 필요한 책들을 조사했다.
2. 그 결과 20명 중 13명이 소설을 선택하였다.
3. 이는 전체의 65퍼센트이다.
4. 20명 중 5명은 공상 과학 책을 선택했다.
5. 그러나 20명 중 2명만이 역사책을 선택했다.
6. 이러한 조사 결과를 통해 학교 도서관은 더 많은 소설을 구해야 한다고 생각한다.
7. 무슨 뜻인지 알겠니?

Before You Read B Look and Write

1. Book Club: Your _____
2. _____: *Robin Hood*
3. Topic of the book: It's about _____ _____ _____ _____ _____ _____ people from the _____ _____.
4. My favorite character: My favorite character is Robin Hood _____ he _____ _____ _____ _____ _____ _____.
5. _____ _____ of the book: _____ bad _____ too much. _____ _____, _____ _____ _____ _____ _____ _____ _____ the most.

1. 책 동아리: 너의 후기들
2. 제목: 로빈 후드
3. 책의 주제: 욕심 많은 왕으로부터 사람을 구하려 고군분투하는 한 남자의 이야기이다.
4. 내가 가장 좋아하는 등장인물: 병사들보다 화살을 더 잘 쏘기 때문에 내가 가장 좋아하는 등장인물은 로빈 후드이다.
5. 책에 대한 나의 논평: 세금을 너무 많이 부과하는 것은 나쁘다. 결국, 돈이 아니라 사람이 가장 중요하다.

Let's Write

1. _____ _____ the _____ _____ on "Who is your favorite character?"

2. Fifteen _____ _____ thirty students chose Hong Gildong.

3. _____ _____ _____, fifty percent of the students _____ _____ _____.

4. I think _____ _____ the _____ _____ _____.

5. _____, _____ _____ _____ Kongiwi and six students chose Robin Hood.

6. _____ _____ chose Nolbu. Maybe _____ _____ the character is _____ be liked _____ _____.

1. '당신이 가장 좋아하는 등장인물은 누구입니까?'라는 설문 조사 결과를 보자.
2. 30명의 학생들 중 15명이 홍길동을 선택했다.
3. 다시 말하면, 학생들 중 50퍼센트가 그 등장인물을 선택했다.
4. 내 생각에 그것은 그 등장인물이 용감하기 때문이다.
5. 그다음에 9명의 학생들이 콩쥐를 선택했고, 6명의 학생들이 로빈 후드를 선택했다.
6. 아무도 놀부를 선택하지 않았다. 아마도 그것은 그 등장인물이 다른 사람들이 좋아하기에 너무 탐욕스럽기 때문일 것이다

※ 다음 우리말을 영어로 쓰시오.

Communication Task

1. 나는 우리 학교 도서관에 필요한 책들을 조사했다.
   ➡ _____

2. 그 결과 20명 중 13명이 소설을 선택하였다.
   ➡ _____

3. 이는 전체의 65퍼센트이다.
   ➡ _____

4. 20명 중 5명은 공상 과학 책을 선택했다.
   ➡ _____

5. 그러나 20명 중 2명만이 역사책을 선택했다.
   ➡ _____

6. 이러한 조사 결과를 통해 학교 도서관은 더 많은 소설을 구해야 한다고 생각한다.
   ➡ _____

7. 무슨 뜻인지 알겠니?
   ➡ _____

Before You Read B Look and Write

1. 책 동아리: 너의 후기들
   ➡ _____

2. 제목: 로빈 후드
   ➡ _____

3. 책의 주제: 욕심 많은 왕으로부터 사람을 구하려 고군분투하는 한 남자의 이야기이다.
   ➡ _____

4. 내가 가장 좋아하는 등장인물: 병사들보다 화살을 더 잘 쏘기 때문에 내가 가장 좋아하는 등장인물은 로빈 후드이다.
   ➡ _____

5. 책에 대한 나의 논평: 세금을 너무 많이 부과하는 것은 나쁘다. 결국, 돈이 아니라 사람이 가장 중요하다.
   ➡ _____

Let's Write

1. '당신이 가장 좋아하는 등장인물은 누구입니까?'라는 설문 조사 결과를 보자.
   ➡ _____

2. 30명의 학생들 중 15명이 홍길동을 선택했다.
   ➡ _____

3. 다시 말하면, 학생들 중 50퍼센트가 그 등장인물을 선택했다.
   ➡ _____

4. 내 생각에 그것은 그 등장인물이 용감하기 때문이다.
   ➡ _____

5. 그다음에 9명의 학생들이 콩쥐를 선택했고, 6명의 학생들이 로빈 후드를 선택했다.
   ➡ _____

6. 아무도 놀부를 선택하지 않았다. 아마도 그것은 그 등장인물이 다른 사람들이 좋아하기에 너무 탐욕스럽기 때문일 것이다.
   ➡ _____

MEMO

영어 기출 문제집

적중100

2학기

정답 및 해설

지학 | 민찬규

중 3

적중100

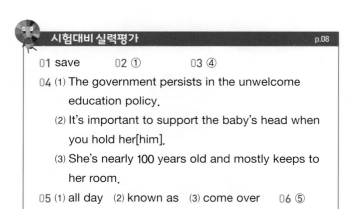

Homes Everywhere

시험대비 실력평가
p.08

01 save   02 ①   03 ④

04 (1) The government persists in the unwelcome education policy.
  (2) It's important to support the baby's head when you hold her[him].
  (3) She's nearly 100 years old and mostly keeps to her room.

05 (1) all day (2) known as (3) come over   06 ⑤

01 hidden(숨겨진)과 concealed(숨겨진)은 동의어 관계에 있는 단어들이다. 따라서 store(저장하다, 보관하다)와 동의어 관계에 있는 단어로는 save(모으다, 저축하다)가 있다.

02 '언덕이나 다른 높이 올라 있는 곳이 없는, 평평한'이라는 영영풀이가 가리키는 단어는 ① flat(평평한)이다.

03 ④ take는 '~을 타다'라는 뜻이 아닌 '가져가다'라는 뜻으로 사용되었다.

04 (1) unwelcome 반갑지 않은 (2) support 지탱하다, 떠받치다 (3) mostly 주로, 일반적으로

05 (1) all day 하루 종일 (2) be known as ~로서 알려지다 (3) come over 들르다

06 hand down ~을 물려주다 / upside down 거꾸로 된, 뒤집힌 / stop A from ~ing A가 ~하지 못하게 막다 / prevent A from ~ing A가 ~하지 못하게 막다

서술형 시험대비
p.09

01 install

02 disappear

03 (1) walk around (2) pull up (3) make sense

04 handed down

05 (1) I cannot imagine why they want to leave.
  (2) New towns were designed to house Seoul's over-population.
  (3) The children playing in the garden appear happy today.

06 (1) Many people usually go to work by bike in Berlin.
  (2) I often like to be on my own.
  (3) What I mostly do during the weekend is reading.

01 '장비나 가구를 사용할 수 있도록 제자리에 고정시키다'라는 뜻을 가진 단어는 install(설치하다)이다.

02 enter(~에 들어가다)와 exit(나가다, 퇴거하다)는 반의어 관계에 있는 단어들이다. 따라서 appear(보이다, 나타나다)와 반의어 관계에 있는 단어는 disappear(사라지다)이다.

03 (1) walk around 돌아다니다 (2) pull up A A를 당겨 올리다 (3) make sense 이치에 맞다

04 hand down ~을 물려주다

05 (1) imagine 상상하다, 짐작하다 (2) house 수용하다 (3) appear 보이다, 나타나다

06 (1) usually 보통, 대개 (2) often 종종 (3) mostly 주로, 일반적으로

교과서 Conversation

핵심 Check
p.10~11

1 ⑤

2 (A) could have   (B) would turn

01 I wish 뒤에는 could를 이용해 현재 사실과 반대되는 내용, 혹은 가능성이 없는 일을 가정한다. 따라서 ⑤ I wish I could have가 정답이다.

02 현재 사실과 반대되는 사실에 대해 가정하는 문장이므로 가정법 과거를 쓴다. 또한 'What would you do ~?'라고 물어봤기 때문에 대답할 때는 'I would ~'라고 답한다.

교과서 대화문 익히기

Check(√) True or False
p.12

1 T 2 F 3 T 4 T

교과서 확인학습
p.15~17

Listen and Speak 1 A

Have, traveling / want, see / take / unique / living / those / to, hope, some day / too

Listen and Speak 1 B

it, / Why, waiting for / wait, out / check / could / kidding, place / build, stay, vacation / Living, sounds these, natural / try / Which, most, live in / strong

Listen and Speak 2 A-1

What / kind / like / what, lived / travel / cool

Listen and Speak 2 A-2

became / build / kind / build / covered / mirrors, invisible / would

Listen and Speak 2 A-3

upside / interesting / easy, upside down / What / like, differently

Listen and Speak 2 B

need, visit / Which / case / would, visited / interested / that, designed / how, inspired / How

Listen and Speak 2 C

What / turn into, able to fly

Real Life Communication A

living, exciting / some / full, could live / would, lived / explore / where, cave / Then, dangerous animals / makes

Real Life Communication B

stay, during / would, were / every day, fishing / sounds

Let's Check 1

This, What / unique, lived / interest, deep sea, explore, unique / That

Let's Check 2

matter, have

시험대비 기본평가   p.18

01 I wish I could try living there.   02 ④
03 I wish I could
04 B wants to live in the stone house most.

01 I wish 뒤에는 could를 이용해 현재 사실과 반대되는 내용, 혹은 가능성이 없는 일을 가정한다. try ~ing 시험삼아 ~해 보다

02 ④ 'G가 언제 터키를 방문할 계획인지'는 위 대화에서 언급되지 않았다.

03 'I wish I could ~.'는 '내가 ~할 수 있으면 좋겠다.'라는 뜻으로, 바람이나 소원을 나타내는 표현이다. I wish 뒤에는 사실과 반대되거나 가능성이 거의 없는 일이 온다.

04 A의 질문에 B가 돌로 만든 집에서 살고 싶다고 대화 후반에 언급했다.

시험대비 실력평가   p.19~20

01 ⓔinterested → interesting
02 What would you do if you visited Spain?
03 inspire
04 (A) lived   (B) would travel
05 ④   06 ①   07 ④   08 ③
09 Then I would be safe from dangerous animals.
10 ②
11 What would you do if you could have a magical power?

01 interest는 '흥미롭게 하다'라는 뜻을 가진 동사로, 어떤 사물이나 사실이 흥미로울 때는 interesting(흥미롭게 하는)이라고 쓴다. interested는 사람이 어떤 사물에 대해 '흥미롭다고 느끼는'이라는 뜻이다. 따라서 ⓔinterested를 interesting이라고 고쳐야 한다.

02 'What would you do if ~?'는 '만약 ~라면 너는 무엇을 하겠니?'라는 뜻으로 상상하여 말하는 표현이다. 이때, 현재 사실에 반대되는 내용을 가정하는 것이므로 if절에는 가정법 과거형을 쓴다.

03 '어떤 사람에게 책이나 영화, 물건을 위한 아이디어를 주다'라는 뜻을 가진 단어는 'inspire'(영감을 주다)이다.

04 현재 사실에 반대되는 상황을 가정할 때에는 가정법 과거형을 사용한다.

05 ④ '어디서 대화를 하고 있는지'는 대화에서 언급되지 않았다.

06 위의 대화에서 B와 G는 ①'꿈에 그리던 집에 대한 상상'에 대해서 이야기하고 있다.

07 '난 거기를 탐험하고 싶어.'라는 문장이 들어갈 곳은, 대화의 문맥상 '정글에 간다면 뭘 할 거니?'라고 물어본 직후인 ④에 들어가야 적절하다.

08 ③'모든 정글들이 신나는 모험으로 가득 차 있다.'는 말은 위 대화에서 언급되지 않았다.

09 safe from ~로부터 안전한 / dangerous 위험한

10 ② 가정법으로 물었으므로 가정법으로 대답해야 한다.

11 '만약 ~라면 너는 뭘 할 거니?'라는 뜻으로 상상하여 말할 때 'What would you do if ~?'를 쓸 수 있으며, 비슷한 표현으로 'Suppose ~', 'What if ~?' 등이 있다.

서술형 시험대비   p.21

01 I would build my own house
02 He would cover his dream house completely with mirrors.
03 I wish I could have a new computer.
04 What would you do if you were there?

3

05 She[He] would go swimming and go fishing.

06 They are talking about the house that[which] is upside down.

07 B would walk upside down and see things differently.

01 상대방이 'What would you do if ~?'라고 물어 볼 때 대답은 'I would ~'라고 한다.

02 B는 자신이 꿈꾸는 집을 거울로 완전히 덮을 것이라고 말했다.

03 바람이나 소원을 나타내는 표현으로 '내가 ~했으면 좋겠다'라는 뜻을 가진 'I wish I could ~'를 쓸 수 있다.

04 '만약 ~라면 너는 무엇을 할 거니?'라는 뜻으로 상상하여 말하는 표현은 'What would you do if ~?'를 쓴다.

05 위 대화의 후반에 언급되었듯이, 수영하러 가고 낚시를 할 것이라고 말했다.

06 위 대화에서 G와 B는 사진 속에서 본 거꾸로 된 집에 대해 이야기하고 있다.

07 위에 언급되었듯이, 거꾸로 걷고 사물을 다르게 볼 것이라고 말했다.

교과서
Grammar

핵심 Check   p.22~23

1 (1) were a robot, I would listen to her
  (2) would buy an apartment in Seoul if I had some money

2 (1) walking   (2) closed

시험대비 기본평가   p.24

01 (1) live → lived   (2) can → could   (3) calls → called
   (4) will → would

02 ③   03 ④   04 ⑤

---

01 문제에서 각 문장이 가정법 문장이라고 했고, 모든 문장들의 구조는 '가정법 과거' 형태로 볼 수 있으므로, 조건절의 동사를 과거로, 주절의 조동사도 과거형으로 고치는 것이 적절하다.

02 모두 5형식으로서, 목적보어를 갖는 문장들이다. call은 목적어와 목적보어 사이에 전치사 of를 필요로 하지 않는다.

03 주절에 조동사의 과거형이 나왔으므로, 가정법 문장이다. 가정법 과거에서 동사의 과거형 또는 조동사의 과거형을 사용하는 것이 적절하다.

04 'keep+목적어(A)+형용사/분사'는 5형식으로 'A가 어떤 상태가 되도록 유지하다'는 의미이고, 'keep+목적어(A)+from+V-ing'는 'A가 ~하지 못하도록 막다'라는 뜻이다. 모든 빈칸을 충족시키는 것은 kept이다.

시험대비 실력평가   p.25~27

01 ④   02 ③, ④
03 to keep themselves safe from invaders
04 Living together in one building keeps them safe.
05 it rained, we could not go to the swimming pool
06 would always havefriends to play with
07 ③   08 ②   09 ⑤
10 have → had, will → would   11 ⑤
12 ②   13 ②   14 ③   15 ⑤

---

01 가정법 과거 형태의 문장들이다. If절에는 동사의 과거형을, 주절에는 조동사의 과거형을 쓰는 것이 적절하다.

02 5형식 동사 made에 관련된 문제이다. '눈속에서 썰매를 타러 가는 것은 Tom과 Sophie를 흥분하게 만들었다.'는 문장의 made와 같은 용법으로 쓰인 것은 ③과 ④이다. ③ '그 경연 쇼에서의 보컬 코치들과 감독은 그 어린 소녀를 세계적으로 유명한 가수로 만들었다.' ④ '그 당시에 해결이 불가능해 보였던 문제들이 광장에 모인 사람들을 더욱 강하게 만들었다.'

03 5형식 동사 keep 관련 문제이다. *keep oneself safe from ~: ~로부터 자신을 안전하게 지키다

04 '동명사 주어' Living과 5형식 동사 keeps에 유의하여 적절하게 배열한다.

05 가정법 과거 시제의 문장이다. If절에 과거동사 rained가 오고, 주절에 조동사의 과거형 could를 쓰는 것에 유의하여 알맞게 배열한다.

06 If절에 과거동사 lived가 있는 가정법 과거 시제의 문장이다. 주절에 조동사의 과거형 would와 빈도부사 always의 순서에 유의하고, friends를 뒤에서 수식하는 to부정사에 with가 함께 있는 것에 유의하여 주어진 단어들을 배열한다.

07 가정법 과거로서 '반대' 개념의 직설법 현재 시제와 적절하게 전환된 문장은 ③번뿐이다.

08 'keep+목적어+목적보어(형용사)'가 적절히 사용된 것을 고른다.

09 'keep/make+목적어+목적보어(형용사)'가 적절히 사용된 것을 고른다. ① keep → keeps ② warmly → warm ③ actively →active ④ make → makes

10 '만약 당신이 사막에서 살고, 함께 살 사람이 없다면, 무엇을 할 것인가?'라는 문장이다. 가정법 과거 문장이라고 했으므로, if절의 동사를 과거형인 lived, had로, 주절의 will도 과거형 would로 고친다.

11 나머지는 5형식 문장으로 쓰였는데, ⑤만 4형식으로 쓰였다. '시골의 그 할머니가 그들에게 전통 한식을 만들어줬다.'라는 뜻이다.

12 ①은 'keep+목적어+목적보어(형용사)'로 5형식 문장이다. 그러나 ②는 'keep+목적어+from+V-ing'로서 '그가 제안한 방법이 당신의 가방이 도둑맞지 않도록 할 것이다.'라는 뜻을 가진 3형식 문장이고, 나머지는 모두 5형식 문장들이기 때문에 정답은 ②이다.

13 가정법 과거 문장이라고 했으므로, if절의 동사가 과거형이고, 주절에 조동사의 과거형이 있는 문장을 찾는다. ① has → had ③ will → would ④ had seen → saw, can → could ⑤ know → knew

14 조건에 맞게 if절의 동사가 과거형이고, 주절에 조동사의 과거형이 있는 문장을 찾는다. ① is → were ② won't → wouldn't ④ have got → get ⑤ know → knew

15 ⑤는 '공손한 질문'을 위한 조동사 Could이다. 나머지 다른 문장들과, <보기>에 주어진 could는 가정법의 주절에 사용된 can의 과거시제형이다.

🦉 서술형 시험대비
p.28~29

01 (1) won't → wouldn't (2) has → had
(3) will → would (4) will → would
(5) would be → would have been
(6) will → would (7) can → could

02 (1) Those wooden poles support Venice
(2) walls would keep people cool in summer and warm
(3) made a huge round building their house
(4) water bus makes it easier to travel from island

03 (1) If it were not for
(2) If there were no
(3) Were it not for
(4) As there are many wooden poles in the ground

04 lived in a house with a soccer field, he could invite

05 (1) made them bored
(2) saw the koalas eating leaves
(3) heard their names called by
(4) made it difficult for them to build

06 I lived in a stone house, the typhoon couldn't shake it

07 Living in the house made of earth keeps us cool

08 (1) If there were food left, the homeless man would not work today.
(2) If he were[was] strong enough, he would not exercise at the gym every day.

01 문제에서 각 문장이 가정법이라고 했으므로, 내용상 가정법 과거시제 문장은 'if절' 또는 'I wish' 뒤의 동사를 과거형으로, be동사는 were또는 was로 고치고, 주절의 조동사는 과거형으로 바꾼다. (5) yesterday로 보아 과거시제이므로 '가정법 과거완료'로 표현한다. 가정법 과거완료의 주절에는 '조동사+have+p.p.'를 쓴다.

02 (2), (3), (4) 5형식 동사 'keep/make+목적어+목적보어(형용사)'를 사용하여, 주어진 단어들을 적절히 배열한다. (4)의 경우, '여행하는 것'을 목적어 'to부정사'로 하여, 5형식을 만들려면 '가목적어 it'을 취하고 '진목적어 to travel'은 뒤로 보내는 것에 유의한다.

03 '땅 속의 많은 나무기둥들이 없다면, 베니스는 매우 다를 텐데.'라는 가정법 문장이다. 직설법으로는, '땅 속의 많은 나무기둥들이 있어서, 베니스는 많이 다르지 않다.'가 된다. 가정법 표현, 'Without = If it were not for = Were it not for'임에 유의하여, 주어진 조건대로 빈칸을 채운다.

04 'Matthew가 축구장이 있는 집에 살고 있지 않기 때문에, 방과 후에 친구들을 초대해서 축구를 할 수 없다.'라는 직설법 문장을 가정법으로 바꾸면 'Matthew가 축구장이 있는 집에 산다면, 방과 후에 친구들을 초대해서 축구를 할 수 있을 텐데.'가 된다. If절에 과거동사, 주절에 조동사 can의 과거형 could에 유의하여 영작한다.

05 5형식 문장에서 목적어 뒤의 목적보어는 '형용사, to부정사, 현재분사, 과거분사' 등이 올 수 있고, 목적어가 to부정사인 경우, 가목적어를 취해야 한다. (1), (3)은 과거분사가, (2)는 현재분사가 목적보어 (4)는 가목적어-진목적어 구조이다.

06 가정법 과거시제를 활용해서 동사를 lived로, 조동사는 could not을 써야 하는데, 글자 수 제한이 있으므로 couldn't로 활용하는 것에 유의하여 영작한다.

5

07 동명사가 주어이므로 live는 Living, 동사 keep은 keeps 형태를 쓴다. 흙으로 만든 집은 the house made of earth로 하는 것에 유의하여, 알맞게 영작한다.

08 가정법 과거는 직설법 현재 반대, 가정법 과거완료는 직설법 과거의 반대를 나타낸다. (3)은 가정법 과거완료이다.

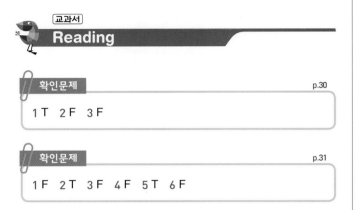

Reading 〔교과서〕

확인문제 p.30

1 T 2 F 3 F

확인문제 p.31

1 F 2 T 3 F 4 F 5 T 6 F

교과서 확인학습 A p.32~33

01 live in
02 use ladders to enter their houses. live in, on
03 others share, with
04 Imagine, live in, that change
05 lived in, would climb, to enter my
06 hidden opening
07 If, appeared, would pull, up to stop, from
08 are made of
09 keep me cool, warm
10 a flat roof, sleep up on the roof
11 lived in, would take a gondola
12 has, islands, On weekend, from island to island
13 from, rises, leaves, full of water
14 However, be able to walk around
15 is known as, floating
16 there are, colorful houses
17 how, why they built the houses on
18 decided to live there, themselves safe from
19 for them to build, swampy
20 installed, wooden poles
21 wooden poles, support, to
22 lived, would, have friends, to play with
23 hear, calling me to come over
24 are, three to five floors
25 is used for
26 store food, tools on

27 where I would sleep, would be on
28 like, living in, have
29 can house up to, work together, share
30 Living, keeps them safe
31 different all over the world, What, like

교과서 확인학습 B p.34~35

1 Different people live in different houses.
2 Some use ladders to enter their houses. Others live in houses on the water.
3 And others share their houses with many people.
4 Imagine you live in one of these houses. How would that change your life?
5 If I lived in a *pueblo*, I would climb up a ladder to enter my house.
6 There's a hidden opening on top of the house.
7 If unwelcome visitors appeared, I would pull the ladder up to stop them from entering.
8 The thick walls are made of earth, straw, and water.
9 They would keep me cool in summer and warm in winter.
10 The house has a flat roof. I would sometimes sleep up on the roof under the moon and stars.
11 If I lived in Venice, I would take a gondola to school every morning.
12 Venice has 118 small islands. On weekends, I would travel from island to island by a *vaporetto*, a water bus.
13 At high tide, the water from the Adriatic Sea often rises and leaves the streets full of water.
14 However, I would be able to walk around the town through the raised walkways.
15 Venice is known as the "floating city."
16 In Venice, there are many colorful houses on the water.
17 You may wonder how and why they built the houses on the water.
18 The old Venetians decided to live there to keep themselves safe from invaders.
19 But it was not easy for them to build their homes on this swampy surface.
20 So they installed more than 10 million wooden poles in the ground.
21 It is these wooden poles that support Venice to this day.

22 If I lived in a *tulou*, a huge round house in Fujian, China, I would always have friends at home to play with.

23 I would sometimes hear my neighbor calling me to come over for tea or dinner.

24 In a *tulou*, there are usually three to five floors.

25 The first floor is used for cooking and eating.

26 And people store food and tools on the second floor.

27 Do you wonder where I would sleep? My bedroom would be on the third or fourth floor.

28 A *tulou* is like a village. The people living in a *tulou* mostly have the same family name.

29 Some large *tulou* can house up to 50 families. They work together and share many things.

30 Living together in one building keeps them safe.

31 Homes are everywhere. But they are different all over the world. What is your home like?

시험대비 실력평가
p.36~39

01 ② 02 ④ 03 ⑤

04 The writer would sometimes sleep up on the roof under the moon and stars.

05 ② 06 swampy

07 There are many colorful houses on the water.

08 ⑤ 09 ③

10 It is a huge round house in Fujian, China.

11 ⑤

12 He or she would sleep on the third or fourth floor.

13 ③ 14 ④

15 There is a hidden opening on top of a *pueblo*.

16 ④ 17 (B)—(D)—(A)—(C)

18 A *vaporetto* is a water bus.

19 steel → wood 20 ⑤ 21 ②

22 calling(또는 call) 23 ⑤ 24 ④

25 Some large *tulous* can house up to 50 families.

01 이어지는 글의 내용은 다양한 사람들이 다양한 집에서 살고 있다는 내용이므로 ②번이 가장 적절하다.

02 주어진 문장의 They가 가리키는 것은 The thick walls이다. 따라서 ④번에 들어가는 것이 가장 적절하다.

03 달갑지 않은 방문객이 나타나면 사다리를 끌어올려 그들이 들어오지 못하게 할 것이라고 하였다. 따라서 ⑤번이 글의 내용과 일치한다.

04 글쓴이는 때때로 나는 달과 별들 아래의 지붕 위에서 잠을 잘 것이라고 하였다.

05 아드리아 해의 물이 자주 범람하고 거리는 물로 가득 차지만 돌출되어 있는 통로로 도심 주변을 걸어다닐 수 있을 것이라는 연결이 자연스럽다. 따라서 ②번이 적절하다.

06 '항상 아주 습한'은 '습지의(swampy)'이다.

07 물 위에 색색의 건물들이 많다고 하였다.

08 지금까지 베니스를 지탱해 주고 있는 것은 천만 개 이상의 나무 기둥이라고 하였다.

09 토루에 사는 사람들은 대부분 같은 성을 가지고 있고 함께 일하고 많은 것을 공유한다고 하였으므로 '마을'과 같다는 말이 가장 적절하다.

10 토루는 중국 푸젠에 있는 거대하고 둥그런 집이라고 하였다.

11 토루는 50가구까지 수용할 수 있으며 이곳에 사는 사람들은 함께 일하고 많은 것을 공유한다고 하였다.

12 침실은 3층이나 4층에 있을 것이라고 하였다.

13 반갑지 않은 방문객이 나타나면 사다리를 끌어올려 그들이 들어오지 못하게 할 것이라고 말하는 것이 자연스러우므로 unwelcome이라고 쓰는 것이 적절하다.

14 위에 언급한 집들 중 하나에 산다고 상상해 보면 삶이 어떻게 바뀔 것인지를 묻고 있으므로 ④번이 가장 적절하다.

15 푸에블로 집 꼭대기에는 숨겨진 구멍이 있다고 하였다.

16 푸에블로에는 평평한 지붕이 있고 달과 별들 아래의 지붕 위에서 잠을 잘 것이라고 하였으므로 ④번이 답이다.

17 (B) 베니스는 '떠다니는 도시'로 알려짐 – (D) 집을 물 위에 지은 이유 설명 – (A) 습지 위에 집을 짓는 것이 쉽지 않음 – (C) 나무 기둥 설치로 베니스 지탱

18 바포레토는 수상버스라고 하였다.

19 나무로 만들어진 기둥(wooden poles)이라고 하였다.

20 조수가 높을 때에는 아드리아 해의 물이 자주 범람하여 거리가 물로 가득 찬다고 하였다.

21 밑줄 친 ⓐ는 주어와 목적어가 같을 때 목적어로 재귀대명사를 쓰는 재귀적 용법에 해당한다. seat는 타동사로 명령문에 생략된 주어 you와 목적어가 같으므로 목적어로 재귀대명사를 쓴 경우이다. 나머지는 모두 강조 용법의 재귀대명사이다.

22 지각동사의 목적어와 목적격 보어의 관계가 능동인 경우 목적격 보어로 동사원형이나 현재분사를 쓸 수 있다. 따라서 calling 혹은 call이라고 쓰는 것이 적절하다.

23 침실이 어디에 있는지 궁금한지 묻는 질문에 대한 답이 ⑤번 다음 문장에 이어지고 있으므로 ⑤번이 적절하다.

24 토루는 3층에서 5층으로 되어 있다고 하였으므로 ④번이 옳다. 토루가 중국의 전통 가옥이라는 말은 나와 있지 않다.

25 몇몇 큰 토루는 50가구까지 수용할 수 있다고 하였다.

01 Some people have to use ladders to enter their houses.

02 If unwelcome visitors appeared, the writer would pull the ladder up to stop them from entering.

03 The walls are made of earth, straw, and water.

04 It is possible to sleep on the roof of the house because it has a flat roof.

05 ladder

06 lived

07 He[She] would travel from island to island by *vaporetto*, a water bus.

08 Venice is known as the "floating city."

09 from themselves → from invaders

10 Do you wonder where I would sleep?

11 어디에나 있는 집

12 the same family name, share many things, cooking and eating, store food and tools, sleeping

01 어떤 사람들은 집에 들어가기 위해 사다리를 이용한다고 하였다.

02 반갑지 않은 방문객이 나타난다면 글쓴이는 사다리를 끌어올려 그들이 들어오지 못하게 할 것이다.

03 두꺼운 벽은 흙, 지푸라기, 물로 만들어져 있다.

04 푸에블로는 평평한 지붕을 가진 집이기 때문에 지붕 위에서 잠을 잘 수 있다.

05 어딘가에 오르기 위해 사용되는 장치로, 두 개의 긴 나무, 금속 혹은 밧줄 사이에 일련의 계단을 가진 것은 '사다리(ladder)'이다.

06 현재 사실과 반대되는 가정을 할 때 쓰는 가정법 과거이므로 If 절에는 과거동사로 쓴다.

07 글쓴이는 수상버스 바포레토를 타고 이 섬 저 섬을 여행할 것이라고 하였다.

08 베니스는 '떠다니는 도시'로 알려져 있다.

09 옛 베니스 사람들은 침략자들로부터 자신들을 안전하게 지키기 위해 도시 베니스를 건설하였다.

10 '내가 어디에서 잠을 잘지'는 동사 wonder의 목적어 역할을 하는 간접의문문으로 쓰는 것에 유의한다. 간접의문문의 어순은 '의문사+주어+동사'이다.

11 앞 문장 homes를 가리키는 말이다. 복수명사를 지칭하므로 they라고 쓴다.

12 토루에 사는 사람들은 대부분 같은 성을 가지고 있다. 그들은 함께 일하고 많은 것을 공유한다. 1층은 요리하고 식사하는 데에 사용되고 2층에 식량과 도구를 보관한다. 3층은 잠을 자기 위해 사용된다.한 재료로 제작된다고 하였다.

01 (1) unwelcome   (2) invisible   02 ②

03 ③

04 What you are saying doesn't make sense.

05 ②   06 ①   07 (B) – (C) – (A)

08 ⑤   09 But the jungle is full of adventure.

10 ②   11 the jungle   12 ②

13 (1) I lived in a house with a swimming pool, I would enjoy

     (2) I don't live in a house with a swimming pool, I won't enjoy

14 (1) had not installed these wooden poles in the ground, they couldn't have lived

     (2) they installed these wooden poles in the ground, they could live

15 ④   16 ③   17 ①   18 ②

19 ③

20 A *pueblo* has a hidden opening on top of the house.

21 ④   22 ②   23 ⑤

24 The raised walkways would make it possible for the writer to walk around the town at high tide.

25 Because there are no beds.

26 The warm *ondol* floors heat your body in the cold winter.

27 ④

01 <보기>의 단어들의 관계는 반의어 관계이다.

02 ②에서 travel은 '여행, 이동'이라는 명사적 의미로 사용되었다.

03 주어진 문장의 take는 '~을 타다'라는 뜻으로 사용되었다. ③은 '여기서 시청까지 가는 버스를 탈 수 있나요?'라는 뜻으로 주어진 문장과 같은 뜻으로 사용되었다.

04 make sense 이치에 맞다

05 'I wish I could ~'는 '내가 ~하면 좋겠다'라는 뜻으로, 바람이나 소원을 나타내는 표현이다.

06 '만약 ~라면 너는 무엇을 할 거니?'라는 뜻으로 상상하여 말하는 표현은 ①'What would you do if ~?'이다.

07 B가 자신이 꿈꾸는 집에 대해 어떻게 생각하느냐고 Alice에게 물었고 이에 그녀는 (B) 특이하다고 생각한다고 말하면서 그 집에서 살면 무엇을 할 것이냐고 되묻는다. 그 대답으로 (C)에서 심해를 탐험하고 특이한 해양 동물을 찾을 것이라고 대답하는 순서로 가는 것이 적절하다. 그리고 마지막으로 이에 대한 Alice의 대답(A)이 오는 것이 문맥상 가장 자연스럽다.

08 ⑤ 'B가 꿈꾸는 집 주변에서 무엇을 찾을 수 있는지'에 대한 대답은 '몇몇 신기한 해양 동물들'(some unique sea animals)

이라고 (C)에 나와 있다.

09 be full of ~로 가득 차 있다

10 (B)는 '만약 ~라면 너는 무엇을 할 거니?'라는 뜻으로 상상하여 말하는 표현으로, 'Suppose ~', 'What if ~?' 등으로 대체할 수 있다.

11 대명사 it은 일반적으로 앞 문장에서 언급한 명사를 가리킨다. 대화의 문맥으로 미루어 보아, 앞 문장에서 물어본 it은 정글(the jungle)을 가리킨다.

12 '한 건물에 함께 사는 것은 우리를 침입자들이나 도둑들로부터 안전하게 지켜준다.'라는 문장이다. ② '우리는 한 건물에서 함께 살고 있는데, 그것은 우리를 침입자들이나 도둑들로부터 안전하게 만들어준다.'와 가장 가까운 뜻이 된다. ① '우리가 한 건물에서 함께 살았을 때, 우리는 안전했다.' ③ '우리가 한 건물에 함께 산다면, 안전할 텐데.'(가정법, 직설법의 반대 의미) ④ '침입자들로부터 안전하게 느끼기 위해서 함께 살고 있다.' ⑤ '침입자들의 위협 때문에 함께 살고 있다.' 등은, 비슷하지만 모두 의미상 거리가 있는 문장들이다.

13 가정법 과거에는 동사의 과거형을 쓰기 때문에 lived와 would를 사용한다. 직설법에는 don't live와 주절에 won't를 쓰는 것에 유의한다.

14 주어진 우리말의 내용상 '가정법 과거완료' 문장이다. If절에 'had p.p.' 형태, 주절에는 '조동사 과거형+have p.p.' 형태를 쓰기 때문에, If절에는 had not installed를, 주절에는 주어진 can't를 couldn't have p.p.로 쓴다. 나무 기둥들이 복수이므로 this는 these로 고쳐서 쓰는 것에 유의한다. 직설법으로 바꿀 때는 not이 없는 과거 시제 installed와 조동사 과거형 could를 사용하면 된다.

15 ④ that morning으로 보아 내용상 가정법 과거완료 문장이다. If절에 'had+p.p.', 주절에는 '조동사 과거+have+p.p.' 형태가 와야 한다. 'didn't fail'을 'hadn't failed'로 고치는 것이 적절하다.

16 'keep+목적어+목적보어' 형태의 5형식 문장에서 목적어와 목적보어의 동작의 관계에 따라 '능동은 현재분사, 수동은 과거분사'를 쓴다. '수업이 끝날 때까지 손을 들고 있도록 했다'는 내용이므로 raised를 raising으로 쓰는 것이 적절하다.

17 '~가 없다면'이라는 가정법 표현은 'If there were no ~'로 나타내며, without 또는 'If it were not for ~'로 대체할 수 있고, 'Were it not for ~'도 표현 가능하다. ① couldn't have lived → couldn't live ⑤ are → were가 적절하다.

18 '~로 들어가다'는 타동사 'enter'이다. 'enter into'는 '~을 시작하

다, (사업에) 착수하다'라는 의미로 쓰인다.

19 위 글은 다양한 사람들이 다양한 집에서 살고 있다는 내용으로 뉴멕시코의 푸에블로가 예시로 제시되어 있다. 따라서 ③번 '세계의 다양한 집들'이 가장 적절하다.

20 푸에블로는 꼭대기에 숨겨진 구멍을 가지고 있다.

21 빈칸 (A)에는 전치사 as가 들어간다. ① be in the mood for: ~할 기분이 나다 ② be ashamed of: ~을 부끄러워하다 ③ be related to: ~와 관련이 있다 ④ be regarded as: ~라고 여겨지다 ⑤ be absent from: ~에 결석하다

22 어떻게, 그리고 왜 베니스인들이 물 위에 집을 지었는지를 설명하는 말 앞에 들어가는 것이 자연스럽다. 따라서 ②번이 적절하다.

23 지금까지 베니스를 지탱해 주고 있는 천만 개 이상의 기둥은 나무로 만들어졌다.

24 조수가 높을 때에는 돌출되어 있는 통로로 도심 주변을 걸어 다닐 수 있을 것이라고 하였다.

25 한옥에서 지냈다면 침대가 없기 때문에 바닥에서 잠을 자게 될 것이라고 하였다.

26 추운 겨울에는 따뜻한 온돌 바닥이 몸을 데워준다고 하였다.

27 한옥 집은 대개 나무, 돌, 지푸라기, 종이, 흙과 같은 천연 재료로 지어져 있다고 하였다.

단원별 예상문제 p.48~51

01 ②

02 (1) take a look
(2) on weekends
(3) for a while

03 ②

04 He would build a snow house and stay there on vacation.

05 ③　　　　　**06** ⑤

07 (A) some pictures　(B) those cave houses
(C) Turkey

08 ④　　　**09** ⑤　　　**10** ②　　　**11** ①

12 ④　　　**13** ⑤

14 If unwelcome visitors appeared, I would pull up the ladder to stop them from entering

15 ④　　　**16** ③　　　**17** ②　　　**18** ⑤

19 It usually has three to five floors.　　**20** ④

21 It was because the Ndebele painted their houses with many colorful symbols when the Boers invaded their land.

22 The symbols expressed feelings such as sadness.

23 ③

01 '어떤 사람에게 살 곳을 제공하다'는 뜻을 가진 단어는 ② house(수용하다)이다.

02 (1) take a look 보다 (2) on weekends 주말마다 (3) for a while 당분간, 잠시 동안

03 위 대화에서 B는 생일 선물로 새 썰매를 받았다고 했으므로 ②'그것을 어서 시험 삼아 타보고 싶다.'라는 말이 들어가야 문맥상 가장 적절하다.

04 대화 후반에 B가 눈으로 만든 집을 짓고 거기서 휴가를 보내고 싶다고 언급했다.

05 G가 날씨를 확인하고 '당분간은 눈이 오지 않을 것'(there will be no snow for a while.)이라고 말했다.

06 주어진 문장에서 대명사 They가 가리키는 것이 무엇인지 파악하는 것이 중요하다. '그것들은 매우 아름다워 보여!'라고 했으므로 복수의 어떤 것을 의미한다. 따라서 대화의 문맥상 they는 those balloons를 가리킨다.

07 (A) 대명사 them이 가리키는 것은 앞 문장에서 언급된 Julia가 보낸 사진을 의미한다. (B) 대명사 They가 가리키는 것은 바로 앞 문장에서 G가 언급한 those cave houses를 가리킨다. (C) there는 대화 속에서 이야기하고 있는 터키(Turkey)를 의미한다.

08 ① can → could ② will → would ③ wins → won ⑤ 가정법 과거완료. would feel → would have felt

09 모든 빈칸에 들어갈 수 있는 단어는 made이다. 모든 문장은 5형식이지만, ⑤는 3형식 동사로 사용되었다. *cozy: 안락한, 아늑한

10 'I wish 가정법' 구문을 쓴다. be 동사의 과거형 were 또는 was와 조동사의 과거형을 알맞게 활용한 문장을 찾는다.

11 가정법 과거완료에 맞게 If절에 'had p.p.'를 쓰되, 이 예문의 경우 비인칭 주어 it을 활용하는 것에 유의한다. 또한, 주절에는 '조동사 과거형+have+p.p.' 형태가 와야 한다. *overflow: (물이) 흘러넘치다.

12 ④를 해석해 보면, '경찰관들이 그 어린 소녀를 폭력배들로부터 안전하게 지켜줬다.'라는 문장이다. 동사 keep은 목적어 뒤에 '형용사'를 '목적보어'로 받아서 목적어의 상태를 설명해 준다. 그러므로 '부사' safely를 '형용사' safe로 고치는 것이 적절하다.

13 5형식 문장들이다. 목적보어는 목적어와의 관계에 맞게 현재분사 또는 과거분사로 쓸 수 있다. ⑤를 해석해 보면, '이 박물관의 소장품들은 방문객들에게 고대 한국 예술에 관해 흥미를 느끼도록 만든다.'라는 문장이다. 방문객들이 '흥미를 느끼는 것'이므로 'interested'가 옳다.

14 가정법이므로 if절에 appear 동사의 과거형과, 주절에 조동사 will의 과거형을 사용하되, 'stop A from V-ing' 구문에 유의한다.

15 각 밑줄 친 make는 ⓐ, ⓕ: 4형식 ⓑ, ⓒ, ⓓ, ⓖ: 5형식 ⓔ: 3형식 등으로 쓰였다.

16 위 글은 대부분 같은 성을 가지고 있는 사람들이 모여 사는 마을과 같은 집인 토루에 관하여 설명하는 글이다. 따라서 '토루: 푸젠의 공동체 집'이 가장 적절하다.

17 '함께 놀 친구'라는 의미이므로 'to play with'라고 쓰는 것이 적절하다.

18 이웃이 차를 마시거나 저녁 식사를 하러 집에 들르라고 부르는 소리를 듣게 될 것이라고 하였으므로 ⑤번이 글의 내용과 일치한다.

19 토루는 대개 3층에서 5층으로 되어 있다고 하였다.

20 주절의 시제 및 내용으로 미루어 보아 가정법 과거 문장임을 알 수 있다.

21 보어인들이 은데벨레족의 땅을 침략했을 때, 은데벨레족은 여러 색의 상징으로 집을 칠하였고 그래서 적들은 그들이 비밀리에 서로 의사소통하고 있었던 것을 이해할 수 없었다.

22 상징들은 슬픔과 같은 감정들을 표현했다.

23 남아프리카 은데벨레족 마을의 집은 독특한 모양과 양식의 집들이라고 하였다. ordinary: 평범한

서술형 실전문제
p.52~53

01 It has wheels and can move like a car.
02 He would travel to many places with his family.
03 (1) building keeps the people safe and
   (2) poles to make them support Venice
04 ④, ④ If the officer knew the driver, he wouldn't give her a ticket. 또는 If the officer knows the driver, he won't give her a ticket.
05 Andrew knew the title of the song, he could sing it at the school festival
06 wish my sisters were as nice as Abigail
07 Others live in houses on the water.
08 Imagine you live in one of these houses.
09 The writer would hear her or his neighbor calling her or him to come over for tea or dinner.
10 The people living in a *tulou* mostly have the same family name.

01 위 대화 초반에 나와 있듯이, 바퀴가 달려 있고 자동차처럼 움직일 수 있다고 한다.

02 위 대화 후반부에 가족들과 함께 많은 곳을 여행할 것이라고 언급했다.

03 5형식 동사 keep과 make의 쓰임새에 관한 문제이다. 특히 (2)의 make는 목적보어 자리에 원형부정사를 쓰는 사역동사로 사용되었음에 유의한다. (1) 한 건물에 함께 사는 것은 사람들은 안전하고 편안하게 지켜준다. (2) 옛 베니스인들은 베니스를 지탱하도록 하기 위해, 천만 개 이상의 나무 기둥을 설치했다.

05 직설법 문장을 해석해 보면, 'Andrew가 그 노래 제목을 모르고, 학교 축제에서 그 곡을 부를 수 없다.'이므로, 가정법 과거시제 'Andrew가 그 노래 제목을 안다면, 학교 축제에서 그 곡을 부를 수 있을 텐데.'라고 하는 것이 적절하다.

06 직설법에서 '누나들이 Abigail처럼 착하면 좋은데, 그렇지 않아 유감이다'라고 했으므로, 'I wish 가정법'을 활용하여, '누나들이 Abigail처럼 착하면 좋을 텐데'로 표현한다.

07 the others는 나머지 전체를 지칭할 때 쓰인다. 물 위에 있는 집에서 사는 다른 사람들을 의미하는 것이므로 others라고 쓰는 것이 적절하다.

08 Imagine의 목적어를 이끄는 명사절 접속사 that이 생략된 문장이다. '~에 살다'는 'live in'으로 표현한다.

09 글쓴이는 이웃이 차를 마시거나 저녁 실사를 하러 집에 들르라고 자신을 부르는 소리를 듣게 될 것이라고 하였다.

10 토루에 사는 사람들은 대부분 같은 성을 가지고 있다고 하였다.

창의사고력 서술형 문제
p.54

|모범답안|

01 (1) I would say hello to the fish every morning
   (2) I could swim with sharks
   (3) I would race with many sea horses
02 would do, would build, covered with, invisible

01 어법에 맞게 적절하게 영작한다. 가정법 과거의 주절이므로 조동사의 과거형이 반드시 들어가도록 한다.

02 최근에 나는 친구와 대화를 하고 있었다. 그녀는 나에게 내가 백만장자가 되면 무엇을 할 것인지 물어 보았다. 나는 거울로 완전히 덮인 나 자신의 집을 지을 것이라고 말했다. 나는 항상 거울이 그 집을 거의 안 보일 수 있게 만들 것이라고 생각해 왔고 그것이 멋지다고 생각한다.

단원별 모의고사
p.55~59

01 ⑤   02 ①   03 be used for
04 I wish I could live in Alaska!

05 ⓒ test out it → test it out
06 ④
07 (A) would   (B) lived
08 ④
09 So I would go see La Sagrada Familia.
10 to see how his design was inspired by nature
11 ①
12 What would you do if
13 ④   14 ①   15 ④   16 ③
17 ②   18 ④   19 ③   20 ③
21 If I could enter a house only by using ladders, it would be fun.
22 ④   23 ⑤
24 At high tide, the water from the Adriatic Sea often rises and leaves the streets full of water.
25 ⑤
26 Because they wanted to keep themselves safe from invaders.
27 ④   28 ⓐ to   ⓑ for
29 Living together in one building keeps them safe.

01 '지구 위에 있는 태양과 달의 인력에 의해 발생하는 바다 수면 높이의 정기적인 상하 움직임'이라는 영영 풀이가 가리키는 단어는 ⑤tide(조수, 흐름)이다.

02 주어진 단어들의 관계는 형용사와 그 부사형의 관계이다. 따라서 high의 부사형은 형용사형과 같은 ①high이다.

03 be used for~로 사용되다

04 현재 사실과 반대되는 내용, 혹은 가능성이 없는 일을 가정할 때, I wish 뒤에는 과거형 동사를 이용한다.

05 동사와 부사로 이루어진 이어동사에서 인칭대명사가 목적어일 때는 두 단어 사이에 쓴다. 따라서 ⓒ 인칭대명사 it은 test와 out 사이에 들어가야 한다.

06 위 대화에서는 거꾸로 된 집에서 살아보는 것을 상상하는 내용이 담겨 있다. ④ '난 혼자서 살기를 원해 왔어.'라는 문장은 대화의 흐름과 관계 없다.

07 'What would you do if ~?'는 '만약 ~한다면 너는 무엇을 할 거니?'라는 뜻으로 상상하여 말하는 표현이다. 이때 현재 사실에 반대되는 내용을 가정할 때는 가정법 과거형을 쓴다.

08 'I wish I could ~.'는 '내가 ~한다면 좋겠다'라는 뜻으로, 바람이나 소원을 나타내는 표현이다.

09 B가 G에게 'What would you do if ~?'라고 물었으므로, G는 'I would~'라고 답하는 것이 옳다.

10 (B)가 가주어 It이 쓰인 문장으로, 그 It은 뒤에 오는 to부정사 구문을 대신하는 가주어이다.

11

11 '~으로'의 뜻을 가진 전치사 as가 적절하다.

12 '만약 ~한다면 너는 무엇을 할 거니?'라는 뜻으로 상상하여 말할 때 'What would you do if ~?'를 쓸 수 있다.

13 ④를 제외한 나머지는 모두 '목적보어'를 받는 5형식 동사 make로 쓰였다. ④는 '간접목적어와 직접목적어'를 받는 4형식 구조의 make이다. '요리 교실의 학생들이 당신에게 맛있는 빵을 만들어 줄 것이다.'

14 ①을 제외한 모든 문장은 가정법 과거 시제이다. ①의 if는 의문사가 없는 간접의문문의 명사절을 이끄는 접속사로 사용되었다.

15 ④를 제외한 나머지는 모두 '목적보어'를 받는 5형식 동사 make로 쓰였다. ④는 '간접목적어와 직접목적어'를 받는 4형식 구조의 make이다. '대학교 연구실의 내 삼촌이 나에게 환상적인 공룡 피규어를 만들어 주었다.'

16 <보기>의 would는 가정법의 주절에서 쓰이는 조동사로서, "Dennis는 친구 Sean이 그녀를 안내해 주라고 부탁하면, Canada에서 온 그 여성을 만날 것이다."라는 문장이다. 같은 가정법의 조동사 would는 ③이다. "그녀가 자신의 기술을 향상시키면, 그 회사의 대표이사가 그 사람을 고용할 것이다." 나머지는 각각 ① 과거의 습관적 행위 ② would like to = want to ④ (상대에게) 공손한 질문 ⑤ will의 과거형 등이다.

17 <보기>의 keep은 '목적보어'를 받는 5형식 동사로 쓰였다. ②도 같은 용법이다. 나머지는 3형식의 타동사로 사용되었고, 각각 ① 간직하다 ③ (월세 등을) 감당하다, 유지하다 ④ (약속 등을) 지키다 ⑤ 'keep A from V-ing: A가 V하지 못하게 금지하다.' 등의 뜻이다.

18 주어진 문장은 'Choo가 상태가 좋으면, 다른 선수들보다 두 배의 홈런을 성공시킬 텐데'라는 가정법 과거 문장이다. 직설법으로는 반대의 현재시제이므로, As가 이끄는 종속절과 주절에 모두 현재시제가 있는 ④가 정답이다.

19 곤돌라가 없다면, 베네치아 사람들은 그들이 원하는 만큼 자유롭게 돌아다닐 수 없을 텐데.'라는 문장이다. '~가 없다면'은 If it were not for = Were it not for = Without = But for 등으로 표현하며, ③ 'Had it not been for'는 'If it had not been for'에서 if를 생략하고 도치된 표현으로 가정법 과거완료시제에 사용한다.

20 ⓒ keep의 목적보어 자리 동사 형태는 능동일 때 현재분사를 쓴다. 'walk → walking' ⓓ 목적보어 자리에는 부사가 아니라 형용사가 와야 한다. 'safely → safe' ⓔ keep의 목적보어 자리이다. 'to stand → standing' ⓗ 동사 allow가 5형식에 쓰일 때 목적보어 자리에는 to부정사가 온다. 'be → to be'

21 가정법 과거이다. If절에 could, 주절에 would, only by using ladders 표현에 유의하여 알맞게 영작한다.

22 옛 베니스인들이 물 위에 집을 지었고 그 이유에 대한 내용이 이어지고 있으므로 ④ '떠 있는 도시'가 가장 적절하다.

23 주어진 문장은 습지 위에 집을 짓는 것이 불가능했지만 그것을 가능하게 만든 방법에 관한 것이며, ⑤번 이후의 문장은 지금까지 베니스를 지탱해 주고 있는 것이 바로 이 나무 기둥들이라고 강조하고 있으므로 ⑤번이 가장 적절하다.

24 조수가 높을 때 아드리아해의 물이 자주 범람하여 거리가 물로 가득 찬다고 하였다.

25 베니스에는 118개의 작은 섬들이 있다. over: ~를 넘는, ~ 이상의

26 옛 베니스인들은 침략자들로부터 자신들을 안전하게 지키기 위해 베니스에서 살기로 결정한 것이었다.

27 밑줄 친 (B)는 It ~ that 강조 구문이다. ④번은 It ~ that 가주어와 진주어이다.

28 ⓐ three to five floors: 3층에서 5층 ⓑ be used for: ~하는 데 사용되다

29 한 건물에 함께 사는 것이 토루에 사는 사람들을 안전하게 지켜준다고 하였다.

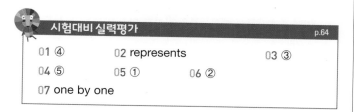

Lesson 8
Behind the Numbers

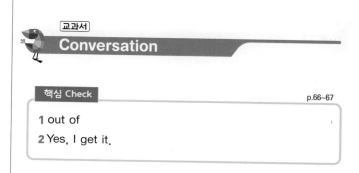

01 • 플라스틱 섬에 관한 기사를 읽어봤니? • 샴푸통과 같은 플라스틱 물품은 재활용할 수 있지만, 깨끗해야 한다. '기사, 물품, 물건'의 의미를 가지는 단어는 'article'이 적절하다.

02 각 주제는 조선 시대의 역사와 문화를 나타냅니다. <영영풀이> '어떤 상징이나 특징으로 표현하다'의 의미로 3인칭 단수 주어 다음에 'represents'가 적절하다.

03 (A) '난 학생들이 가장 좋아하는 간식에 대한 기사를 쓰고 있어. 나는 그들의 건강이 걱정 돼.'라는 의미로 'be worried about' 이 '~에 관해 걱정하다'의 의미로 적절하다. 'be related to'는 '~와 연관되어 있다'의 의미이다. (B) '나는 내년에 대통령 선거에 출마할 것이다.'라는 뜻으로 '~에 입후보하다'라는 'run for' 가 적절하다.

04 ⑤는 '용감한-겁이 많은'의 뜻을 가진 반의어 관계이고, 나머지는 유의어 관계이다. ①은 '주장하다', ②는 '일치하다, 같다', ③은 '애쓰다, 분투하다', ④는 '소설'이란 뜻이다.

05 '정부가 공공 서비스에 대한 지불을 하도록 정부에 내야 하는 돈' 의 의미로 'tax(세금)'가 적절하다.

06 '작가에 의해 지어진 등장인물과 사건에 대한 긴 이야기'의 의미로 'novel(소설)'이 적절하다.

07 one by one: 하나씩

서술형 시험대비   p.65

01 (1) facial   (2) celebrated   (3) election
   (4) adventures
02 solution
03 (1) repeated   (2) struggle   (3) greedy
   (4) matter, matters
04 (1) celebrate, 기념하다   (2) wav, 손을 흔들다
   (3) sum, 총계   (4) greedy, 탐욕스러운

01 (1) 침팬지는 얼굴의 표정과 소리를 통해서 감정을 표현할 수 있습니다. / 명사 'expression'을 수식하는 형용사 'facial'이 적

절하다. (2) 사실, Valentine's Day는 세계의 대부분의 지역에서 기념한다. / Valentine's Day가 기념되는 수동 의미로 수동태 'be celebrated'가 적절하다. (3) 학교에서 반장 선거가 있었어. / 관사 'an' 뒤에는 명사가 오기 때문에 동사 'elect'를 명사 'election'으로 바꾸어 준다. (4) 이러한 스포츠는 사람들에게 빠른 속도의 스릴 또는 모험을 느낄 수 있는 기회를 줍니다.

02 • 정부는 도움을 필요로 하는 사람들에게 돈을 주는 가장 좋은 해결책이다. • 그들은 그 용액에 향을 내기 위해 여러 허브와 꽃을 첨가했습니다. • 우리는 갈등에 대한 더 나은 해결책을 찾아야 한다. / 'solution'은 '해결책', '용액', '방안' 등의 의미를 가지고 있다.

03 (1) repeat: 반복하다 (2) struggle: 고군분투하다 (3) greedy: 탐욕스러운 (4) matter: 중요하다

04 (1) 특정한 행사가 중요하다는 것을 보여주기 위해 특별하고 즐거운 활동에 참여하다 (2) 손을 들고 손가락을 움직여 인사로 신호하다 (3) 수학적 과정에 의해 결정되는 둘 또는 그 이상의 숫자 혹은 수량의 전체 (4) 필요한 것보다 더 많은 돈이나 음식 등을 원하는

교과서 Conversation

교과서 대화문 익히기

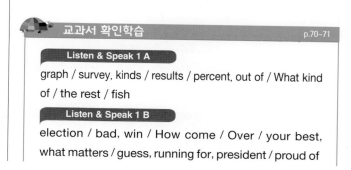

교과서 확인학습   p.70~71

Listen & Speak 1 A

graph / survey, kinds / results / percent, out of / What kind of / the rest / fish

Listen & Speak 1 B

election / bad, win / How come / Over / your best, what matters / guess, running for, president / proud of

03 '내 말이 무슨 뜻인지 알겠어?'라는 물음에, B가 '그것을 전에 본 적이 있어.'라고 말하는 것은 어색하다.

04 B의 세 번째 말에서 '화난 표정을 지을 때는 많은 근육이 필요하다'고 말하므로 얼굴 근육을 많이 사용한다는 것을 알 수 있다. 그러므로 'relaxed(이완된)'를 'tired(피곤한)'로 바꾸는 것이 적절하다.

05 80%의 학생들이 애완동물을 가지고 있지 않다는 것은 도표와 다르다.

06 (C) 방과 후 수업으로 테니스 수업을 더 해야 한다는 말에 → (D) 그렇게 말하는 이유를 묻고 → (A) 이유에 대해 상술을 하고 이해했냐고 묻자 → (B) 알았다고 대답하는 것이 자연스럽다.

07 빈칸에는 '숫자 4를 11로 만들기 위해 막대기 하나를 옮겨야 한다'라는 내용이 들어가는 것이 적절하다.

08 '의문사+조동사+주어+동사 ~?' 어순을 사용하고, 'minus'는 전치사로 '~을 뺀'의 의미로 주어인 'four'를 수식하는 역할을 한다. 'equal'이 동사로 '~와 같다'라는 의미이다.

09 '당신은 번거롭게 티켓을 출력할 필요가 없습니다.'라는 의미가 적절하므로 'need to'를 'don't need to'로 바꾸어야 한다.

시험대비 기본평가 p.72

01 Do you see what I mean?
02 ④
03 ②

01 Do you see what I mean?은 '내 말이 무슨 뜻인지 알겠어?'라는 뜻으로 상대방에게 어떤 상황에 대해 그것을 이해했는지 묻는 표현이다.

02 대화의 내용상 상대방에게 어떤 상황에 대해 그것을 이해했는지 묻는 표현이 오는 것이 적절하다. ④번은 '막대를 옮겼니?'의 뜻이다.

03 대화의 흐름상 '왜 선거에서 이기지 못했니?'의 의미가 오는 것이 적절하다.

시험대비 실력평가 p.73~74

01 ③   02 ⑤   03 ④   04 ③
05 ②   06 ④   07 ②
08 How could four minus five equal six?   09 ④

01 뒤에서 Henry가 한 말로 보아 건강에 대해 염려한다는 내용이 적절하다.

02 Henry가 조사한 내용을 통해 대부분의 학생들이 fast food를 좋아하는 것을 알 수 있다.

서술형 시험대비 p.75

01 Eighty students liked them.
02 Do you see what I mean?
03 out of, romance movies, thirty percent of, Two out of, ten percent
04 move one of the sticks in number four to make it eleven

01 질문: '얼마나 많은 학생들이 간식으로 피자와 프라이드치킨을 좋아했는가?' / 100명 중에 80%가 피자와 프라이드치킨을 좋아한다고 했으므로 80명의 학생들이 그것을 좋아한다는 것을 알 수 있다.

02 "Do you see what I mean?"은 '내 말이 무슨 뜻인지 알겠어?' 라는 뜻으로 상대방에게 어떤 상황에 대해 그것을 이해했는지 묻는 표현이다.

03 원 도표를 보면, 20명 중 6명이 로맨스 영화를 좋아하는데, 그것은 전체의 30%에 해당된다. 그리고 20명 중 2명이 공포영화를 좋아하는데 그것은 전체의 10%에 해당된다는 것을 알 수 있다.

04 '너는 숫자 4를 11로 만들기 위해 막대기 하나를 옮기면 돼.'라는 의미가 적절하다.

Grammar

p.76~77

핵심 Check

1 (1) too, to (2) enough (3) for (4) enough
2 (1) is (2) comes
3 Nobody

시험대비 기본평가

p.78

01 (1) 없음 → 없음 (2) believe → believes
  (3) studying → study (4) it → 제거
02 seems 또는 seemed **03** ⑤
04 (1) I slept so late that I couldn't get up early.
  (2) He was so wise that he could accept the offer.
  (3) The box was so heavy that I couldn't lift it.
  (4) The problem was too difficult for me to solve.
  (5) She was lucky enough to be chosen for the team.

01 (1) 'None of 복수 명사' 뒤에 단수 동사나 복수 동사가 오므로 어법상 적절하다. (2) Not everyone 뒤에는 단수 동사가 오므로 believe를 believes로 고치는 것이 적절하다. (3) 'too 형/부 to 동사원형' 구문이므로 studying을 study로 고치는 것이 적절하다. (4) 'too 형/부 to 동사원형' 구문에서 주어와 to부정사의 목적어가 일치하는 경우, 목적어를 삭제한다.

02 'None of+불가산명사' 뒤에는 단수 동사가 오므로 현재형일 경우 seems가 오고, 과거형일 때는 seemed가 오는 것이 적절하다.

03 too 형/부 to동사원형 구문에서 주어와 to부정사의 목적어가 일치하는 경우, 목적어를 삭제한다.

04 (1), (3), (4) too 형/부 to 동사원형 구문은 so 형/부 that 주어 can't 동사원형으로 바꿔 쓸 수 있다. (2)와 (5) 형/부 enough to 동사원형 구문은 so 형/부 that 주어 can 동사원형으로 바꿔 쓸 수 있다.

시험대비 실력평가

p.79~81

01 so → too	**02** ②	**03** ②	**04** ①
05 ④	**06** ④, ⑤	**07** ⑤	**08** ⑤
09 ④	**10** so, that, them		**11** ①
12 ④	**13** ⑤	**14** ②	**15** ①
16 ③	**17** ①		
18 (1) none (2) Not (3) for	**19** ③, ⑤		**20** ⑤

01 나는 그 차가 너무 뜨거워서 마실 수 없다. 'too 형용사 to 동사원형' 구문으로 so를 too로 고치는 것이 적절하다.

02 그에게 그 자동차는 너무 비싸서 살 수 없다. 'too 형/부 to 동사원형' 구문으로 to부정사의 의미상의 주어는 'for+목적격'이므로 빈칸에 for가 적절하다.

03 다행히도, 화재가 났을 때 집에는 아무도 없었다. 'no one+단수 동사'이므로 were를 was로 고쳐야 한다. 그러므로 ②를 고르는 것이 적절하다.

04 '모든 이가 그것을 볼 수는 없다'는 '부분 부정'이므로 everyone을 수식할 어휘로 빈칸에 not을 넣는 것이 적절하다. 'not+전체를 나타내는 말'은 부분 부정'의 의미이다.

05 첫 번째 문장은 '무슨 일이 없다'는 의미가 들어가야 하므로 nothing이 적절하다. 두 번째 문장은 '모든 사람들이 ~하지 않습니다.'라는 부분 부정이 들어가야 하므로 not everyone이 적절하다. 세 번째 문장은 no one이 주어이므로 단수 동사가 적절하다.

06 승객 중 심하게 다친 사람은 아무도 없었다. 'None of 복수명사' 뒤에는 단수 동사나 복수 동사가 온다.

07 '그 책은 ____가 읽기엔 어렵다.'의 의미로 'too 형/부 to 동사원형' 구문이다. to부정사의 의미사의 주어는 'for+목적격'이므로 주격으로 쓰인 ⑤는 부적절하다.

08 그 농담은 너무 무례해서 차마 옮길 수가 없다. 'too 형/부 to동사원형' 구문으로 주어와 to부정사의 목적어가 일치하는 경우 목적어를 삭제한다.

09 • 그 무리들 중 누구도 서로 알지 못했다. ④ 그 무리에 있는 어느 누구도 서로를 알지 못했다. ① 그 무리에 있는 모두는 서로를 알았다. ② 그 무리들에 있는 모두가 서로를 아는 것은 아니었다. ③ 그 무리들에서 몇몇은 서로를 알고 있었고, 다른 이들은 서로를 몰랐다. ⑤ 그 무리들에서 몇몇은 서로를 알고 있었고, 다른 몇몇은 서로를 모르고 있었으며 또 다른 몇몇은 새로운 멤버들이었다.

10 so~that ... 구문으로 바꿔 쓰는 문제이다.

11 '모든 사람들이 ~하지는 않다.'이므로 '부분 부정'이다. 그러므로 ① 을 고르는 것이 적절하다. ② 네 환상을 깨고 싶진 않지만 모든 사람이 너만큼 정직하지는 않다.(= 당신만큼 정직한 사람은 없다. 전체 부정) ③ 네 환상을 깨고 싶지는 않지만 모든 이가 너만큼 정직하지는 않다. ④ 네 환상을 깨고 싶지만 모든 사람이 너만큼 정직하지는 않다. ⑤ 네 환상을 깨고 싶지만 모든 사람이 너만큼 정직하지는 않다.

12 그녀는 너무 수줍음이 많아서 누구에게 도와 달라고 하지를 못

했다. 'too 형용사/부사 to 동사원형' 구문이므로 asking을 ask로 고치는 것이 적절하다.

13 밖에서 식사를 해도 될 정도로 날이 따뜻해요. 'It's 형/부 enough to동사원형' 구문은 'It's so 형/부 that 주어 can 동사원형'으로 바꿔 쓸 수 있다. ① 너무 따뜻해서 밖에서 식사할 수 없다. ② 따뜻하지만 밖에서 식사할 수 없다. ③ 밖에서 식사할 만큼 따뜻하지 않다. ④ 밖에서 식사할 만큼 시원하다.

14 • 평서문은 The cable is long enough to reach the socket.이므로 의문문으로 전환될 때 첫 번째 빈칸에는 Is, 두 번째 빈칸에는 enough to를 넣는 것이 적절하다.

15 ① 아무도 다치지 않았다는 것을 알고 우리는 놀랐다. no one 은 단수로 받으므로 were를 was로 고치는 것이 적절하다. ② 상심해서 죽은 사람은 없다. ③ 아무도 그녀의 판단에 이의를 제기한 적이 없다. ④ 주인공에 아직 아무도 선정이 되지 않았다. ⑤ 아무도 오지 않을 거라는 것이 곧 분명해졌다.

16 모두가 이 새로운 유행이 아시아 영화계를 위해 바람직하다고 생각하는 것은 아니다. 주어 'Not everyone' 뒤에 단수 동사가 적절하다.

17 • 반드시 아무도 이것에 대해서 알지 못하도록 해라. 주어 'no one' 뒤에 이어지는 동사는 단수이며 의미상 finds out이 오는 것이 적절하다.

18 어법에 맞게 배열하면, (1) It is none of your business. (2) Not everyone thinks alike. (3) The snow was too deep for him to walk.

19 ③ 이제 그들이 그것을 연기하기에는 너무 늦다. 'too 형용사 to 동사원형' 구문으로 of를 for로 고치는 것이 적절하다. ⑤ 세일 가격이 너무 좋아서 놓칠 수가 없었다. 'too 형/부 to 동사원형' 구문으로 주어와 to부정사의 목적어가 일치하는 경우 목적어를 삭제한다. ① 좀 조용히 해 달라는 것이 너무 많은 요구인가요? 'too 부사 to 동사원형' 구문의 의문문 형태이다. ② 제가 주문을 취소하기에 너무 늦었나요? 'too 형용사 to 동사원형' 구문의 의문문 형태이다. ④ 그날 밤은 항해를 하기엔 폭풍우가 너무 심했다.

20 죽음은 삶보다 보편적이다. 모든 사람은 죽기 마련이지만 모든 이가 사는 것은 아니다. 전제가 죽음은 삶보다 보편적이라고 했으므로 (A)는 '죽다' 동사와 어울리는 보편적인 사실이 들어가야 하므로 everyone이 적절하다. (B)는 '살다' 동사와 어울리면서 앞 문장에서 'than life'와 논리적으로 알맞은 not everyone이 들어가는 것이 적절하다.

01 No one was supposed to know about it.
02 he can't ask me → I can't ask him
03 (1) (f)or (2) (N)o
04 (1) The machine is so dangerous that people can't handle it.
 (2) The shop is too crowded to look around.
05 (1) No one could have predicted the final outcome.
 (2) Not everyone could have predicted the final outcome.
 (3) She has been well enough to go out lately.
 (4) Is she well enough to travel?
06 (1) He's strong enough to lift a car.
 (2) The food wasn't enough to satisfy his hunger.
 (3) She is so tall that she can reach the top of the bookcase.
07 (1) Nobody parked their car in the garage.
 (2) Some parked their car in the garage, but others didn't.
08 The door is too stiff to open.
09 (1) no one (2) no one
10 read
11 (1) No one was to be
 (2) enough sugar to make
 (3) enough time for us to
 (4) so tired that he couldn't climb up

01 'No one+단수 동사'이므로 were를 was로 고치는 것이 적절하다.

02 난 이제 너무 겁이 나서 그에게 물어 볼 수가 없어요. 'too 형/부 to 동사원형'은 'so 형/부 that 주어 can't 동사원형'으로 바꿔 쓸 수 있다. (A)에서 내가 그에게 물어보는 것이 겁이 난 것이므로 (B)에서 that절 이하의 주어와 목적어를 I와 him으로 바꿔주는 것이 적절하다.

03 (1) to부정사의 의미상의 주어는 'for+목적격'이므로 빈칸에 for를 쓰는 것이 적절하다. (2) 빈칸 앞에 주어진 철자와 문맥상 내용을 보면 '아무도 모른다'는 내용이 들어가야 하므로 no를 쓰는 것이 적절하다.

04 'so 형/부 that 주어 can't 동사원형'은 'too 형/부 to 동사원형'과 같다. 'too 형/부 to 동사원형' 구문에서 to부정사의 의미상의 주어가 일반 사람들을 지칭할 경우 생략이 가능하다.

05 (1)은 우리말에 맞게 보기에서 could have predicted와 outcome을 이용하여 전체 부정의 문장(No one ~)을 쓰는 것이 적절하다. (2) '모두가 ~한 것은 아니다.' 부분 부정 (3) '최근에 그녀의 컨디션이 좋아진 것'으로 'she has been well'을

쓰고, '~하기에 충분하다.'는 'be well enough to'로 쓰는 것이 적절하다. (4)의 평서문은 She is well enough to travel. 이므로 이를 의문문으로 전환하여 쓰고, '~할 정도로 충분하다.' 표현은 'be well enough to'로 쓴다.

06 (1) '충분히 ~할 정도'의 표현은 형/부 enough to동사원형으로 할 수 있으므로 strong enough to lift, (3) so~that ... 구문

07 (1) 아무도 차고에 그들의 차를 주차하지 않았다. 'No one 대신 Nobody를 써도 같은 뜻이다. (2) 모두가 차고에 그들의 차를 주차한 것은 아니었다. 'Not everyone'은 '부분 부정'의 문장으로 주어진 단어를 활용하여 'Some parked ~, but others didn't.'로 다시 쓰는 것이 적절하다.

08 보기의 우리말을 영작할 때 어순은 the door / is / too / stiff / to / open. 이다. 주어진 단어에서 it은 open의 목적어로 쓸 수 없다. 'too ~ to ...' 구문에서 주어와 to부정사의 목적어가 일치하는 경우, 목적어를 생략한다.

09 (1) '~는 없다'라는 전체 부정은 'no one'으로 나타낸다. (2) '아무도 ~ 않다'를 'no one'으로 나타낸다.

10 'too+형용사+to 동사원형' 구문으로 빈칸에 '읽다'의 동사원형 형태가 와야 하므로 read를 쓰는 것이 적절하다.

11 (1) 우리말에 '한 사람도'라고 되어 있고 주어진 단어에 no가 있으므로 no one을 주어로 하고, to be가 있으므로 수동태로 영작한다. (2) '만들기에 충분한 설탕'은 'enough sugar to make'로 쓴다. (3) to go의 의미상의 주어로 'for us'를 쓰고'충분한 시간'은 enough time으로 쓴다. (4) so ~ that 주어 can't …: 너무 ~해서 …할 수 없다.

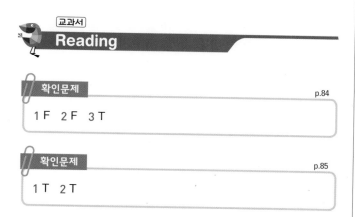

교과서 Reading

확인문제   p.84

1 F   2 F   3 T

확인문제   p.85

1 T   2 T

교과서 확인학습 A
p.86~87

01 was doing his math homework, struggling with
02 too hard to read, draw, these, needs graphs

03 put down, picked up
04 decided to read himself, was about to open
05 looked up from, to see who was talking
06 who was
07 Close, repeat after
08 You can talk, repeat
09 repeated the words, heard, shouting
10 When, on horses
11 chasing, with arrows, shouted
12 It's, for you to stand
13 pulled, rode
14 arrived at, stopped, got off
15 my name is
16 the Robin Hood from
17 Who are you, are you
18 why I'm here, must be, saved, from, Is there anything, for
19 get back, that, took, taxed them
20 too greedy to share, enough money to buy
21 help them get, back, However, no one can get
22 take me to the tower, count the number of
23 hid up, counted, one by one
24 There are, from, to
25 three soldiers until noon, eight soldiers until
26 Lastly, until, go inside between, and noon
27 don't get it
28 might make this easier to
29 drew, showed it
30 the most dangerous time
31 Four times more soldiers, than, what I mean
32 get it, so much
33 realize the importance of graphs, that, them
34 walked out of, looked back, waving
35 waved back, himself, adventure, do I go back, should say

교과서 확인학습 B
p.88~89

01 Pascal was doing his math homework in his room. He was struggling with graphs.
02 "It's too hard to read and draw graphs. Why do I need these anyway? No one needs graphs in real life."
03 He put down his pen and picked up his favorite book, *Robin Hood*.
04 He decided to read himself to sleep. When he

was about to open the book, he heard a voice.

05 He looked up from the book to see who was talking.

06 He couldn't believe his eyes. It was his dog, Manny, who was talking!

07 "Close your eyes and repeat after me. *Cogito ergo sum*," said Manny.

08 "You can talk?" "Just repeat! *Cogito ergo sum*."

09 Pascal closed his eyes and repeated the words. Suddenly, he heard men shouting.

10 When he opened his eyes, he saw soldiers on horses.

11 They were chasing a man with arrows in his hand. The man saw Pascal and shouted.

12 "It's too dangerous for you to stand there. Come on."

13 The man pulled Pascal onto his horse and rode into the woods.

14 When they arrived at a house, the man stopped and got off his horse.

15 "Hello, my name is Robin Hood."

16 "Wow! Are you the Robin Hood from the book?"

17 "No, I'm the Robin Hood of Sherwood Forest. Who are you and why are you here?"

18 "My name is Pascal. I don't know why I'm here, but there must be a reason. You saved me from the soldiers. Thank you so much. Is there anything I can do for you?"

19 "Well, can you help us get back the money that the king took from the people? He taxed them too much.

20 He is too greedy to share with the people, so they don't have enough money to buy food.

21 I want to help them get their money back. However, there are many soldiers in the tower, so no one can get inside."

22 "Hmm... I think I have a solution. But first, can you take me to the tower? I need to count the number of soldiers."

23 Robin and Pascal hid up in a tree and counted the soldiers one by one.

24 "There are five soldiers from midnight to six in the morning.

25 Next, there are three soldiers until noon, and then there are eight soldiers until six in the evening.

26 Lastly, there are twelve soldiers until midnight. So, you should go inside between six in the morning and noon."

27 "What? I don't get it."

28 Pascal thought for a moment. 'Hmm... A graph might make this easier to understand.'

29 Pascal drew a graph and showed it to Robin.

30 "Look, the most dangerous time is between six in the evening and midnight.

31 Four times more soldiers work at that time than from six in the morning until noon. Do you see what I mean?"

32 "Aha! I get it now. Thank you so much, Pascal!"

33 "You're welcome. Now I realize the importance of graphs. No one can say that we don't need them anymore."

34 Pascal walked out of the woods. When he looked back, he saw Robin Hood waving at him.

35 Pascal waved back and said to himself, "It was a great adventure. How do I go back? Oh, I know. I should say the words *Cogito ergo sum*!"

시험대비 실력평가 p.90~93

01 ③　　　02 repeat　　　03 ④　　　04 ⑤

05 ④

06 Pascal wants Robin to take him to the tower.

07 ⑤　　　08 ⑤

09 Robin Hood stopped and got off his horse when they arrived at a house.

10 ④　　　11 ③

12 He saw Robin Hood waving at him.

13 Pascal was doing his math homework in his room.

14 ④　　　15 ④　　　16 ⑤　　　17 ⑤

18 ⑤

19 He wants to help people get their money back.

20 ④　　　21 파스칼이 로빈에게 설명해 준 것

22 He realized the importance of graphs.　23 ⑤

---

01 주어진 문장은 파스칼이 책을 펴려고 할 때 목소리를 들었다는 것이므로, 누가 이야기를 하는지 보기 위해 책에서 눈을 들어 보았다는 내용 앞에 위치하는 것이 자연스럽다.

02 무언가를 다시 또는 한 번 이상 말하거나 쓰다는 '반복하다, 한 번 더 말하다'이다.

03 Manny는 파스칼에게 자신을 따라 말하라고 하였다.

04 이어지는 파스칼의 말로 보아 로빈 후드는 그에게 누구이며 왜 여기에 있는지를 물어본 것임을 알 수 있다.

05 사람들의 돈을 다시 찾을 수 있도록 돕고 싶지만 탑 안에 병사들

이 많아서 아무도 들어갈 수 없다는 연결이 자연스럽다. 따라서 However가 적절하다.

06 파스칼은 로빈이 자신을 탑에 데려가 주기를 원한다.

07 모두 파스칼을 가리키지만 ⑤번은 로빈 후드를 가리키고 있다.

08 말을 탄 병사들이 화살을 들고 있는 로빈 후드를 뒤쫓고 있는 상황에서 로빈 후드는 파스칼을 말에 올려 태우고 숲으로 말을 몰았다. 따라서 ⑤번이 가장 적절하다.

09 그들이 한 집에 이르렀을 때, 로빈 후드는 멈추고 말에서 내렸다.

10 오전 여섯 시부터 정오까지보다 저녁 여섯시와 자정 사이에 네 배나 더 많은 병사들이 일하므로 가장 위험한 시간이다. 따라서 the most dangerous라고 쓰는 것이 적절하다.

11 파스칼은 그래프의 중요성을 깨달으며 아무도 그래프가 더 이상 필요 없다고 말할 수 없을 것이라고 하였다.

12 파스칼이 뒤돌아봤을 때 그는 로빈 후드가 그에게 손을 흔들고 있는 것을 보았다.

13 파스칼은 그의 방에서 수학 숙제를 하고 있었다.

14 파스칼은 아무도 실제 생활에서는 그래프를 필요로 하지 않는다고 하였으므로 ④번이 가장 적절하다.

15 파스칼은 그래프 문제에 고군분투하고 있었고, Manny는 파스칼의 개다. Manny는 파스칼에게 눈을 감고 자신의 말을 따라 말하라고 하였고 파스칼은 Manny의 말대로 했다.

16 왕이 사람들에게 세금을 너무 많이 부과하고 사람들이 음식을 살 충분한 돈이 없다고 하였으므로 왕은 '탐욕스러운' 사람임을 알 수 있다.

17 로빈은 파스칼이 그곳에 서 있는 것이 너무 위험하다며 파스칼을 그의 말에 올려 태웠다.

18 밑줄 친 ⓐ는 강한 추측을 나타내어 '~임에 틀림없다'라는 의미로 쓰이고 있다. ① 꼭 필요한 것 ②, ③, ④ ~해야만 한다 ⑤ ~임에 틀림없다

19 로빈은 사람들의 돈을 다시 찾을 수 있도록 돕고 싶다고 하였다.

20 자정부터 새벽 여섯 시까지는 다섯 명의 병사들이 있고 정오까지는 세 명의 병사들이 있다. 그 외의 시간에는 그보다 더 많은 병사들이 있으므로 새벽 여섯시에서 정오 사이에 들어가야 한다고 말하는 것이 적절하다.

21 로빈이 언제 들어가는 것이 좋은지 파스칼이 설명했지만 그가 알아듣지 못하자 그래프가 자신의 설명을 이해하는 걸 쉽게 해줄지도 모른다고 말한 것이다.

22 파스칼은 그래프의 중요성을 깨달았다고 하였다.

23 파스칼은 손을 흔드는 로빈에게 손을 흔들어 답하고는 정말 멋진 모험이라고 생각하였다.

01 He had hard time with graphs.
02 He picked up his favorite book, *Robin Hood*.
03 It was because his dog, Manny, could talk.
04 When he was about to open the book, he heard a voice.
05 He saw soldiers on horses.
06 He had arrows in his hand.
07 It was because the king taxed the people too much.
08 the woods, get the money back
09 It was because there were many soldiers in the tower.
10 They counted the soldiers one by one.
11 There are eight soldiers from midnight to noon.
12 He used a graph.
13 He saw Robin Hood waving at him.

01 'struggle with'는 '~에 고군분투하다'는 의미로 'have hard time with'와 같은 의미로 쓰인다.

02 파스칼은 그의 펜을 내려놓고, 그가 가장 좋아하는 책, '로빈 후드'를 집어 들었다.

03 눈을 들어 올려 보았을 때 파스칼이 놀란 이유는 그의 개가 말을 할 수 있어서였다.

04 파스칼이 책을 펴려고 할 때, 그는 목소리를 들었다.

05 눈을 떴을 때 파스칼은 말을 탄 병사들을 보았다.

06 로빈은 손에 화살을 들고 있었다.

07 왕이 사람들에게 세금을 너무 많이 부과해서 음식을 살 충분한 돈이 없다고 하였다.

08 파스칼을 태우고 숲으로 말을 타고 간 로빈은 파스칼에게 상황을 설명하고 사람들에게 돈을 돌려줄 수 있도록 자신을 도와달라고 하였다.

09 아무도 탑 안으로 들어갈 수 없다고 말한 이유는 탑 안에 병사들이 많아서이다.

10 로빈과 파스칼은 나무에 숨어서 병사들의 수를 한 명씩 세었다.

11 자정부터 새벽 여섯 시까지는 다섯 명의 병사들이 있고 정오까지는 세 명의 병사들이 있으므로 자정부터 정오까지는 총 여덟 명의 병사들이 있다.

12 로빈을 이해시키기 위해서 파스칼은 그래프를 사용하였다.

13 파스칼이 뒤돌아봤을 때 그는 로빈 후드가 자기에게 손을 흔들고 있는 것을 보았다.

19

01 novel　02 ④　03 ②　04 ⑤
05 get off　06 ④　07 ③　08 ①
09 In other words, most students liked pizza more
　　than any other snack.
10 ③　　11 ③
12 (1) I'm too scared to go on my own.
　　(2) I'm too busy to take a rest.
　　(3) He is so honest that he can't tell a lie.
　　(4) None of the passengers and crew were
　　　　injured.
13 (1) They were so brave that they could face the
　　　　strong enemy.
　　(2) He is so clever that he can solve the riddle.
14 ②　　15 ④
16 This chance is too good to miss.　17 ③
18 ②　　19 ④　　20 ⑤　　21 ⑤
22 ②
23 Robin asked Pascal if he could help him get
　　back people's money.
24 ③　　25 the sound　26 ④

01 유의어 관계이다. 나타내다 : 소설

02 (A) 노벨상은 세계에서 가장 인정받는 상으로 여겨지고 있다.
　　(B) 나도 네게 똑같은 걸 막 물어보려던 참이었어. be about
　　to: 막 ~하려고 하다

03 신체의 특정 부분을 움직일 수 있도록 도와주는 신체 조직: 근육
　　(muscle)

04 활에서 쏘는 한 쪽 끝에 날카로운 뾰족한 끝을 가진 얇은 막대:
　　화살(arrow)

05 get off: 내리다

06 ④번의 'salty'는 형용사로 '맛이 짠, 짭짤한'의 의미이다. '소금'
　　은 'salt'다.

07 대화는 반장 선거에 출마한 내용으로 'run for'가 적절하다.

08 6 더하기 2를 11로 만들기 위해서 숫자 6의 왼쪽 아래에 있는
　　막대를 옮겨서 9로 만들면 된다.

10 주어진 문장은 내 말이 무슨 뜻인지 알겠어?'라는 뜻으로 'I get
　　it.(이해했어.)'라는 문장 앞에 위치하는 것이 자연스럽다.

11 ③번에 대한 답은 대화에서 언급되어 있지 않다.

12 (1), (2) '너무 ~해서 …할 수 없다'로 'too 형/부 to동사원형' 구
　　문을 활용한다. 괄호 안의 단어를 활용하여 (1) 'too scared to
　　go on my own.', (2) 'too busy to take a rest.'로 쓴다, (3)
　　괄호 안의 단어를 활용하여 'so honest that he can't tell a lie.'
　　로 쓴다. (4) 전체 부정 문장으로 주어가 복수이므로 '아무도 ~하

지 않았다.'는 none of를 활용하고 were injured로 쓴다.

13 '형/부 enough to동사원형'은 'so 형/부 that 주어 can 동사원
　　형'으로 바꿔 쓸 수 있다. (1) 그들은 강한 적을 대적할 만큼 충
　　분히 용감했다. (2) 그는 아주 영리해서 그 수수께끼를 풀 수 있
　　다.

14 ② 바다에서 아무도 수영하지 않는다. 'No one+단수 동사'를
　　써야 하므로 어법상 적절하다. ① 아무도 교복을 입고 있지 않는
　　다. are를 is로 고쳐야 한다. ③ 아무도 그 소식에 기뻐하는 사
　　람이 없었다. were를 was로 고치는 것이 적절하다. ④ 아무도
　　가방을 가지고 다니지 않습니다. carry를 carries로 고치는 것
　　이 적절하다. ⑤ 그가 틀릴 때 그를 고쳐주는 이가 아무도 없다.
　　correct를 corrects로 고치는 것이 적절하다.

15 ④ The toy was too expensive for me to buy.가 적절하다.

16 'too 형/부 to 동사원형' 구문에서 주어와 to부정사의 목적어가
　　일치하는 경우, 목적어를 삭제한다. 그러므로 miss의 목적어로
　　쓰여 있는 it을 삭제하는 것이 적절하다.

17 그 개는 너무 커서 박스 안에 들어갈 수 없다. 'too 형/부 to 동
　　사원형'은 'so 형/부 that 주어 can't 동사원형'과 같으므로 can
　　을 can't로 고쳐야 한다.

18 빈칸 (A)에는 전치사 with가 들어간다. ① refer to: ~을 참고하
　　다, 보다 ② be concerned with: ~와 관련이 있다 ③ in terms
　　of: ~라는 점에서 ④ result from: ~이 원인이다 ⑤ bring
　　about: ~을 야기하다, 초래하다

19 목소리를 듣고 누가 말하는지 보기 위해 책에서 눈을 들어 올렸
　　다고 말하는 것이 가장 자연스럽다.

20 파스칼은 눈을 감은 채로 Manny의 말을 따라하였다.

21 병사들의 수를 셀 필요가 있다고 말하는 것이 자연스럽다. a
　　number of: 많은, the number of: ~의 수

22 밑줄 친 (A)는 money를 수식하는 형용사로 쓰인 to부정사이
　　다. ① 진주어 ② 형용사적 용법 ③ 부사적 용법 중 목적 ④ 명
　　사적 용법 중 목적격 보어 ⑤ 부사적 용법 중 감정의 원인

23 로빈은 파스칼에게 사람들의 돈을 되찾을 수 있도록 도와줄 수
　　있는지 물었다.

24 위 글은 세계 여러 문화에서 숫자가 가지는 의미에 관한 것이다.
　　따라서 ③번이 가장 적절하다.

25 숫자 4라는 단어의 소리는 중국 단어에서 죽음이라는 단어의 소
　　리와 비슷하다는 의미이다.

26 성 안토니오는 잃어버린 물건들이나 사람들을 위해 기도했다고
　　하였다.

01 midnight   02 ④   03 ③   04 ⑤

05 ④

06 How come you didn't win?

07 run for   08 ⑤

09 Do you get what I mean?

10 (A) it takes a lot of muscles to look angry

   (B) it's not good to stay angry for a long time

11 (1) Forty percent of the students like red.

   (2) Twenty percent of the students like blue.

12 Not everyone

13 (1) No one was at home.

   (2) No one has told me about the new rules.

   (3) Not everyone is able to join these active groups.

   (4) Not everyone seems to be happy.

14 (1) He was too young to understand it.

   (2) Alex was too shy to talk to her.

   (3) The manual was too complicated for him to understand.

15 ⓐ waving   ⓑ waved   16 ②

17 Twelve soldiers work from six in the evening to midnight.

18 ⑤   19 ④   20 ②

21 There were four characters.

22 ⑤

---

01 반의어 관계이다. 탐욕스러운–관대한 : 정오–자정

02 신문에 나오는 글: 기사(article)

03 그림에서 숫자 4를 11로 만들어야 하므로 'five'를 'four'로 바꾸어야 한다.

04 대화의 소년은 Emma가 말한 내용을 이해했다고 말한다.

05 'percent of'는 'of' 뒤에 오는 명사의 수에 동사를 일치시킨다. '단수명사+단수동사 / 복수명사+복수동사'를 사용한다. 'doesn't'를 'don't'로 고쳐야 한다.

06 'How come?'은 놀람을 표현하는 말로 '왜(Why?)'의 의미를 가진다. 'How come' 뒤에는 '주어+동사'가 올 수 있다. 'How come you didn't win?'의 줄임말이다.

07 '선거에서 후보자로 경쟁하다'의 의미로 'run for(출마하다)'가 적절하다.

08 이 조사에서 학생들이 얼마나 많은 종류의 간식을 먹을 수 있는지는 언급되어 있지 않다.

09 'Do you see what I mean?'과 같은 표현으로 'Do you get what I mean?', 'Do you understand?' 등을 사용할 수 있다.

10 (A) '~하는 데 …을 필요로 하다'라는 구문은 'it takes+목적어

+to V'를 이용한다. (B) 가주어(it) ~ 진주어(to V) 구문을 이용한다.

11 질문: 도표에서 무엇을 알 수 있는가?

12 '모두가 ~하는 것은 아니다.'라는 의미를 지니는 '부분 부정'이므로 not everyone이 적절하다. 'no one'은 '전체 부정'이다.

13 nobody = no one, not+everyone: 부분 부정 (1) 집에는 아무도 없었다. nobody는 no one으로 바꿔 쓸 수 있고 두 단어 모두 단수 취급을 하므로 was를 쓰는 것이 적절하다. (2) 아무도 내게 새로운 규칙에 대해 말해주지 않았다. (3) 모든 사람이 이 활동적인 모임에 참여할 수 있는 것은 아니다. (4) 모든 사람들이 행복한 것 같지는 않아 보인다.

14 (1) 그는 너무 어려서 그것을 이해할 수 없었다. (2) Alex는 너무 부끄러워서 그녀에게 말을 걸 수 없었다. (3) 그 매뉴얼은 너무 복잡해서 그가 이해할 수 없었다.

15 지각동사의 목적어와 목적격 보어의 관계가 능동인 경우, 목적격 보어로 현재분사나 동사원형을 모두 쓸 수 있다. 단, 이 경우에는 진행을 강조하는 현재분사 waving다.

16 밑줄 친 (A)는 이해가 안 된다는 말이다. 따라서 ②번이 적절하다.

17 오후 여섯시부터 자정까지 일하는 병사들은 열 두 명이라고 하였다.

18 파스칼이 그래프를 그려서 로빈에게 보여줬을 때, 로빈은 즉시 이해하였다.

19 두 사람이 병사들의 수를 센 이유는 안으로 들어가기에 가장 좋은 시간을 찾기 위해서임을 알 수 있다.

20 다른 어구를 사용하여 앞 문장과 똑같은 내용을 말하고 있으므로 '다시 말해서(In other words)'가 가장 적절하다.

21 학생들은 홍길동, 콩쥐, 로빈 후드, 놀부 중 하나의 캐릭터를 선택할 수 있었다.

22 ⑤ 놀부는 너무 탐욕스러워서 선택되지 않았다고 하였다. ④ 서른 명의 학생 중 아홉 명이 콩쥐를 선택하였으므로, 삼십 퍼센트의 학생이 콩쥐를 선택한 셈이다.

---

01 (A) I'm worried about their health.

   (B) Do you see what I mean?

02 (1) big enough to fit me

   (2) enough food to go

   (3) enough money to buy me a drink

03 (1) about   (2) pets (3) five out of   (4) ten students

(5) fish
04 (1) Despite Covid-19, not everyone wears a mask.
  (2) During this rainy season, no one was walking on the streets due to heavy rain.
  (3) [1] The pandemic is so severe that you[we] can't travel to Berlin.
    [2] The pandemic is too severe for me to travel to Berlin.
05 he saw Robin Hood waving at him
06 It was between six in the evening and midnight.
07 Four times more soldiers worked at that time than from six in the morning until noon.
08 Pascal drew a graph to make it easier for Robin to understand.
09 the character is so greedy that it can't be liked by others.
10 Twenty percent of students chose Robin Hood.

01 (A) '에 관해 걱정하다'라는 의미로 'be worried about'을 사용한다. (B) 동사 'see'의 목적어 자리에 사용된 문장으로 'mean'의 목적어가 빠져 있는 불완전한 문장이므로 'that'을 관계대명사 'what'으로 바꾸는 것이 적절하다.

02 (1) 빈칸에는 '나에게 맞을 만큼 충분히 큰'이 들어가야 하므로 '형/부 enough to동사원형' 구문을 활용하여 'big enough to fit me'로 쓰는 것이 적절하다. (2) 빈칸에는 '골고루 돌아갈 만큼 충분한 음식'이 들어가야 하므로 'enough 명사 to동사원형' 구문을 활용하여 'enough food to go'로 쓰는 것이 적절하다. (3) 빈칸에는 '나에게 음료수를 살 만큼 충분한 돈'이 들어가야 하므로 'enough money to buy me a drink'로 쓰는 것이 적절하다.

03 (1) '이 그래프는 무엇에 관한 거야?'라는 의미로 'What ~ about?'이 적절하고, (2)는 '애완동물'에 관한 조사라는 것을 알 수 있다. (3) '25명의 학생들 중 5명'의 의미로 'out of+전체'가 적절하다. (4) 개를 가지고 있는 학생은 10명이다. (5) 7명의 학생은 물고기를 가지고 있다.

05 글의 내용이 과거시제로 전개되고 있으므로 see를 과거 시제로 표현한다. 지각동사의 목적어와 목적격 보어의 관계가 능동인 경우 목적격 보어로 동사원형이나 현재분사를 쓰지만 여기서는 waving이 더 적절하다.

06 파스칼에 따르면 저녁 여섯 시에서 자정까지가 가장 위험한 시간이다.

07 오전 여섯 시부터 정오까지보다 네 배나 더 많은 병사들이 저녁 여섯 시에서 자정까지 일한다고 하였다.

08 파스칼은 로빈이 이해하기 더 쉽게 만들기 위해서 그래프를 그린 것이다.

09 too ~ to V = so ~ that 주어 can't V: 너무 ~해서 V할 수 없는

10 서른 명의 학생 중 여섯 명이 로빈 후드를 선택하였으므로 20퍼센트의 학생이 로빈 후드를 선택했다고 말할 수 있다.

창의사고력 서술형 문제 p.108

|모범답안|
01 thirteen out of, percent of the total, Five out of twenty students, science-fiction books, two out of twenty students, history books
02 (1) 65%   (2) 25%   (3) 10%
03 Fifteen, Hong Gildong, fifty, courageous, nine, Kongiwi, six, Robin Hood, Nolbu, too greedy to be

01 나는 우리 학교 도서관에 필요한 책들을 조사했다. 그 결과 20명 중 13명이 소설을 선택하였다. 이는 전체의 65퍼센트이다. 20명 중 5명은 공상 과학책을 선택했다. 그러나 20명 중 2명만이 역사책을 선택했다.

02 (1) 65% of students in my class read 'novels'. 또는 Most students in my class read 'novels'. (2) 25% of students in my class read 'science-fiction books'. (3) 10% of students in my class read 'history books'. (4) No one in my class reads 'fiction'. 또는 Nobody in my class reads 'fiction'.

단원별 모의고사 p.109~113

01 ⑤   02 lastly   03 ③   04 ④
05 ④
06 Thinking outside the box can be helpful sometimes.
07 it takes only a few muscles to smile
08 facial muscles, smile, angry
09 ④
10 (1) You are too big to ride this bike.
  (2) John's son is too smart to hang out with his friends.
  (3) This coffee is too bitter to drink.
  (4) This apple pie is so delicious that I can't stop buying it.
  (5) This rope is too thick to cut with scissors.
11 ②, ④   12 ①, ②

13 (1) No one really stands out among new recruits.

   (2) Therefore, nobody is able to help the gorillas.

   (3) 없음

   (4) Would you be kind enough to close the window?

14 ②

15 (1) thinks   (2) too   (3) can't   (4) it

16 (C)–(B)–(A)   17 ⑤   18 ⑤

19 It is too dangerous for you to stand there.

20 ②

21 They were chasing a man with arrows in his hand.

22 ④   23 ①, ③   24 ④

25 It was because he needed to count the number of soldiers.

---

01 ⑤번은 'rich(부유한)'에 관한 설명이다. 'greedy(탐욕스러운)'의 영어 설명은 'wanting more money, power, food, etc. than you really need(당신이 정말로 필요로 하는 것보다 더 많은 돈, 힘, 음식 등을 원하는)'이다.

02 반의어 관계이다. 행운의 - 불행의 : 첫째로 – 마지막으로

03 '무슨 문제 있니? 너 무척 속상해 보여.'라는 A의 말에 B가 '안됐구나.'라고 대답하는 것은 어색하다.

04 '앞서 제시한 설명보다 더 간단한 설명을 소개하는 데 사용되는'의 의미로 'in other words(다시 말해)'가 적절하다.

05 ④번의 'Do you see what I mean?'은 '내 말이 무슨 뜻인지 알겠어?'라는 의미는 맞지만, 'What do you mean?'은 상대방의 말이 이해되지 않을 때 '무슨 말이야?'라고 되묻는 표현이다.

06 '틀 밖에서 생각하다'라는 표현은 'think outside the box'이다.

07 웃을 때는 몇 개의 근육만 필요하다는 의미이다.

08 화난 표정을 지을 때는 많은 근육이 필요하지만, 웃을 때는 많은 근육을 필요로 하지 않아. 그러니 오랫동안 화난 상태로 있지 마.

09 (d) 'don't need to'는 '~할 필요가 없다'라는 의미이다.

10 (1), (2), (3), (5)는 'too 형/부 to 동사원형' 구문이다. 'too 형/부 to 동사원형' 구문에서 주어와 to 부정사의 목적어가 일치하는 경우 목적어를 생략해야 하는 것에 주의해야 한다. (5)는 'so 형/부 that 주어 can't 동사원형' 구문이다.

11 • 너무 추워서 우리는 밖에서 를 할 수 없다. 'too 형/부 to 동사원형' 구문이므로 빈칸에 going과 swimming을 넣는 것은 적절치 않다.

12 ① 그는 너무 일이 많아서 쉴 틈이 없었다. '너무 ~해서 …하지 못하다.'는 'so 형/부 that 주어 can't 동사원형' 형태이다, could

---

를 couldn't로 고쳐야 한다. ② 그 컨테이너는 그가 들기에 너무 무거웠다. 'too 형/부 to동사원형' 구문에서 주어와 to부정사의 목적어가 일치하는 경우, 목적어를 생략하므로 lift의 목적어 it을 지워야 한다.

13 (1)과 (2)는 전체 부정 문장으로 No one과 nobody 뒤에는 단수동사를 쓰므로 각각 stand를 stands로, are를 is로 고치는 것이 적절하다. (3) '모든 사람이 ~하는 것은 아니다.'라는 '부분 부정'의 표현은 'not everyone'을 쓰고 이어서 '조동사+동사원형'이 쓰였으므로 어색한 곳이 없다. (4) '형/부 enough to 동사원형' 구문으로 to부정사로 쓰는 것이 적절하다.

14 ② 모든 학생이 애완동물을 기르는 것은 아니다. 그래프에서 보면 no pets에 학생 수가 없으므로 학생들은 모두 애완동물을 기른다고 추측할 수 있다. ① 대부분의 학생들은 개를 키운다. ③ 어느 누구도 고양이를 기르지 않는다. ④ 학급 친구들 중 대략 40퍼센트는 물고기를 키운다. ⑤ 모두가 애완동물을 기른다.

15 우리말에 맞게 배열하면, (1) Not everyone thinks like that. (2) She said the situation was just too stressful for her to deal. (3) I am so full that I can't eat more. (4) The stone was so heavy that he couldn't move it.

16 파스칼은 그래프 문제에 고군분투하다가 (C) 그래프를 읽고 그리는 것이 너무 어렵다며 (B) 펜을 내려놓고 그가 가장 좋아하는 책을 막 펴려고 할 때 어떤 목소리를 들었고 (A) 누가 말하고 있는지 보기 위해 책에서 눈을 들어 올려다보았다.

17 파스칼이 얼마나 오랫동안 숙제를 했는지는 위 글을 읽고 답할 수 없다.

18 be about to V: 막 V하려고 하다

19 '너무 ~해서 …할 수 없는'은 'too ~ to V'로 표현할 수 있다.

20 get off: ~에서 내리다

21 병사들은 손에 화살을 든 남자를 쫓고 있었다.

22 ④번 'greedy'는 '탐욕스러운'이라는 의미이지만, 풀이는 '관대한(generous)'에 해당한다.

23 탐욕스러운 왕이 사람들에게서 가져간 돈을 되찾고자 하므로 Robin의 성품은 정의롭고 용감하다고 말할 수 있다.

24 병사들이 숲에서 로빈을 발견할 때까지 계속해서 추격했다는 말은 위 글에 나와 있지 않다.

25 파스칼이 로빈에게 탑에 데려가 달라고 한 이유는 병사들의 수를 셀 필요가 있어서였다.

23

교과서 파헤치기

Lesson 7

01 평평한	02 지붕	03 숨겨진
04 동굴	05 거대한, 굉장히 큰	06 주로, 일반적으로
07 형형색색의	08 통로	09 반갑지 않은
10 설치하다	11 조수, 흐름	12 습지의
13 나무로 된	14 사다리	15 표면, 지면, 수면
16 짚, 지푸라기	17 백만장자	
18 눈에 보이지 않는, 투명한		19 구멍
20 지탱하다, 떠받치다		21 모든 곳에, 어디나
22 떠다니는	23 높이 올린	24 수용하다
25 보이다, 나타나다	26 저장하다, 보관하다	
27 침략자	28 두꺼운, 살찐	29 상상하다
30 마을, 촌락	31 보통, 대개	32 그러나, 하지만
33 오르다, 올라가다	34 공유하다	35 거꾸로 된, 뒤집힌
36 들르다	37 ~로서 알려지다	38 ~을 물려주다
39 돌아다니다	40 당분간, 잠시 동안	41 ~로 가득 찬
42 A가 ~ 하지 못하게 막다		
43 ~로 구성되다, ~로 만들어지다		

01 usually	02 earth	03 opening
04 raised	05 swampy	06 appear
07 roof	08 invader	09 support
10 unwelcome	11 install	12 cave
13 store	14 colorful	15 imagine
16 flat	17 sometimes	18 hidden
19 surface	20 floating	21 huge
22 thick	23 millionaire	24 house
25 invisible	26 straw	27 wooden
28 ladder	29 mostly	30 walkway
31 rise	32 tide	33 everywhere
34 share	35 on top of	36 all day
37 hand down	38 come over	39 stop A from ~ing
40 be known as	41 walk around	42 pull A up
43 be made up of		

1 invisible, 눈에 보이지 않는, 투명한   2 flat, 평평한
3 house, 수용하다   4 straw, 짚   5 cave, 동굴
6 install, 설치하다   7 opening, 구멍
8 millionaire, 백만장자   9 swampy, 습지의
10 store, 저장하다, 보관하다   11 walkway, 통로
12 thick, 두꺼운   13 invader, 침략자
14 support, 지탱하다, 떠받치다   15 ladder, 사다리
16 tide, 조수

Listen and Speak 1 A

Have, traveling / want, see / take / unique, living / those, beautiful / to, hope, some day / too

Listen and Speak 1 B

it, / Why, waiting for / wait, out / check / could / kidding, cold place / build, stay, vacation / Living, sounds

Listen and Speak 1 C

these, natural / try living / Which, most, live in / strong

Listen and Speak 2 A-1

What / kind / move like / what, lived / travel, with / cool

Listen and Speak 2 A-2

became, millionaire / build / kind, build / covered with / mirrors, almost invisible / would

Listen and Speak 2 A-3

upside down / interesting / easy, because, upside down / try living / What, lived / like, differently

Listen and Speak 2 B

need, visit / Which country / case / would, visited / interested / that, church, designed / how, inspired by nature / How, as

Listen and Speak 2 C

What, magical power / turn into, able to fly freely

Real Life Communication A

living, exciting, so / some dangerous / full, could live / would, lived / explore / where, cave / stay in, Then, dangerous animals / makes sense

Real Life Communication B

stay, during / would, were / go swimming every day, go fishing / sounds

Let's Check 1

This, What, think / deep sea, unique, would, lived / interest, deep sea, So, explore, unique / That

Let's Check 2

matter, wish, could have

Listen and Speak 1 A

G: Have you heard from Julia? She's traveling in Turkey, right?

B: Yes, she sent me some pictures. Do you want to see them?

G: Yes, please.

B: Okay, take a look.

G: Oh, look at those cave houses! They look so unique, don't they? I wish I could try living there.

B: I like those balloons. They look so beautiful!

G: I think Turkey is a wonderful place to visit. I hope to visit there some day.

B: Me too!

Listen and Speak 1 B

B: Will it snow today?

G: I have no idea. Why are you waiting for snow, Taeho?

B: I got a new sled for my birthday. I can't wait to test it out.

G: Let me check the weather. Umm, there will be no snow for a while.

B: I wish I could live in Alaska. Then I could go sledding all day!

G: No kidding! Alaska is a very cold place.

B: I think it would be fun. I want to build a snow house and stay there on vacation.

G: Living in a snow house sounds fun!

Listen and Speak 1 C

A: Look at these houses. They look very natural.

B: Wow, I wish I could try living here.

A: Which house would you most like to live in?

B: I wish I could live in the stone house. It looks very strong.

Listen and Speak 2 A-1

B: This is my dream house, Alice. What do you think?

G: Oh, the house has wheels! Is it a kind of car?

B: Yes, it can move like a car.

G: So what would you do if you lived in that house?

B: I would travel to many places with my family.

G: That sounds cool.

Listen and Speak 2 A-2

G: What would you do if you became a millionaire, Juwon?

B: I would build my own house.

G: What kind of house would you build?

B: I would build a house that is completely covered with mirrors.

G: Why?

B: The mirrors would make the house almost invisible. Wouldn't that be cool?

G: That would be cool!

Listen and Speak 2 A-3

G: Look. The house in this picture is upside down.

B: That's interesting. Does anybody live there?

G: No, it would not be easy to live there because the inside is also upside down.

B: Really? But I want to try living there.

G: What would you do if you lived in that house?

B: I would walk upside down like Spider-Man. I could also see things differently.

Listen and Speak 2 B

G: Dohun, we need to start our project on our dream country to visit.

B: That's right. Which country do you want to visit, Emma?

G: In my case, I want to visit Spain.

B: What would you do if you visited Spain?

G: I'm interested in buildings. So I would go see La Sagrada Familia.

B: Isn't that the church Antoni Gaudi designed?

G: Yes, it is. It would be interesting to see how his design was inspired by nature.

B: Hmm... . How about Gaudí and Spain as the title for our project?

G: I love it!

Listen and Speak 2 C

A: What would you do if you could have a magical power?

B: I would turn into a bird. Then I would be able to fly freely in the sky.

A: That's cool.

Real Life Communication A

Jinho: I think living in a jungle would be really exciting. Don't you think so?

Claire: But there are some dangerous animals in the jungle, Jinho.

Jinho: I know. But the jungle is full of adventure. I wish I could live there.

Claire: What would you do if you lived in the jungle?

Jinho: I would explore it. Maybe I could make some animal friends.

Claire: Then where would you sleep? In a cave?

Jinho: No, I would stay in a tree house. Then I would be safe from dangerous animals.

Claire: That makes sense.

Real Life Communication B

A: I wish I could stay in a house on the water during my vacation.

B: What would you do if you were there?

A: I would go swimming every day. I would also go fishing.

B: That sounds fun.

Let's Check 1

B: This is my dream house. What do you think, Alice?

G: Oh, it's in the deep sea. It looks so unique. So, what would you do if you lived in that house?

B: I have an interest in deep sea animals. So I would explore the deep sea and find some unique sea animals.

G: That sounds cool!

Let's Check 2

A: What's the matter?

B: My computer is so slow. I wish I could have a new computer.

본문 TEST Step 1　　　　　　　　　p.11~12

01 Different, live in, houses
02 Some, ladders, enter, Others
03 others share, houses with
04 Imagine, one, change, life
05 lived, would climb, enter
06 There's, hidden opening, top
07 unwelcome, appeared, stop, from
08 thick, made of, straw
09 keep me cool, warm
10 flat roof, up, under
11 If, lived, would take
12 On, from, to, by
13 tide, rises, full of
14 However, around, through, raised
15 is known as, floating
16 there are, colorful houses
17 wonder how, why, built
18 decided, keep, safe, invaders
19 easy, build, swampy surface
20 So, installed, wooden poles
21 wooden poles, support, to
22 lived, huge round, with
23 neighbor calling, come over

---

24 three to five floors
25 floor is used for
26 store food, tools, floor
27 would, on, third, floor
28 like, living, mostly, same
29 up to, work together
30 Living together, keeps, safe
31 everywhere, different, What, like

본문 TEST Step 2　　　　　　　　　p.13~14

01 Different, live in
02 use ladders to enter their houses, Others live in, on
03 others share, with
04 Imagine, live in one of, that change
05 lived in, would climb, to enter my
06 hidden opening on top
07 If, appeared, would pull, up to stop, from
08 are made of
09 keep me cool, warm
10 a flat roof, sleep up on the roof
11 lived in, would take a gondola
12 has, islands, On weekend, from island to island
13 high tide, from, rises, leaves, full of water
14 However, be able to walk around, raised walkways
15 is known as, floating
16 there are, colorful houses
17 wonder how, why they built the houses on
18 decided to live there, themselves safe from invaders
19 for them to build, swampy surface
20 installed, wooden poles
21 wooden poles, support, to
22 lived, huge round, would, have friends, to play with
23 hear, calling me to come over
24 are, three to five floors
25 is used for
26 store food, tools on, second floor
27 where I would sleep, would be on
28 like, living in, have, family name
29 can house up to, work together, share
30 Living, keeps them safe
31 different all over the world, What, like

---

1 다양한 사람들이 다양한 집에서 살고 있습니다.

2 어떤 사람들은 집에 들어가기 위해 사다리를 이용합니다. 다른 사람들은 물 위에 있는 집에서 살고 있습니다.

3 그리고 또 다른 사람들은 많은 사람들과 함께 집을 공유합니다.

4 여러분이 이 집들 중 하나에 산다고 상상해 보세요. 여러분의 삶은 어떻게 바뀔까요?

5 내가 만약 푸에블로에 산다면, 나는 집에 들어가기 위해 사다리를 오를 것이다.

6 집 꼭대기에는 숨겨진 구멍이 있다.

7 반갑지 않은 방문객이 나타난다면 나는 사다리를 끌어올려 그들이 들어오지 못하게 할 것이다.

8 두꺼운 벽은 흙, 지푸라기, 물로 만들어져 있다.

9 그것들은 여름에는 시원하게, 겨울에는 따뜻하게 유지시켜 준다.

10 집에는 평평한 지붕이 있다. 때때로 나는 달과 별들 아래의 지붕 위에서 잠을 잘 것이다.

11 내가 만약 베니스에 산다면, 나는 매일 아침 곤돌라를 타고 학교에 갈 것이다.

12 베니스는 118개의 작은 섬이 있다. 주말마다 나는 수상 버스인 바포레토를 타고 이 섬 저 섬을 여행할 것이다.

13 조수가 높을 때에는 아드리아 해의 물이 자주 범람하고 거리는 물로 가득 찬다.

14 그러나 나는 돌출되어 있는 통로로 도심 주변을 걸어다닐 수 있을 것이다.

15 베니스는 '떠다니는 도시'로 알려져 있다.

16 베니스에는 물 위에 있는 색색의 건물들이 많다.

17 여러분은 어떻게, 그리고 왜 그들이 물 위에 집을 지었는지 궁금할 것이다.

18 옛 베니스 사람들은 침략자들로부터 자신들을 안전하게 지키기 위해 그곳에 살기로 결정했다.

19 하지만 그들이 이 습지 위에 집을 짓는 것은 쉽지 않았다.

20 그래서 그들은 땅에 천만 개 이상의 나무 기둥을 설치했다.

21 이 나무 기둥들이 바로 지금까지 베니스를 지탱해 주고 있는 것이다.

22 내가 만약 거대하고 둥그런 집인 중국 푸젠의 토루(tulou)에 산다면, 나는 항상 집에 함께 놀 친구들이 있을 것이다.

23 때때로 나의 이웃이 차를 마시거나 저녁 식사를 하러 집에 들르라고 나를 부르는 소리를 듣게 될 것이다.

24 토루는 대개 3층에서 5층으로 되어 있다.

25 1층은 요리하고 식사하는 데에 사용된다.

26 그리고 사람들은 2층에 식량과 도구를 보관한다.

27 내가 어디에서 잠을 잘지 궁금한가? 내 침실은 3층이나 4층에 있을 것이다.

28 토루는 마을과 같다. 토루에 사는 사람들은 대부분 같은 성(姓)을 가지고 있다.

29 몇몇 큰 토루는 50가구까지 수용할 수 있다. 그들은 함께 일하고 많은 것을 공유한다.

30 한 건물에 함께 사는 것은 그들을 안전하게 지켜 준다.

31 집은 어디에나 있습니다. 그러나 전 세계의 집은 모두 다릅니다. 여러분의 집은 어떤가요?

1 Different people live in different houses.

2 Some use ladders to enter their houses. Others live in houses on the water.

3 And others share their houses with many people.

4 Imagine you live in one of these houses. How would that change your life?

5 If I lived in a *pueblo*, I would climb up a ladder to enter my house.

6 There's a hidden opening on top of the house.

7 If unwelcome visitors appeared, I would pull the ladder up to stop them from entering.

8 The thick walls are made of earth, straw, and water.

9 They would keep me cool in summer and warm in winter.

10 The house has a flat roof. I would sometimes sleep up on the roof under the moon and stars.

11 If I lived in Venice, I would take a gondola to school every morning.

12 Venice has 118 small islands. On weekends, I would travel from island to island by a *vaporetto*, a water bus.

13 At high tide, the water from the Adriatic Sea often rises and leaves the streets full of water.

14 However, I would be able to walk around the town through the raised walkways.

15 Venice is known as the "floating city."

16 In Venice, there are many colorful houses on the water.

17 You may wonder how and why they built the houses on the water.

18 The old Venetians decided to live there to keep themselves safe from invaders.

19 But it was not easy for them to build their homes on this swampy surface.

20 So they installed more than 10 million wooden poles in the ground.

21 It is these wooden poles that support Venice to this day.

22 If I lived in a *tulou*, a huge round house in Fujian, China, I would always have friends at home to

play with.

23 I would sometimes hear my neighbor calling me to come over for tea or dinner.

24 In a *tulou*, there are usually three to five floors.

25 The first floor is used for cooking and eating.

26 And people store food and tools on the second floor.

27 Do you wonder where I would sleep? My bedroom would be on the third or fourth floor.

28 A *tulou* is like a village. The people living in a *tulou* mostly have the same family name.

29 Some large *tulou* can house up to 50 families. They work together and share many things.

30 Living together in one building keeps them safe.

31 Homes are everywhere. But they are different all over the world. What is your home like?

Let's Write

1. might wonder where you can stay

2. Why don't you stay

3. a traditional Korean house

4. stayed, would sleep, because there are no beds

5. are mostly built with, such as wood, straw, and earth

6. help you keep your skin healthy

7. warm *ondol* floors heat your body

8. are covered with thin paper

9. help keep you cool

Culture & Life

1. walked down, would see houses with many unique patterns

2. Each house tells

3. might be about neighbors' babies

4. Others, personal opinions

5. A long time ago, were at war with

6. invaded their land, with many colorful symbols

7. what, secretly communicating to each other

8. expressed feelings such as sadness

9. were handed down from, to

10. kept their traditions alive

Let's Write

1. When you visit Korea, you might wonder where you can stay.

2. Why don't you stay in a *hanok*?

3. A *hanok* is a traditional Korean house.

4. If you stayed in a *hanok*, you would sleep on the floor because there are no beds.

5. *Hanok* houses are mostly built with natural materials such as wood, stone, straw, paper, and earth.

6. These materials help you keep your skin healthy.

7. In the cold winter, the warm *ondol* floors heat your body.

8. The doors in *hanok* are covered with thin paper.

9. They help keep you cool in summer.

Culture & Life

1. If you walked down a street in the village of the Ndebele in South Africa, you would see houses with many unique patterns and styles.

2. Each house tells a different story.

3. Some stories might be about neighbors' babies.

4. Others express personal opinions.

5. A long time ago, the Ndebele were at war with the Boers.

6. When the Boers invaded their land, the Ndebele painted their houses with many colorful symbols.

7. So, their enemies couldn't understand what they were secretly communicating to each other.

8. The symbols expressed feelings such as sadness.

9. Those symbols were handed down from mothers to daughters.

10. And they have kept their traditions alive.

11 lastly, 마지막으로   12 novel, 소설
13 sum, 총계, 계산   14 tax, 세금   15 claim, 주장하다
16 celebrate, 기념하다

단어 TEST Step 1   p.23

01 글, 기사	02 고장 내다	03 이유
04 투표하다	05 손을 흔들다	06 모험
07 용감한	08 반복하다, 따라 말하다	
09 근육	10 같다	11 설문조사하다
12 게다가, 어쨌든	13 나타내다	14 중요하다
15 선거	16 군인, 병사	17 뒤쫓다
18 계산, 총계	19 중요성	20 갑자기
21 자정	22 얼굴의	23 독이 있는
24 투쟁하다, 분투하다		25 깨닫다
26 도움이 되는	27 기념하다	28 해결책
29 주장하다	30 탐욕스러운, 욕심 많은	
31 결과	32 일치하다	33 마지막으로
34 공상 과학의	35 되찾다	36 ~와 연관되어 있다
37 하나씩	38 출마하다	39 집어들다
40 다시 말하면	41 막 ~하려고 하다	42 ~을 자랑스러워하다
43 ~로 여겨지다		

단어 TEST Step 2   p.24

01 soldier	02 typewriter	03 survey
04 tax	05 match	06 sum
07 claim	08 vote	09 solution
10 facial	11 adventure	12 reason
13 courageous	14 election	15 celebrate
16 article	17 anyway	18 equal
19 midnight	20 represent	21 chase
22 struggle	23 greedy	24 suddenly
25 helpful	26 muscle	27 importance
28 poisonous	29 result	30 salty
31 science-fiction	32 realize	33 arrow
34 wave	35 hide up	36 be proud of
37 look up	38 be about to	39 in other words
40 be related to	41 one by one	42 be regarded as
43 not ~ anymore		

단어 TEST Step 3   p.25

1 matter, 중요하다   2 soldier, 군인, 병사
3 midnight, 자정   4 realize, 깨닫다
5 poisonous, 독이 있는   6 shout, 외치다, 소리치다
7 article, 글, 기사   8 represent, 나타내다
9 wave, 손을 흔들다   10 greedy, 탐욕스러운, 욕심 많은

대화문 TEST Step 1   p.26~27

Listen & Speak 1 A

graph about / survey, kinds / results / percent.
Only, out of / What kind of / have cats / the rest /
fish

Listen & Speak 1 B

election / bad, win / How come / Over, voted for /
your best, what matters / guess, while running for,
president / proud of

Listen & Speak 2 A

help, with / have to, to make, sum, How, minus,
equal / need to, sticks, sticks, to make, what I mean /
what, minus, equals, How / Thinking outside the box,
helpful

Listen & Speak 2 B

the matter, look upset / broke, angry / I'm sorry to
hear, facial, be tired / What do you mean / takes,
muscles to look, a few, what / get, to stay, for a long
time / it's, better to smile

Real Life Communication

doing, article, favorite snacks / (I')m worried about /
surveyed, results, eighty percent / Do you see, mean
/ I get it, What else / Twelve percent, chose, as
favorite / try to, healthier

Let's Check

These days, paper tickets, store, in, show, screen,
go in, don't need to go through, trouble of printing,
what I mean

대화문 TEST Step 2   p.28~29

Listen & Speak 1 A

B: Minju, what is this graph about?

G: I did a survey on the kinds of pets my classmates
   have.

B: What were the results?

G: Eighty percent of the students have pets. Only
   five out of twenty-five students don't have pets.

B: What kind of pets do they have?

G: Well, ten students have dogs and three students
   have cats.

B: What about the rest?

G: Seven students have fish.

M: Mason, how was the election?

B: It was bad. I didn't win.

M: How come?

B: Yura won. Over sixty percent of the students voted for her.

M: Well, you tried your best and that's what matters.

B: I guess so. I have learned many things while running for class president.

M: I'm really proud of you.

B: Thanks, Dad.

B: Emma, can you help me with this math problem?

G: Sure, what is it?

B: You have to move one stick to make this sum right. How could four minus five equal six?

G: Oh, it's simple. You need to move one of the sticks in number four to make it eleven. Do you see what I mean?

B: Yes, now I see what you mean. Eleven minus five equals six. How clever!

G: Thinking outside the box can be helpful sometimes.

B: Jian, what's the matter? You look upset.

G: My brother broke my computer. I'm so angry.

B: I'm sorry to hear that, but your facial muscles must be tired.

G: What do you mean?

B: Well, it takes a lot of muscles to look angry, but only a few to smile. Do you see what I mean?

G: Oh, I get it. I guess it's not good to stay angry for a long time.

B: That's right. Remember, it's always better to smile!

Mina: Henry, what are you doing?

Henry: I'm writing an article about students' favorite snacks. I'm worried about their health.

Mina: Why?

Henry: Well, I surveyed 100 students and the results show that eighty percent of the students liked pizza and fried chicken for snacks. Do you see what I mean?

Mina: Oh, I get it. Students really like fast food. What else did they like?

Henry: Twelve percent of the students chose chocolate cake as their favorite.

Mina: Wow, students should really try to eat healthier snacks!

B: These days, you don't need paper tickets to watch a movie or go to a concert. You just need to store your ticket in your cell phone. Then show the ticket on your phone's screen before you go in. You don't need to go through the trouble of printing out tickets. Do you see what I mean?

본문 TEST Step 1   p.30~32

01 doing, math, struggling with
02 too, draw, anyway, real
03 put down, picked up
04 decided, himself, about, heard
05 looked up from, talking
06 couldn't believe, who was
07 Close, eyes, repeat after
08 can talk, Just repeat
09 repeated, words, heard, shouting
10 When, opened, soldiers on
11 chasing, with arrows, shouted
12 dangerous for you, stand
13 pulled, onto, rode, woods
14 arrived, stopped, got off
15 my name is
16 Are, from, book
17 Who, why, here
18 must, reason, soldiers, anything
19 get back, took, taxed
20 greedy, share, enough, buy
21 get, back, so, inside
22 solution, take, count, number
23 hid up, counted, by
24 There are, from, to
25 three soldiers until noon
26 Lastly, until, between, and
27 don't get it
28 moment, might make, easier
29 drew, graph, showed, to
30 the most dangerous, midnight
31 work, than, what, mean
32 get it, so much
33 realize, importance, that, anymore
34 walked out, back, waving
35 waved back, himself, adventure

01 was doing his math homework, struggling with

02 too hard to read, draw, these, needs graphs, real life

03 put down, picked up

04 decided to read himself, was about to open, heard

05 looked up from, to see who was talking

06 who was

07 Close, repeat after

08 You can talk, repeat

09 repeated the words, Suddenly, heard, shouting

10 When, on horses

11 chasing, with arrows, shouted

12 It's, for you to stand

13 pulled, onto, rode

14 arrived at, stopped, got off

15 my name is

16 the Robin Hood from

17 Who are you, are you

18 why I'm here, must be, saved, from, Is there anything, for

19 get back, that, took, taxed them

20 too greedy to share, enough money to buy

21 help them get, back, However, no one can get inside

22 take me to the tower, count the number of

23 hid up, counted, one by one

24 There are, from, to

25 three soldiers until noon, eight soldiers until

26 Lastly, there are, until, go inside between, and noon

27 don't get it

28 moment, might make this easier to

29 drew, showed it

30 the most dangerous time, between, and

31 Four times more soldiers, than, until, what I mean

32 get it, so much

33 realize the importance of graphs, No one, that, them

34 walked out of, looked back, waving

35 waved back, himself, adventure, do I go back, should say

1 파스칼은 그의 방에서 수학 숙제를 하고 있었습니다. 그는 그래프 문제에 고군분투하고 있었습니다.

2 "그래프를 읽고 그리는 것은 너무 어려워. 게다가 내가 왜 그래프가 필요하겠어? 아무도 실제 생활에서는 그래프가 필요하지 않아."

3 그는 그의 펜을 내려놓고, 그가 가장 좋아하는 책, '로빈 후드'를 집어 들었습니다.

4 그는 책을 읽으며 잠들기로 했습니다. 그가 책을 펴려고 할 때, 그는 목소리를 들었습니다.

5 누가 말하고 있는지 보기 위해 그는 책에서 눈을 들어 올려다보았습니다.

6 그는 그의 눈을 믿을 수 없었습니다. 말하는 것은 바로 자신의 개, Manny였습니다!

7 "눈을 감고 내 말을 따라 말하세요. 코기토 에르고 숨." Manny가 말했습니다.

8 "너는 말할 수 있니?" "그냥 따라 하세요! 코기토 에르고 숨."

9 파스칼은 그의 눈을 감고 그 단어들을 따라 말했습니다. 갑자기 그는 남자들이 소리치는 것을 들었습니다.

10 그가 눈을 떴을 때, 그는 말을 탄 병사들을 보았습니다.

11 그들은 손에 화살을 든 남자를 뒤쫓고 있었습니다. 그 남자는 파스칼을 보고 소리쳤습니다.

12 "네가 거기 서 있는 것은 너무 위험해. 이리 와."

13 그 남자는 파스칼을 그의 말에 올려 태우고 숲으로 말을 몰았습니다.

14 그들이 한 집 앞에 이르렀을 때, 그 남자는 멈추고 말에서 내렸습니다.

15 "안녕, 내 이름은 로빈 후드야."

16 "와우! 당신이 책 속의 로빈 후드인가요?"

17 "아니, 나는 셔우드 숲의 로빈 후드야. 너는 누구이고 왜 여기에 있니?"

18 "제 이름은 파스칼이에요. 저는 제가 왜 여기 있는지 모르지만 이유가 분명 있을 거예요. 당신은 저를 병사들로부터 구해줬어요. 정말 감사드려요. 제가 당신을 위해 할 수 있는 것이 있을까요?"

19 "음, 우리가 왕이 사람들에게서 가져간 돈을 되찾는 것을 도와줄 수 있니? 그는 그들에게 세금을 너무 많이 부과했어.

20 그는 너무 탐욕스러워서 사람들과 나누지 않아, 그래서 그들은 음식을 살 충분한 돈이 없어.

21 나는 그들의 돈을 다시 찾을 수 있도록 돕고 싶어. 하지만 탑 안에 병사들이 많아서 아무도 들어갈 수 없어."

22 "흠… 제게 해결책이 있는 것 같아요. 그러나 우선 저를 탑에 데려가 주실 수 있나요? 저는 병사들의 수를 세야 해요."

23 로빈과 파스칼은 나무에 숨어서 병사들의 수를 한 명씩 세었습니다.

24 "자정부터 새벽 여섯 시까지는 다섯 명의 병사들이 있어요.

25 그다음, 정오까지는 세 명의 병사들이 있고, 오후 여섯 시까지는 여덟 명의 병사들이 있어요.

31

26 마지막으로, 자정까지는 열두 명의 병사들이 있어요. 그래서 당신은 새벽 여섯 시에서 정오 사이에 들어가야 해요."

27 "뭐라고? 나는 이해하지 못했어."

28 파스칼은 잠시 생각에 잠겼습니다. '흠…그래프가 이것을 이해하는 것을 쉽게 해 줄지도 몰라.'

29 파스칼은 그래프를 그려서 그것을 로빈에게 보여주었습니다.

30 "보세요, 가장 위험한 시간은 저녁 여섯 시에서 자정까지예요.

31 오전 여섯 시부터 정오까지보다 그 시간에 네 배나 더 많은 병사들이 일해요. 제 말이 무슨 뜻인지 아시겠어요?"

32 "아하! 이제 이해했어. 너무 고마워, 파스칼!"

33 "천만에요. 이제 저는 그래프의 중요성을 깨달았어요. 아무도 그래프가 더 이상 필요 없다고 말할 수 없을 거예요."

34 파스칼은 숲에서 걸어 나왔습니다. 그가 뒤돌아봤을 때, 그는 로빈 후드가 그에게 손을 흔들고 있는 것을 보았습니다.

35 파스칼은 손을 흔들어 답하고 혼잣말을 했습니다. "정말 멋진 모험이었어. 나는 어떻게 돌아가지? 오, 알겠어. 나는 코기토 에르고 숨이라는 말을 해야 해!"

본문 TEST Step 4~Step 5   p.37~41

01 Pascal was doing his math homework in his room. He was struggling with graphs.

02 "It's too hard to read and draw graphs. Why do I need these anyway? No one needs graphs in real life."

03 He put down his pen and picked up his favorite book, *Robin Hood*.

04 He decided to read himself to sleep. When he was about to open the book, he heard a voice.

05 He looked up from the book to see who was talking.

06 He couldn't believe his eyes. It was his dog, Manny, who was talking!

07 "Close your eyes and repeat after me. *Cogito ergo sum*," said Manny.

08 "You can talk?" "Just repeat! *Cogito ergo sum*."

09 Pascal closed his eyes and repeated the words. Suddenly, he heard men shouting.

10 When he opened his eyes, he saw soldiers on horses.

11 They were chasing a man with arrows in his hand. The man saw Pascal and shouted.

12 "It's too dangerous for you to stand there. Come on."

13 The man pulled Pascal onto his horse and rode into the woods.

14 When they arrived at a house, the man stopped and got off his horse.

15 "Hello, my name is Robin Hood."

16 "Wow! Are you the Robin Hood from the book?"

17 "No, I'm the Robin Hood of Sherwood Forest. Who are you and why are you here?"

18 "My name is Pascal. I don't know why I'm here, but there must be a reason. You saved me from the soldiers. Thank you so much. Is there anything I can do for you?"

19 "Well, can you help us get back the money that the king took from the people? He taxed them too much.

20 He is too greedy to share with the people, so they don't have enough money to buy food.

21 I want to help them get their money back. However, there are many soldiers in the tower, so no one can get inside."

22 "Hmm… I think I have a solution. But first, can you take me to the tower? I need to count the number of soldiers."

23 Robin and Pascal hid up in a tree and counted the soldiers one by one.

24 "There are five soldiers from midnight to six in the morning.

25 Next, there are three soldiers until noon, and then there are eight soldiers until six in the evening.

26 Lastly, there are twelve soldiers until midnight. So, you should go inside between six in the morning and noon."

27 "What? I don't get it."

28 Pascal thought for a moment. 'Hmm… A graph might make this easier to understand.'

29 Pascal drew a graph and showed it to Robin.

30 "Look, the most dangerous time is between six in the evening and midnight.

31 Four times more soldiers work at that time than from six in the morning until noon. Do you see what I mean?"

32 "Aha! I get it now. Thank you so much, Pascal!"

33 "You're welcome. Now I realize the importance of graphs. No one can say that we don't need them anymore."

34 Pascal walked out of the woods. When he looked back, he saw Robin Hood waving at him.

35 Pascal waved back and said to himself, "It was a great adventure. How do I go back? Oh, I know. I should say the words *Cogito ergo sum*!"

Communication Task

1. we want for our school library
2. The result, that, out of, chose novels
3. sixty-five percent, total
4. Five out of twenty students, science-fiction books
5. However, two out of twenty students
6. survey result, I think, should get more novels
7. what, mean

Before You Read B Look and Write

1. Reviews
2. Title
3. a man who struggles to help, greedy king
4. because, shoots arrows better than soldiers
5. My opinion, It's, to tax, After all, not money but people matter

Let's Write

1. Look at, survey result
2. out of
3. In other words, chose the character
4. it's because, character is courageous
5. Next, nine students chose
6. No one, it's because, too greedy to, by others

Communication Task

1. I did a survey on the books we want for our school library.
2. The result says that thirteen out of twenty students chose novels.
3. That is sixty-five percent of the total.
4. Five out of twenty students chose science-fiction books.
5. However, only two out of twenty students chose history books.
6. From this survey result, I think the school library should get more novels.
7. Do you see what I mean?

Before You Read B Look and Write

1. Book Club: Your Reviews
2. Title: *Robin Hood*
3. Topic of the book: It's about a man who struggles to help people from the greedy king.
4. My favorite character: My favorite character is Robin Hood because he shoots arrows better than soldiers.

5. My opinion of the book: It's bad to tax too much. After all, not money but people matter the most.

Let's Write

1. Look at the survey result on "Who is your favorite character?"
2. Fifteen out of thirty students chose Hong Gildong.
3. In other words, fifty percent of the students chose the character.
4. I think it's because the character is courageous.
5. Next, nine students chose Kongiwi and six students chose Robin Hood.
6. No one chose Nolbu. Maybe it's because the character is too greedy to be liked by others.

MEMO

MEMO

적중 100

영어 기출 문제집

정답 및 해설

지학 | 민찬규